PERIODIC CLASSIFICATION OF THE ELEMENTS
(BASED ON $C^{12} = 12.0000$) 1961 ATOMIC WEIGHTS

Light Metals — Heavy Metals — Nonmetals

IA	IIA	IIIB	IVB	VB	VIB	VIIB	VIIIB			IB	IIB	IIIA	IVA	VA	VIA	VIIA	VIIIA
1 H 1.0080																	2 He 4.003
3 Li 6.939	4 Be 9.012											5 B 10.81	6 C 12.011	7 N 14.007	8 O 15.9994	9 F 18.998	10 Ne 20.183
11 Na 22.990	12 Mg 24.31											13 Al 26.98	14 Si 28.09	15 P 30.974	16 S 32.064	17 Cl 35.453	18 Ar 39.948
19 K 39.102	20 Ca 40.08	21 Sc 44.96	22 Ti 47.90	23 V 50.94	24 Cr 52.00	25 Mn 54.94	26 Fe 55.85	27 Co 58.93	28 Ni 58.71	29 Cu 63.54	30 Zn 65.37	31 Ga 69.72	32 Ge 72.59	33 As 74.92	34 Se 78.96	35 Br 79.909	36 Kr 83.80
37 Rb 85.47	38 Sr 87.62	39 Y 88.91	40 Zr 91.22	41 Nb 92.91	42 Mo 95.94	43 Tc (99)	44 Ru 101.1	45 Rh 102.90	46 Pd 106.4	47 Ag 107.870	48 Cd 112.40	49 In 114.82	50 Sn 118.69	51 Sb 121.75	52 Te 127.60	53 I 126.90	54 Xe 131.30
55 Cs 132.91	56 Ba 137.34	57 to 71	72 Hf 178.49	73 Ta 180.95	74 W 183.85	75 Re 186.2	76 Os 190.2	77 Ir 192.2	78 Pt 195.09	79 Au 197.0	80 Hg 200.59	81 Tl 204.37	82 Pb 207.19	83 Bi 208.98	84 Po (210)	85 At (210)	86 Rn (222)
87 Fr (223)	88 Ra 226.05	89 to 103															

Lanthanide series	57 La 138.91	58 Ce 140.12	59 Pr 140.91	60 Nd 144.24	61 Pm (147)	62 Sm 150.35	63 Eu 151.96	64 Gd 157.25	65 Tb 158.92	66 Dy 162.50	67 Ho 164.93	68 Er 167.26	69 Tm 168.93	70 Yb 173.04	71 Lu 174.97
Actinide series	89 Ac (227)	90 Th 232.04	91 Pa (231)	92 U 238.03	93 Np (237)	94 Pu (242)	95 Am (243)	96 Cm (247)	97 Bk (249)	98 Cf (251)	99 Es (254)	100 Fm (253)	101 Md (256)	102 No (254)	103 Lw (257)

FUNDAMENTAL CONSTANTS

Symbol	Name	Value
c	Velocity of light	2.9979×10^{10} cm sec^{-1}
e	Electronic charge	1.6021×10^{-19} coulomb
N_0	Avagadro's number	6.0225×10^{23}
h	Planck's constant	6.6256×10^{-27} erg sec
F	Faraday constant	96,487 coulomb eq^{-1}
R	Gas constant	82.056 cm^3 atm mole^{-1} deg^{-1}
		1.9872 cal mole^{-1} deg^{-1}
		8.3143 joule mole^{-1} deg^{-1}
k	Boltzmann constant	1.3805×10^{-16} erg deg^{-1}

GREEK ALPHABET

Greek letter	Greek name	Greek letter	Greek name
A α	Alpha	N ν	Nu
B β	Beta	Ξ ξ	Xi
Γ γ	Gamma	O o	Omicron
Δ δ	Delta	Π π	Pi
E ε	Epsilon	P ρ	Rho
Z ζ	Zeta	Σ σ	Sigma
H η	Eta	T τ	Tau
Θ θ	Theta	Υ υ	Upsilon
I ι	Iota	Φ ϕ	Phi
K κ	Kappa	X χ	Chi
Λ λ	Lambda	Ψ ψ	Psi
M μ	Mu	Ω ω	Omega

MODERN
METHODS
OF CHEMICAL
ANALYSIS

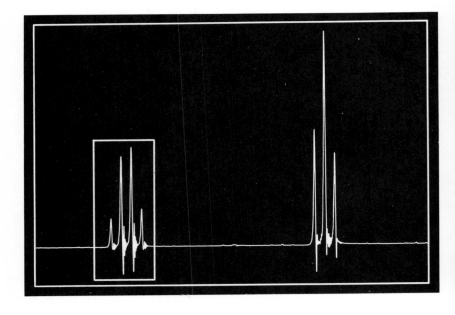

Cover Design: *The quartet of peaks on the cover is from the n.m.r. spectrum of diethyl ether. The entire spectrum is reproduced above as it appears in the film,* Nuclear Magnetic Resonance, *produced by the Chemistry Department, UCLA, and distributed by John Wiley & Sons.*

MODERN
METHODS
OF CHEMICAL
ANALYSIS

Robert L. Pecsok
University of California,
Los Angeles

L. Donald Shields
California State College,
Fullerton

John Wiley & Sons, Inc.
New York   London   Sidney

WILEY INTERNATIONAL EDITION

To Mary and Patty

PREFACE

In his Fisher Award Address to the American Chemical Society in 1965, Professor C. N. Reilley noted that: "Perhaps the only constant feature of science is that of change." This is nowhere more apparent than in the field of analytical chemistry. From the beginning of chemistry as a science, precise analytical measurements not only have provided the necessary tests of theory but also have led to modifications of existing theories or entirely new developments. For many years the balance and buret were adequate for most of the analyses a chemist needed to perform. But these tools, precise though they may be, fail to provide the specificity required to treat mixtures, the speed and versatility needed to follow fast reactions, and the detailed information which can help to unravel the structure of a complicated molecule. Now even the beginning student should know something about *modern* analytical methods, especially those of separation, spectrometric methods for study of structure, and electrochemical and radiochemical methods.

This introductory text represents a significant departure from the familiar textbook on quantitative analysis. We have not emphasized the determination of composition of samples per se. Important as this aspect of analytical chemistry may be, it is even more desirable that the student acquire an early familiarity with the techniques that chemists currently employ to gather data for whatever purpose. The degree of understanding that the student will acquire depends in part on his background, but even more on his motivation. To this end we have emphasized immediate applications to organic chemistry as well as biochemistry, bearing in mind that often many students at this level are likely to be oriented toward the life sciences. Thus we have tried to achieve a new blend of topics, all of an analytical flavor but geared to every branch of chemistry.

We have taken advantage of the now well-established trend to include gravimetric and volumetric analyses in the general chemistry course. The student is assumed to be proficient in the use of the standard equipment in his desk. When precise titrations have been performed in a previous course, there is little need to repeat them, per se, in the next year. Because of the nature of the examples, a prior or concurrent course in elementary organic chemistry is necessary. Although this text is especially applicable to a one-semester or two-quarter course at the sophomore level, it provides an introduction to instrumental methods which will be useful to technicians and others who desire a survey of new techniques. Obviously, the depth of coverage and degree of sophistication represent a compromise. One might argue, for example, that nuclear magnetic resonance (n.m.r.) should be reserved for advanced courses where it can be treated from a more fundamental approach. Our reply is that a student beginning his study of organic chemistry can no doubt learn much more from an n.m.r. spectrum than from a boiling point or solubility product. Therefore, our discussion of n.m.r. could seem superficial to the expert, but we hope it will be understandable and useful to a novice. The same can be said about many of the other topics such as gas chromatography and mass spectrometry. We have aimed at a presentation of principles, kinds of information obtained, and the interpretation of results rather than the detailed operation of commercial instruments.

A study of analytical methods is necessarily laboratory oriented, but there is no real virtue in interrupting the text with laboratory directions. In a companion volume, *Experiments in Modern Methods of Chemical Analysis*, there are illustrative experiments based on problems in organic and biochemistry. In addition, many suitable experiments are found in *Experimental Organic Chemistry* by M. C. Caserio and in *Experiments for Instrumental Methods* by C. N. Reilley and D. T. Sawyer. Some excellent supporting films are available in the areas of infrared, n.m.r., and mass spectrometry. Low-cost *p*H meters, spectrophotometers, and gas chromatographs are already commercially available, and reasonably priced n.m.r. and mass spectrometers are on the horizon. By judicious scheduling with two lectures and one four-hour laboratory per week, we have obtained enough instruments for 500 students per year for less than $150 per student.

Although we have not formally divided the book into parts, the instructor may choose equally well to begin with Chapter 2, 8, or 14. Chapters 2–7 concern separation techniques starting from simple phase changes and going through various kinds of chromatography. Chapters 8–13 treat the nature of electromagnetic radiation and its interaction with matter, including qualitative and quantitative spectrophotometry, nuclear magnetic resonance, and mass spectrometry. Chapters 14–17 cover the more classical topics of electrochemistry and acid-base chemistry in aqueous and non-aqueous solvents. Finally, Chapters 18–19 introduce kinetics as applied to rates of reaction and radioactivity.

As in any text, there is very little herein that is new. We have attempted to present a new combination of topics and, perhaps, some different approaches to presenting sophisticated techniques at an introductory level. Although no single topic is treated exhaustively, there is sufficient depth so that the students will not need to congest the library nor be obliged to purchase supplementary monographs. Detailed and original references would be of little use at this level. Instead, at the end of each chapter we have listed a few useful and generally available monographs and advanced texts. A set of problems is included in most chapters.

We are grateful to the first generation of students who used a preliminary version of this text. Their comments have been invaluable. Thanks are also due to those of our colleagues who offered numerous suggestions—the list is long: C. S. Foote, D. A. Lightner, J. L. Sudmeier, C. N. Reilley, D. T. Sawyer, W. P. Schaefer, L. B. Rogers, D. W. Ellis, A. J. Diefenderfer, and many others. The cooperation of the publisher, especially T. L. Sears, B. Scheier, and Barbara

Ravizza who designed the cover and the book, is greatly appreciated. Most important of all, we are grateful to our wives who provided the essential ingredients—encouragement, patience, and understanding as well as help in typing and advice on the niceties of the English language.

Robert L. Pecsok
and L. Donald Shields

Los Angeles and Fullerton, California
January 1968

CONTENTS

16 THE ROLE OF THE SOLVENT
IN ACID-BASE CHEMISTRY   395

17 EFFECTS OF MOLECULAR STRUCTURE
ON ACIDITY   417

18 KINETICS   433

1 INTRODUCTION

If chemistry is aptly described as "what chemists do," it must be that "analytical chemistry is what analytical chemists do." However, it is no easier to pinpoint the subject matter of analytical chemistry than it is to describe chemistry as a whole. Biologists, geophysicists, engineers—all practice chemistry to some extent, and nearly all chemists practice analytical chemistry; for, among other things, chemistry is the study of the composition and behavior of the natural world. Anyone wishing to know more about the composition of substances must employ analytical methods to determine the kinds and amounts of compounds, elements, atoms, and sub-atomic particles present in a given sample, as well as to examine the detailed arrangements of the various species. And to study the behavior of materials, analytical methods must be used before, during, and after certain reactions or "changes."

The recent rapid advances in our knowledge of the physical world parallel a similar rapid advance in the science of analytical methods. However, neither the balance nor buret, which provided most of our analytical measurements in the 1940's, has been relegated to the museum—both are still indispensable in any chemical laboratory, and often are the ultimate weapons in calibrating a fancier instrumental method. They were good enough to allow Nobel Laureate T. W. Richards to prove the existence of isotopes by very precise determinations of the atomic weight of lead from various sources. But now mass spectrometry permits atomic weights to be determined more precisely and with a fraction of the effort. Similarly, the American Petroleum Institute invested many thousands of man-hours in attempting to isolate the hundreds of components in petroleum and gasoline by tedious fractional distillations. Today the same results can be obtained by one man in a few hours with a gas chromatograph. Most of our present knowledge about the detailed structure of compounds and atoms has been gained by studying the interaction of electromagnetic radiation with matter—through various forms of spectroscopy.

Even the beginning student soon becomes aware of the importance of modern analytical methods in all branches of science. This is not to say that breakthroughs in chemistry must wait for the analytical chemist to invent new methods, though most new techniques and instruments have been invented by chemists with analytical problems to solve. Chromatography was first introduced by bio-chemists. Nuclear magnetic resonance spectroscopy and mass spectroscopy were first studied by physicists. Yet, for the most part, scientists who are not analytical chemists tend to consider analytical methods as tools of the trade. They are primarily interested in the results they can provide.

The analytical chemist, on the other hand, is concerned with methods *per se*. He must become familiar with the theoretical principles and instrumentation of all methods. In so doing, he often becomes involved in bio-, organic, inorganic, and physical chemistry. He seeks to improve methods, searches for new areas of application, and points out the limitations so that the technique will not be misused. Accuracy, precision, reproducibility, and reliability are everyday words in his vocabulary. In a real sense, the analytical chemist is the keeper of chemistry's tools and techniques. This is no small assignment, and in this book we attempt merely to introduce some of the methods which all chemistry students will use in the more specialized branches of chemistry.

The determination of a melting point is hardly a modern analytical technique, but it illustrates how an extremely simple experiment can identify a substance or measure its purity. The melting process involves a two-phase system and is best understood from a study of a "phase diagram." The same principles apply to distillation, a somewhat more sophisticated separation technique where the concept of a column process is introduced. In distillation, there is a distribution of material between a gas phase and a liquid phase, whereas in extraction there is a distribution of material between two immiscible liquid phases. Otherwise the two processes have much in common. In extraction we develop the concept of a distribution coefficient which describes how a component is apportioned between two phases. The concepts of distribution (from extraction) and flow through columns (from distillation) form the basic framework for chromatographic methods in which a complex mixture is separated into its components by selective retardation as the sample is washed through a packed column or over a specially prepared paper surface. Chromatographic methods include some of the most powerful and useful separating techniques yet devised.

As a second major topic, the study of the interaction of electromagnetic radiation with matter serves as a background for the great variety of spectroscopic methods. At one end of the spectrum we find X-rays which not only tell us much about the details of atomic structure, but can also draw the blueprint for the structure of a crystal. At the other end of the spectrum we have relatively low-energy radiation in the radio frequency range. Normally these low-level frequencies are of concern to communication engineers, but when combined in the proper way with an intense magnetic field, this kind of energy can interact with certain nuclei, giving us a new tool called "nuclear magnetic resonance."

At intermediate frequencies, we find ultraviolet and infrared radiation—both capable of yielding much information about the nature of molecules. Sandwiched in the middle is visible radiation. While the inorganic chemist may use visible radiation to study transition metal complexes, the layman may use it for a simple "eyeball" determination of the strength of his cup of tea.

In most spectroscopic methods, the sample is exposed to some kind of radiation. In mass spectrometry, the sample is bombarded with a beam of electrons which ionizes and "cracks" the molecules into many pieces. The spectrometer then sorts the electrically charged fragments in order of their mass-to-charge ratio.

The third major topic is the more traditional study of chemical equilibria. Stoichiometry and equilibrium are the foundation of classical gravimetric, volumetric, and electrometric analytical methods. The treatment here will extend the elementary concepts to more complex systems and include the use of solvents other than water. We will see that the strength of an acid is related to its structure. Thus, in addition to determining the concentration of an acid, a titration can give us information about its structure.

Finally, we will examine how the rates of chemical reactions can be measured and how rate data, taken under controlled conditions, can unravel the detailed mechanism of how the reaction really occurs. Problems in reaction kinetics are first of all problems in analytical chemistry—the concentration of one or more of the species must be determined while the reaction is going on. This may be difficult if the reaction is essentially instantaneous. As a simpler example of reaction kinetics, we will consider the spontaneous decay of a radioactive isotope which can be followed with a counter.

The methods we have selected by no means exhaust the list available to the modern chemist. No matter what list is chosen, it is soon outdated. Rather than completeness, our objective is to present a variety of principles and concepts which underlie most of the instruments and techniques in current use.

We should point out that most of the instruments the chemist now uses routinely were not available 25 years ago or were available only as laboratory curiosities in a few research laboratories. There is no doubt that in the next 25 years we will see an even more spectacular change in the types of analytical methods used routinely and the kind of information they are able to unfold.

With a sound background, the student will be better prepared and more eager to keep current. The first of the general references listed below is one of the best sources of information on new developments as they come along.

GENERAL REFERENCES

Annual Reviews—a special biannual issue of *Analytical Chemistry*, in which the literature is reviewed in all areas of analytical chemistry. This review is usually the quickest and easiest way to begin a literature search.

4

I. M. Kolthoff and P. J. Elving, *Treatise on Analytical Chemistry*, Interscience, New York, 1959 ff. An encyclopedic work in many volumes in which experts discuss all fields of analytical chemistry by methods and by applications. This work is the best single source for analytical methods.

A. Weissberger, *Physical Methods of Organic Chemistry*, Interscience, New York, 1959 ff. Another many-volume work with discussions in depth. Parts of it have been revised several times.

F. L. J. Sixma and H. Wynberg, *A Manual of Physical Methods in Organic Chemistry*, Wiley, New York, 1964. A condensed version of the theoretical principles of most of the methods covered in this text, as well as experimental procedures.

H. H. Willard, L. L. Merritt, Jr., and J. A. Dean, *Instrumental Methods of Analysis*, 4th ed., Van Nostrand, Princeton, N. J., 1965. Theory, instrumentation, and experimental procedures.

2 SEPARATIONS BASED ON PHASE CHANGES

Chemical analysis, whether the intent is to determine structure or composition, involves measurements of various kinds. We might begin by weighing a sample and, after a series of chemical reactions, also weigh one of the products. We might measure the amount of light that the sample absorbs; or we might measure the potential of an electrode placed in contact with the sample. Whatever the measurement, if it is to be useful, we must have some idea of *what* is being measured. We will be misled if we weigh the gold in an ore sample unless we are sure that we have isolated all of the gold in a pure form. With some analytical methods, the presence of other substances does not invalidate the measurement; that is, the method is *selective*. But the degree of selectivity varies, and by and large we are faced with the problem of isolating, or separating, a particular substance from the gross sample before we can make a meaningful measurement.

The most common and surely the simplest separation results if the sample components can be distributed between two phases, say, a gas and a liquid, or a solid and a liquid, or two immiscible liquids. If some of the sample components prefer one phase and other components prefer the other phase, we have the basis of a separation. The mechanical separation of the two phases is relatively simple. The key to a successful separation is the control of conditions (temperature, solvent, pH, etc.) so that the equilibrium distribution places the components as completely as possible in one phase or the other.

As a chemist, you will have a variety of powerful and elegant separation techniques available, but if you are to use them wisely, you must understand the principles that determine the distribution of species between the phases. These principles are the basis of crystallization, distillation, extraction, and chromatography. We will begin with a study of a very simple system; namely, the phase distribution of a pure compound.

PHASE DIAGRAMS

Dependent on the temperature and pressure, water exists as a solid, liquid, or gas. The molecules of both liquid and solid water possess a certain amount

5

of kinetic energy, and occasionally those at the surface escape into the vapor phase. The kinetic energy increases with temperature, therefore the tendency to escape also increases. Thermal energy is thus converted to kinetic energy, resulting in a greater rate of escape of molecules from the liquid or solid phase to the vapor phase. Conversely, molecules in the vapor phase occasionally strike the surface of the liquid or solid phase and are captured. The two processes of vaporization and condensation occur simultaneously at rates determined by the temperature and by the concentration of molecules in the vapor phase. The concentration in the vapor phase is directly related to the pressure and it is convenient to use pressure as measure of concentration. If a vapor contains more than one kind of molecule, each substance exerts its own *partial pressure*. The total pressure is the sum of the partial pressures. In this discussion, the system contains only water molecules and the partial and total pressures are equal.

In a closed system, the vapor pressure will rapidly reach a constant value which means that the rates of vaporization and condensation are equal. This equilibrium vapor pressure is characteristic for each substance at a given temperature.

So far we have considered the "distribution" of a pure substance between vapor and liquid, or vapor and solid. There are also conversions from liquid to solid and vice versa. It requires energy to release molecules from the more stable arrangement in a solid. As we would expect, the rates of melting and freezing depend on temperature.

A great deal of information about a substance can be compressed into a single picture called a *phase diagram*. In Figure 2-1 which is the phase diagram for water, the area is divided into three sections labeled solid, liquid, and vapor. Curve *A* separating the solid and vapor phases actually shows the equilibrium vapor pressure of the solid as a function of temperature. If the pressure above the solid is less than this, then the solid will begin to vaporize. If the pressure is greater, some of the vapor will condense. Similarly curve *B* between the liquid and vapor phase regions depicts the vapor pressure of the liquid as a function of temperature. The dashed portion of this line (curve *D*) extending into the solid region represents the vapor pressure of a *supercooled liquid*, a metastable state which sometimes arises when the liquid fails to freeze even though it is below its normal freezing temperature. Curve *C* separating the liquid and solid phases shows the melting point as a function of pressure. The melting point of ice decreases slightly with pressure because of the decrease in volume that occurs when ice melts.

For a given temperature and pressure, the phase diagram indicates which of the three phases is the stable one. Unless the temperature-pressure combination falls on one of the curves, only one phase is stable. Points on the curves give the combinations of pressure and temperature which will allow two phases to

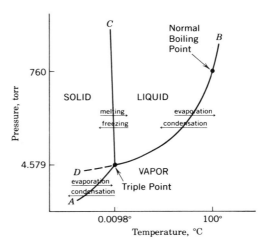

FIGURE 2-1.   Phase diagram for water (not to scale).

coexist in equilibrium. There is one unique combination, *the triple point*, at which all three phases can exist.

The concepts just described are basic to the understanding of more practical techniques using melting points and boiling points. We will refer often to information obtained from phase diagrams.

MELTING-POINT METHODS

The melting point of a pure substance is characteristic of that substance and serves to identify it. If the substance is not pure, it will melt over a range of temperature. The change in the melting point thus indicates the purity of the substance. Finally, zone melting is a powerful technique for the ultimate purification of many substances. Both in theory and in practice, these methods are perhaps the simplest of all analytical techniques.

MELTING POINT OF A PURE SUBSTANCE

The melting point of a pure solid (or the freezing point of a pure liquid) is the temperature at which the solid and liquid phases are in equilibrium. For practical purposes, let us assume that the external pressure is one atmosphere. However, because little change in volume occurs upon melting, the effect of any change in pressure is slight. At the melting point, the solid must have the same vapor pressure as the liquid. If it did not, the phase having the higher vapor pressure would distill into the other. In Figure 2-1, the vapor pressure of the solid and liquid phases are equal at a unique temperature, the point where the curves *A* and *B* intersect. Curve *C* is nearly vertical, and at 1 atmosphere, the melting point of water is exactly (by definition) 0° C.

The very simple apparatus shown in Figure 2-2 is adequate to determine the melting point. A few milligrams of sample are placed in a thin-walled capillary tube. The tube is attached to a thermometer with the sample close to the ther-

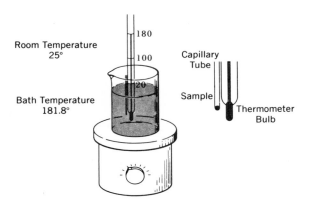

FIGURE 2-2. Simple apparatus for determining the melting point. Close-up of position of sample.

mometer bulb. This assembly is heated in a bath at a reasonable rate until the temperature reaches within 10° of the melting point. Then the heating is adjusted so that the final approach to the melting point does not exceed a rate of 1° per minute. This slow rate is necessary so that the bath, sample, and thermometer will always be at the same temperature. Although this simple equipment is adequate for the job, more sophisticated apparatus is available for increased accuracy, speed, and convenience.

There are several sources of error in this determination, some of which are easily corrected. Adequate heat transfer must be provided by using a properly stirred bath, a thin-walled capillary, a compact sample, and, above all, a very slow rate of heating in the region of the melting point.

Thermometers are not to be trusted unless they have been certified and calibrated at two temperatures. Immersion in both ice slush and boiling water at a known pressure, for example, serves this purpose, although any correction that may be necessary will depend on the degree of immersion for which the thermometer is designed. As a rule, the bulb of a thermometer exhibits a temperature different from that of its stem. With only partial immersion in the heated zone, the density of the mercury varies along the stem. In this case, the volume occupied by the mercury is too small and a correction, ΔT, must be applied:

$$\Delta T = 0.000154 \; l(t - n) \tag{2-1}$$

where 0.000154 is the linear expansion of mercury in a glass tube, l the length of the exposed column of mercury in degrees, t the observed temperature, and n the average temperature of the emergent stem.

example/problem 2-1: The thermometer in Figure 2-2 reads $180°$ and is immersed to the $20°$ mark. The correction is:

$$\Delta T = 0.000154 \times (180 - 20) \times \left(180 - \frac{180 + 25}{2}\right)$$

$$= 1.8°$$

The corrected reading is therefore $181.8° \, C$.

Some thermometers are calibrated for partial immersion and do not require this correction if they are immersed to the indicated mark on the stem.

Another source of error is the presence of impurities. Their effects are complex but significant, and will be discussed in some detail. Among other things, the freezing point depression which is caused by impurities is the basis of the well-known method of determining molecular weights. To explain this effect we will return to a modification of the phase diagram which applies to mixtures.

FREEZING POINT OF MIXTURES

Odd as it may seem, we will approach freezing points through vapor pressure curves. Let us consider an isolated system consisting of solid and liquid camphor at its melting point, $179° \, C$. The vapor pressure curves for this system of pure camphor are the solid lines A and B in Figure 2-3. A small amount of naphthalene added to the system will dissolve in the liquid camphor. The concentration of camphor molecules at the liquid surface is now less than before adding the naphthalene. As a consequence, the rate of vaporization of liquid camphor is decreased proportionately and its vapor pressure is decreased. The dashed line, C, in Figure 2-3 gives the vapor pressure of liquid camphor containing a small amount of naphthalene. The actual displacement of curve C from curve B is given by *Raoult's law* which states that the vapor pressure, P_c, of a solvent (in this case, camphor) in a solution, is equal to the vapor pressure of the pure solvent P_c° multiplied by the mole fraction, X_c, of the solvent in the solution:

$$P_c = X_c P_c^\circ \tag{2-2}$$

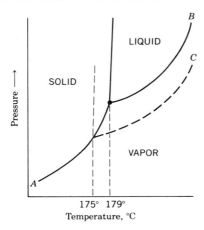

FIGURE 2-3. Phase diagram for camphor with a small amount of naphthalene added (Curve C).

Mole fraction is a measure of concentration and is equal to the number of moles of the given substance divided by the total number of moles of all substances in the same phase. The addition of a small amount of naphthalene does not alter the vapor pressure of solid camphor because the naphthalene dissolves entirely in the liquid phase, leaving the solid pure.

As in Figure 2-1, the intersection of the two vapor pressure curves, A and B, or A and C, in Figure 2-3, must define the freezing point. Thus the addition of an impurity lowers the freezing point of the liquid. If more impurity is added, there will be a still greater change in the freezing point. For *dilute* solutions, all changes will be small and we can represent the curves of Figure 2-3 as straight lines as shown in Figure 2-4. The obvious conclusion is that the change in freezing point, ΔT_f, is directly proportional to the amount of naphthalene added. If we measure concentration as molality (moles of solute per 1000 g of solvent), the proportionality constant is called the *molal freezing point depression constant*, K_f. For dilute solutions a simple equation describes this behavior:

$$\Delta T_f = K_f m \tag{2-3}$$

where m is the molality of the solute. The value of K_f depends only on the nature of solvent and not of the solute. Values of K_f for a few solvents are given in Table 2-1. If a known weight of a solute is dissolved in a known amount of solvent, a determination of the freezing point depression will yield the molality

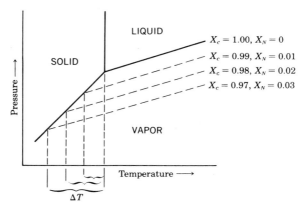

FIGURE 2-4. Expanded portion of phase diagram for camphor with several amounts of naphthalene added.

of the solution, from which the molecular weight of the solute can be computed. Although simple in principle, exact determination requires great care.

example / problem 2-2: Determine the molecular weight of an unknown from the following data: 4.35 g of the unknown were dissolved in 200 g of liquid camphor, giving a solution with a freezing point of $173.5°$ C.

$$\Delta T_f = 179.0° - 173.5° = 5.5°$$

$$\Delta T_f = K_f m$$

$$5.5 = 38.0 \times m$$

$$m = 5.5/38.0 = 0.145 \text{ mole}/1000 \text{ g solvent}$$

$$0.145/5 = 0.029 \text{ mole}/200 \text{ g solvent}$$

$$\text{Molecular wt.} = \frac{4.35 \text{ g}}{0.029 \text{ mole}} = 150$$

TABLE 2-1 MOLAL FREEZING POINT CONSTANTS

Solvent	Freezing Point	K_f, deg/mole
Acetic acid	$17°$ C	-3.9
Benzene	5.4	-5.12
Camphor	179	-38.0
Ethylene dibromide	10.1	-11.8
Naphthalene	80	-6.8
Water	0	-1.86

12   In treating freezing points of mixtures, we generally assume that the liquid phase is homogeneous; i.e., the two liquids are miscible. But the two solid substances may or may not form a homogeneous phase. A solid phase whose composition is the same throughout is, for the present discussion, called a *solid solution*. Some mixtures of solids are able to form homogeneous solid solutions while others remain as mixtures of two pure solid phases.

Mixtures with No Solid Solutions.   If we start with pure naphthalene, m.p. 80° C, and add camphor, the argument is the same as for adding naphthalene to pure camphor. The two effects are combined in Figure 2-5, in which the melting point is plotted as a function of the mole % composition of the liquid phase. The two curves intersect at 32.3° C, where the composition is 58 mole % camphor-42 mole % naphthalene. This point is known as the *eutectic* point, the lowest possible melting point of any mixture of these two compounds.

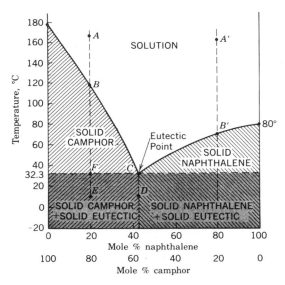

FIGURE 2-5.   Melting point-composition diagram for the naphthalene-camphor system.

Much more information can be derived from this graph. If a liquid mixture containing 20 mole % naphthalene (point *A*) is cooled, it will begin to freeze at 117° C (point *B*), but the solid which appears is pure camphor. As the mixture freezes, the liquid phase becomes enriched in naphthalene and its melting point must fall until the eutectic point is reached (point C). Here the composition of the remaining liquid is 42 mole % naphthalene, and stays unchanged as both camphor and naphthalene continue to freeze in the same ratio. An analogous treatment holds for a mixture containing 80 mole % naphthalene (point A'), but in the opposite direction ($A'B'CD$). An initial mixture containing 42 mole % naphthalene will melt or freeze at 32.3° C without change of composition of either phase.

Consider next a mixture of solids containing 20 mole % naphthalene which is to be heated. When the temperature reaches 32.3° C, it will begin to melt and produce a liquid phase of the eutectic composition, 42 mole % naphthalene. It should continue to melt at this temperature until no more solid naphthalene remains. The temperature will then rise as the liquid phase has now found equilibrium with pure solid camphor, the composition of the liquid following the curve to the left of the eutectic point. The liquid thus becomes enriched with camphor until no solid camphor is left. At this point the composition of the liquid phase is the same as that of the original solid mixture, 20 mole % naphthalene.

The process just described may be confusing to follow on the phase diagram because the solid originally consists of part eutectic mixture and part pure camphor, with an average composition of 20 mole % naphthalene. A temperature-time diagram is also useful in illustrating the same process. In Figure 2-6 the temperature increases steadily along AB until the melting point of the eutectic

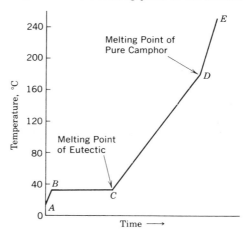

FIGURE 2-6. Heating curve for a solid sample with an average composition 20 mole % naphthalene-80 mole % camphor.

is reached. While the eutectic is melting, the temperature remains essentially constant, *BC*. At point *B* the average composition of the solid is 20 mole % naphthalene, but at point *C* only pure camphor remains as a solid. As the remaining camphor melts, the temperature follows curve *CD* in Figure 2-6 with a liquid composition following curve *CB* in Figure 2-5. After the solid is completely melted, the temperature increases more rapidly along curve *DE* in Figure 2-6.

It should be clear that unless it has a eutectic composition, a mixture of two compounds will melt over a range of temperature. A broad melting point is indeed an indication of the presence of an impurity; however, a broad melting point may also result from poor heat transfer or decomposition of the sample.

Freezing Points with Solid Solutions. The naphthalene-camphor system represents a special class of mixtures in which no solid solutions or mixed compounds form. Whenever solid solutions are possible, the melting point diagram takes a different form like that for the system naphthalene-β-naphthol shown in Figure 2-7. The upper curve represents the composition of the liquid and the lower curve the composition of the solid in equilibrium with the liquid

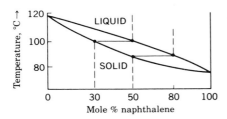

FIGURE 2-7. Temperature-composition curve for the naphthalene-β-naphthol system.

at the same temperature. Horizontal tie-lines intersecting the two curves give the composition of the liquid and solid phases which are in equilibrium at the tie-line temperature. For example, a 50-50 mixture of the two solids will begin to melt at 90° C, but the liquid phase produced will contain a considerable enrichment of the lower melting component (80 mole % naphthalene). Similarly, a 50-50 mixture of the two liquids will begin to freeze at 100° C, but the solid phase produced will contain 70 mole % β-naphthol, again a considerable enrichment but not pure β-naphthol as would occur if no solid solutions were formed. The liquid and solid curves of Figure 2-7 are similar to the vapor and liquid curves used to explain distillation. We will discuss the shape of these curves in the section on Distillation.

Identification by Melting Point. The sharp melting point of a pure compound serves as a means of identification. However, the usual "pure" organic compound seldom has a melting point range of less than 0.3 to 0.5° C. Thus there are often several compounds all having essentially the same melting point. Pure samples of the suspected compounds permit a more positive identification. Portions of the unknown are mixed with each of the known compounds and the melting point of each mixture is taken. The "mixed melting point" of all such mixtures will be lowered except when the two compounds are identical.

ZONE MELTING

The melting point behavior of mixtures is put to good use in the powerful technique of zone melting, or zone refining. As shown in Figure 2-8, the basic apparatus consists of a tube and traveling furnace. The long narrow column is

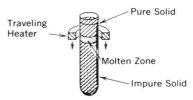

FIGURE 2-8. Essential features of the zone melting apparatus. The impurities, represented as dots, collect in the molten zone.

filled with the impure liquid substance which is then quickly frozen. A small zone at the top is melted by the furnace. As the furnace moves slowly from top to bottom of the column, the melted zone follows along, with melting occurring at the lower interface and freezing at the upper. The success of this technique depends on fast and efficient heat transfer into and out of the column.

Suppose that the column is filled with camphor containing a 1% impurity of naphthalene. At the beginning, the melted zone will thus contain 99% camphor. As the zone progresses down the column, pure camphor will freeze out at the top of the zone while all of the naphthalene remains in the liquid phase. The melted zone will continuously be enriched in naphthalene until it reaches the bottom of the column, or until it reaches the eutectic composition (see Figure 2-5). Ideally, a single pass of the furnace should produce pure camphor and concentrate all of the naphthalene in one zone length at the bottom of the column. In practice, heat transfer is far from perfect, and the freezing crystals may be contaminated by occlusion and absorption. Nevertheless, after a few successive passes of the melted zone through the charge, the purification will be essentially complete.

In a system where solid solutions are possible, the situation is less favorable. The solid which freezes out is not a pure compound but is somewhat enriched in the lower melting component (see Figure 2-7). With each successive pass of the furnace, the purity increases; however, it may take many passes to reach the desired result. Fortunately, this equipment can be automated very easily. A rotating helical column, as shown in Figure 2-9, is most effective. Several melted zones are thus passed through the column simultaneously.

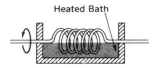

Heated Bath

FIGURE 2-9. Rotating helical column for continuous zone melting.

Zone refining is one of the best methods of preparing ultrapure materials; e.g., germanium for transistors with less than 1 part in 10 billion impurity, and primary standard benzoic acid of 99.99% purity.

CRYSTALLIZATION

Although zone melting is a powerful purification technique, it does require repeated melting of the sample. Many organic substances are thermally unstable and will decompose in such a drastic process. A more gentle and commonly used method of purification of solids is crystallization. Here the solid phase is formed by precipitation from solution rather than by freezing from a melt. In either case, in crystal formation there is a great tendency to build an organized lattice of a single substance, leaving impurities in the liquid phase.

In brief, crystallization from solution consists of preparing a saturated solution of the substance in question at the boiling point of the solvent, filtering the hot solution to remove insoluble impurities, cooling the filtrate to effect crystallization, filtering, washing, and drying the crystals. Although some losses due to solubility are inevitable, good yields of pure product can be realized. The success of the procedure can often be judged by the appearance of well-formed crystals, or by checking the melting points of starting material and product.

Selection of the Solvent. Perhaps the most important part of the procedure is the choice of the best solvent. Often this must be done by trial-and-error, using small samples of the compound in a few drops of the solvents. A list of useful solvents is given in Table 2-2. Several criteria are used in selecting the best solvent:

1. The solvent should have a large temperature coefficient for the solubility of the substance; that is, it should dissolve a large amount when hot and a small amount when cold.
2. Impurities should be either insoluble when hot or soluble when cold.
3. The solvent should have moderate volatility; not too volatile to handle easily at its boiling point, but easily removed when drying the crystals.
4. The solvent should be chemically inert toward the substance.

TABLE 2-2 Some Useful Solvents

Solvent	Boiling Point, °C	Freezing Point, °C	Dielectric Constant
Diethyl ether	35	−116	4.3
Carbon disulfide	46	−111	2.6
Acetone	56	−95	20.7
Chloroform	61	−64	4.8
Methanol	65	−98	33.6
Tetrahydrofuran	66	−65	7.6
Di-isopropyl ether	68	−60	3.9
Carbon tetrachloride	76	−23	2.2
Ethyl acetate	77	−84	6.0
Ethanol	78	−117	24.3
Benzene	80	5.5	2.3
Cyclohexane	81	6.5	2.0
Iso-propanol	82	−89	18.1
Water	100	0	80.4
Dioxane	102	12	2.2
Toluene	111	−95	2.4
Acetic acid (glacial)	118	17	6.2
N,N-Dimethylformamide	154	−61	34.8
Diethylene glycol	245	−10	37.7

In the absence of more specific information, the most useful general rule is that "like dissolves like"—polar substances are best crystallized from polar solvents, and vice versa. As a rough guide to polarity, the dielectric constants listed in Table 2-2 may be helpful. The larger the dielectric constant, the more polar the solvent. A mixture of two solvents may be better than either one alone; for example, ethanol-water, benzene-cyclohexane, ethanol-ethyl acetate, benzene-ether.

18   *Preparation of the Solution.*   To obtain an optimum yield, it is important to use the minimum amount of solvent. If a large excess of the solvent has been used, it should be evaporated until the solution is nearly saturated. A slight excess of solvent is desirable because the next step is filtration to remove insoluble impurities. When a mixture of two solvents is to be used, the solid is first dissolved in the solvent in which it is more soluble. The second solvent (in which it is less soluble) is added slowly to the hot solution until the solution starts to become cloudy. More of the first solvent is then added until the solution again becomes clear. Alternatively, the second solvent may be added after the filtration step. If the solution is just saturated before the filtration, some crystallization will almost inevitably occur in the funnel. The hot solution is filtered through a short-stem funnel without suction, keeping it as near boiling as possible. A few milliliters of additional solvent are used to rinse the flask and funnel.

Crystallization.   The best crystals are formed by slowly cooling the solution. Crystals which are formed too rapidly tend to be very small, sometimes even collodial. They are difficult to filter and adsorb impurities on their surfaces. On the other hand, very large crystals may occlude portions of the solvent which cannot be removed by washing. The lower the final temperature, the greater the yield, although at some point the impurities may also crystallize, voiding the entire procedure. If the product is appreciably soluble, the solubility may be decreased by adding a second solvent in which it is less soluble.

The slow cooling is usually accomplished by simply allowing the flask to stand undisturbed—it may take hours to reach equilibrium. Many solutions tend to become supersaturated and once crystallization begins, crystals shoot rapidly through the solution, occluding most of the impurities. On the other hand, in stubborn cases crystallization may not start at all, whence various forms of magic must be invoked; for example, scratching the inside of the flask with a stirring rod or withdrawing the stirring rod, hoping that crystallization will start on the rod as the solvent evaporates. Whenever crystals of the substance are available from elsewhere, it is usually possible to start crystallization by "seeding," that is, adding a tiny speck of crystal to the supersaturated solution.

Separation of the Crystals.   Suction filtration of the cold mixture is the best way to remove the supernatant. Since the adhering solution, "mother liquor," contains the soluble impurities, the crystals must be sucked as dry as possible by pressing them against the bottom of the filter. They are then washed with several portions of fresh, cold solvent, keeping all volumes minimal. Adequate drying may require vacuum or heat as necessary.

Some loss of product is inevitable because of its solubility in the mother liquor. If it is important to increase the yield, the volume of the mother liquor can be reduced by evaporation, whereupon a second "crop" of crystals results.

The purity of the second crop will probably be less than that of the first and this should be checked by melting-point determination. Low percentage losses are generally tolerable.

DISTILLATION METHODS

Anyone who has passed by an oil refinery will be impressed by the vast array of distillation columns, or fractionating towers, that dominate the skyline. Fractional distillation is perhaps the commonest of industrial processes for separating mixtures on a large scale.

On the laboratory scale, the alchemist's retort is one of the oldest and simplest pieces of scientific apparatus. Now a museum piece, the retort has been replaced by more efficient and more versatile fractionating columns. The technology of making distillation columns has reached an advanced stage and is not likely to change much in the near future. Small-scale distillation is already being replaced to some extent by various chromatographic methods, but for medium- and large-scale separations of volatile compounds, distillation is usually the method of choice.

Temperature Dependence of Vapor Pressure. We have already used the temperature dependence of vapor pressure of liquids and solids to define the melting point. Curve B in Figure 2-1 shows that the vapor pressure of a liquid increases rapidly with temperature. Since vapor pressure measures the tendency of molecules to escape from the liquid to the vapor state, we would expect this behavior. Vapor pressure data for some straight chain hydrocrabons are given in Table 2-3. For many substances, the *Clapeyron equation* expresses the vapor pressure adequately. This equation is treated rigorously in thermodynamics, but for our purposes we will use one of the integrated forms:

$$\log P = -\frac{\Delta H_v}{2.3RT} + \text{const.} \tag{2-4}$$

or

$$\log \frac{P_2}{P_1} = -\frac{\Delta H_v}{2.3R}\left(\frac{1}{T_2} - \frac{1}{T_1}\right) \tag{2-5}$$

where ΔH_v is the heat of vaporization in cal/mole and R is the gas constant (1.987 cal/mole^{-1} deg^{-1}). Over a considerable range of temperature, ΔH_v is constant and can be determined by measuring the slope of a plot of the data according to Equation 2-4, as shown in Figure 2-10. Once we have a value for ΔH_v, Equation 2-5 is convenient for computing the vapor pressure, P_2, at temperature T_2 from the known value, P_1, at another temperature, T_1.

example / problem 2-3: What is the heat of vaporization and the vapor pressure of *n*-pentane at 25°C? The data from Table 2-3 are plotted in Figure 2-10, from which the slope is

TABLE 2-3 Vapor Pressures of Paraffins in Torr*

Temp.	n-Pentane	n-Hexane	n-Heptane	n-Octane
0° C	183	40	11	3
10	282	70	21	6
20	420	120	36	10
30	611	170	58	18
40	873	280	92	31
50	1193	410	141	49
60	1605	565	209	78
70	2119	770	302	118
80	2735	1050	427	175
90	3498	1390	589	253
100	4410	1840	795	354
110			1047	482
120			1367	646
130				859

*1 torr = 1 mm Hg

-1.4×10^3 deg^{-1} giving a value for ΔH_v of 6400 cal/mole. From the graph, the vapor pressure at 25° C ($1/T = 0.00336$) is 500 torr or using Equation 2-5 and values for 20° C we have

$$\log \frac{P_2}{420} = \frac{-6400}{2.3 \times 1.987}\left(\frac{1}{298} - \frac{1}{293}\right)$$

$$\log P_2 - \log 420 = 0.07$$

$$\log P_2 = 2.69$$

$$P_2 = 490 \text{ torr}$$

Boiling Point of a Pure Liquid. When a liquid is heated, its vapor pressure increases until it reaches the external pressure. When these two pressures are equal, the liquid is at its *boiling point*. Under these conditions the rates of evaporation and condensation are equal. The boiling point depends on the total external pressure (normally 1 atmosphere) and decreases rapidly as the external pressure is lowered. Boiling points given in reference tables usually refer to 760 torr unless otherwise specified.

example / problem 2-4: What is the boiling point of n-pentane at 760 torr? At 100 torr? From Equation 2-5 and values for 40°, we have:

$$\log \frac{760}{873} = \frac{-6400}{2.3 \times 1.987}\left(\frac{1}{T_b} - \frac{1}{313}\right)$$

$$T_b = 309° \text{ (36° C) at 760 torr}$$

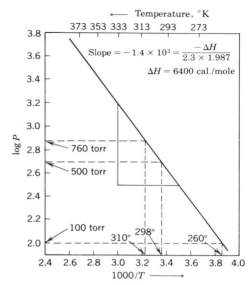

FIGURE 2-10. Vapor pressure-temperature plot for *n*-pentane according to Equation 2-4.

and for the T_b at reduced pressure (100 torr), using values for $0°$ C we have:

$$\log \frac{100}{183} = \frac{6400}{2.3 \times 1.987} \left(\frac{1}{T_b} - \frac{1}{273} \right)$$

$$T_b = 260° \ (-13° \text{C}) \text{ at } 100 \text{ torr}$$

From Figure 2-10, the corresponding boiling points are $310°$ and $260°$.

At lower pressure the boiling point is not only at a lower temperature, but also changes faster with a change in pressure. Compounds which are sensitive to heat may often be distilled at temperatures well below their normal boiling points by reducing the pressure inside the apparatus as shown in Figure 2-11. A mixture of compounds A and B, whose boiling points are also given in Figure 2-11, would be more easily separated at low pressure because the difference in boiling points is larger. In order to explain the distillation of mixtures, we will return to Raoult's law and the vapor pressure of solutions.

Boiling Point vs. Composition. Raoult's law, introduced on page 9, states that the partial vapor pressure of a constituent, P_A, is equal to the product of the mole fraction, X_A, and the vapor pressure of the pure constituent, P_A°:

$$P_A = X_A P_A^\circ \tag{2-2}$$

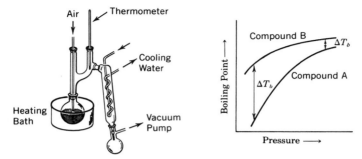

FIGURE 2-11. Apparatus for distilling under reduced pressure and the effect of pressure on the boiling points of two compounds to be separated.

This law is valid only for an ideal solution, or to put it the other way around, *an ideal solution is one that obeys Raoult's law*. Ideal behavior is most likely to be observed if the solute and solvent are chemically similar. For example, a mixture of *n*-hexane and *n*-heptane has essentially ideal behavior, as shown in Figure 2-12. The partial pressure of each component increases in direct proportion to the composition of the solution and the total pressure is the sum of the two.

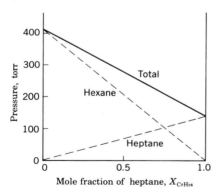

FIGURE 2-12. Vapor pressure-composition curves for the hexane-heptane system at 50° C.

More often the linear relation expressed in Equation 2-2 is valid only in highly dilute solutions, and even then only for the major component—the solvent. In this instance, the vapor pressure of the solute, P_B, often obeys another law, *Henry's law*:

$$P_B = kX_B \qquad (2\text{-}6) \qquad \textbf{23}$$

where k is a constant not equal to P_B°.

If A is the solvent and B the solute, the solution is likely to be ideal only if interaction between two molecules of A is similar to that between two of B, and also similar to that between A and B; otherwise, the solution will probably be non-ideal.

The data for Figure 2-12 pertain to a constant temperature. In Figure 2-13, the total vapor pressure for a mixture of n-hexane and n-heptane is plotted vs.

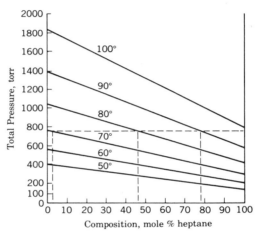

FIGURE 2-13. Effect of temperature on the total vapor pressure for the hexane-heptane system.

the composition of the mixture. The family of curves shows the effect of temperature. The intersection of each curve with the horizontal dashed line at 760 torr gives the boiling temperature of the corresponding mixture; that is, a solution which is 2.5 mole % heptane will boil at 70° C, 46 mole % heptane will boil at 80°, and 78 mole % heptane at 90°. If we had enough lines on the graph, we could read the boiling point of any mixture of n-hexane and n-heptane.

It is more informative to plot the boiling point itself as a function of composition at a constant pressure of 760 torr. Also, it is equally important to consider the composition of the vapor which is escaping from the solution. Let X_A and X_B represent the mole fractions of A and B in the liquid phase, and Y_A and Y_B the mole fractions of A and B in the vapor phase. The total pressure is of course equal to:

$$P_T = P_A + P_B \qquad (2\text{-}7)$$

and from Raoult's law:

$$P_A = X_A P_A^\circ \quad \text{and} \quad P_B = X_B P_B^\circ \qquad (2\text{-}8)$$

But in the vapor phase, there is also a simple relationship between partial pressure and composition:

$$\frac{P_A}{P_T} = Y_A \quad \text{and} \quad \frac{P_B}{P_T} = Y_B \qquad (2\text{-}9)$$

Now the ratio of P_A/P_B is readily obtained from Equations 2-8 and 2-9:

$$\frac{P_A}{P_B} = \frac{Y_A}{Y_B} = \frac{X_A P_A^\circ}{X_B P_B^\circ} \qquad (2\text{-}10)$$

If component A is the more volatile component, then $P_A^\circ > P_B^\circ$; therefore, X_A/X_B must be less than Y_A/Y_B. This is *the fundamental principle of fractional distillation*; namely, that in the process of boiling a solution, the vapor becomes enriched in the more volatile component.

example / problem 2-5: What is the composition of the vapor which is in equilibrium with a liquid containing 46 mole % heptane-54 mole % hexane at its boiling point?
From Figure 2-13, the mixture boils at 80° C.
The vapor pressure of hexane is $X_{C_6} P_{C_6}^\circ = 0.54 \times 1050 = 567$ torr.
The vapor pressure of heptane is $X_{C_7} P_{C_7}^\circ = 0.46 \times 427 = 193$ torr.

The vapor composition is $\dfrac{567}{760} \times 100 = 74.5$ mole % hexane

and $\dfrac{193}{760} \times 100 = 25.5$ mole % heptane.

Thus, an enrichment from 54 to 74.5 mole % hexane.

A similar calculation for a liquid containing 78 mole % heptane which boils at 90° C gives a vapor containing only 60 mole % heptane, or an enrichment from 22 to 40 mole % in the more volatile component (hexane). Many more similar calculations would give the two lines on Figure 2-14 in which pairs of points at the ends of horizontal tie-lines give the composition of the vapor and liquid which are in equilibrium at the boiling point of the given mixture.

The enrichment of the vapor so obtained is a function of the relative vapor pressures of the two components. A single distillation of a solution cannot yield pure products. However, an understanding of the enrichment process is basic to the study of fractional distillation.

Non-Ideal Solutions. When a solution displays a total vapor pressure greater than that predicted by Raoult's law, it is said to show a *positive deviation*. The

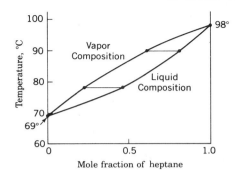

FIGURE 2-14. Boiling point-composition diagram for the hexane-heptane system. Upper curve is the vapor composition and the lower curve is the liquid composition of boiling mixtures. Horizontal tie-lines connect vapor and liquid compositions in equilibrium at various temperatures. Lower curve is also the boiling point as a function of composition.

molecules of each substance seem to prefer their own kind and have an abnormally large tendency to escape from a mixture. The solution thus has an abnormally low boiling point. Perhaps the best known example is ethanol-water; its boiling point-composition diagram is shown in Figure 2-15. A minimum boiling point is observed at a composition of about 96% ethanol. To the left of this minimum, water is the more volatile component, and to the right, ethanol is the more volatile. A solution containing 96% ethanol has the lowest boiling point and is known as an *azeotropic mixture* because it cannot be separated by distillation alone.

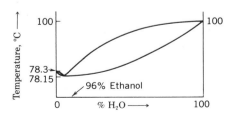

FIGURE 2-15. Boiling point-composition diagram for the ethanol-water system.

If the vapor pressure of a mixture is lower than that predicted by Raoult's law, the solution has a *negative deviation*. These mixtures exhibit an abnormally high boiling point, as exemplified by the acetone-chloroform system shown in Figure 2-16. This behavior is to be expected whenever the two components react in some way with each other (formation of loose molecular complexes).

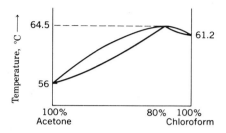

FIGURE 2-16. Boiling point-composition for the acetone-chloroform system.

The composition of the solution remaining in the still always approaches that corresponding to the maximum boiling point and then boils with a constant composition. This, too, is an azeotrope; a better known example of this kind is constant boiling hydrochloric acid which boils at 108.6° C at 1 atmosphere with a composition of 20.2% (6N) HCl.

Azeotropic mixtures appear without rhyme or reason; there is no way to predict their occurrence *a priori*. There are no doubt many more azeotropes than are normally recognized because they frequently occur with a composition of nearly 100% of one of the components. Some typical cases are given in Table 2-4.

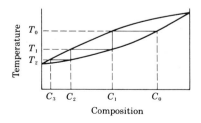

FIGURE 2-17. The enrichment process during the fractional distillation of *n*-hexane and *n*-heptane.

TABLE 2-4 Typical Azeotropic Mixtures

A. With Minimum Boiling Point

Component	Boiling Point of Pure Comp., °C	Minimum Boiling Point, °C
66.7% Benzene	80.2	71.9
33.3% Isopropanol	82.5	
11.7% *tert*-Butanol	82.8	79.9
88.3% Water	100.0	
44% Methanol	64.7	62.3
56% Ethyl acetate	77.1	

B. With Maximum Boiling Point

Component	Boiling Point of Pure Comp., °C	Maximum Boiling Point, °C
31.3% Acetic acid	118.1	162
68.7% Triethylamine	89.4	
77% Formic acid	101	107.1
23% Water	100	
42% Phenol	181.5	186.2
58% Aniline	184.4	

FRACTIONAL DISTILLATION

We have shown that, except for azeotropes, simple distillation results in a partial separation of two components—the vapor phase is enriched in the more volatile component. Neither phase is pure, however. In the technique of fractional distillation, we repeat this partial separation process many times, each time causing a further separation.

Let us return to the hexane-heptane system which is replotted in Figure 2-17, and consider the following very effective, but very impractical experiment. We begin with a large amount of solution of composition C_0—so large an amount that subsequent removal of vapor will not change its composition materially. When it is heated to T_0 it will begin to boil, producing a vapor of composition C_1. This vapor is condensed in a separate part of the apparatus producing a liquid of the same composition, C_1, with a boiling point T_1. This condensate is now brought to temperature T_1 and a small amount of its vapor is collected. The second condensate has a composition C_2 and a boiling point of T_2. This stepwise process can be repeated until the last vapor is essentially pure hexane. But we can remove only a small amount of vapor each time. Unless we have an infinite amount of starting material, the yield is infinitesimally small.

Bubble-Cap Column. The experiment just described is better carried out in a bubble-cap column, as illustrated in Figure 2-18. The original mixture is heated in the still pot A to its boiling point. The vapor passes through plate B and is deflected and condensed by the bubble cap. Plate B is maintained at the boiling point of the mixture contained therein, which is, of course, somewhat lower than that of the original mixture in the still pot. The vapors formed in plate B are condensed at the bubble cap in plate C, and so forth up to the top of the column. The excess liquid in each plate flows through the overflow tube down to the next plate. A condenser is placed at the top of the column. When

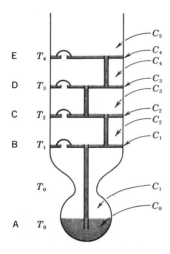

FIGURE 2-18. Operation of a bubble-cap distillation column.

the system has reached equilibrium, the composition of the vapor and liquid in each plate corresponds to the steps drawn in Figure 2-17. Accordingly, the vapors in each plate are progressively enriched in the more volatile component.

By adding a sufficient number of plates, it is possible to separate two components to any required degree of purity. However, the addition of plates requires that more of the mixture will be "held up" within the column. Furthermore, as soon as any product is removed from the top of the column, the equilibrium existing in the top plate is disturbed and this effect is shortly reflected down the column. Any departure from equilibrium results in a less effective separation. Therefore, it is necessary to make a compromise between desirable yield per unit time, or throughput, and purity. The effective number of plates is equal to the number of theoretical enrichment steps, and this is always less than the actual number of plates in the column.

Reflux Ratio. Condensation of the vapors takes place at the top of any column, and the condensate is either withdrawn as product or returned to the column. The ratio of the amount returned to that withdrawn is called the reflux ratio, R, which can vary from zero to infinity. For large-scale industrial purposes, a low value of R (often less than unity) is desirable in order to increase the yield of distillate. For analytical uses, large values of R are needed (10 to 50 are common) in order to obtain better separation. The reflux ratio may be fixed by the geometry of the column head or may be varied in some columns by adjusting the position of the take-off, or by altering the position of a stopcock, possibly with an automatic timing device. As a rule of thumb, the reflux ratio should be approximately equal to the number of plates in the column.

Fractionating Columns. In practice, bubble-cap columns are not convenient for laboratory work. The yield is too small relative to the large amount of material contained in the column; in other words a bubble-cap column has a small *throughput* with a large *holdup.* An approximation of the phenomenon occurring in the bubble-cap column can be achieved by inserting baffles, projections, or various kinds of loose or porous packing materials in an open column. Vapors are thus condensed and partially revaporized many times as they pass up the column, and there is a continuous flow of condensate back down the column. If the column is properly insulated, its temperature will gradually decrease toward the top of the column. The effectiveness of such a column depends on many factors, such as the design of the packing, temperature control, the length of the column and the rate at which product is removed. In order to measure the column's efficiency under operating conditions, we compare the result (degree of separation) obtained from the given column with that to be expected from an ideal bubble-cap column giving the same degree of separation. The number of actual plates in the corresponding bubble-cap column defines the *number of "theoretical plates"* in the given column. An equivalent description of the number of theoretical plates is the number of steps required in the boiling point-composition diagram to reach the same degree of separation; one equilibrium separation is achieved in each theoretical plate. The fundamental unit of efficiency is the *height equivalent to a theoretical plate*, HETP, which is equal to the length of the column divided by the number of theoretical plates. It should be noted that the number of theoretical plates, and HETP, depends on the nature

30

of the mixture to be separated. We will return to the theoretical plate concept many times in the discussions of extraction and chromatography.

In practice the number of theoretical plates in a column is determined with calibration mixtures designed for this purpose. The details are left for more specialized texts. However, it is helpful to have some idea of the number of plates required to make a reasonably good separation. As a rough approximation, let us assume (1) that a "good" separation should yield a product at the top of the column with a composition of at least 95% of the more volatile component while leaving a still-pot composition of 95% of the less volatile component, (2) that a typical mixture has an average boiling point of 150° C, and (3) that the column is operated with total reflux. Then for a binary mixture whose pure components have boiling points differing by ΔT_b, the minimum number of plates required for a "good" separation is given in Table 2-5. Simple unpacked columns rarely have more than one theoretical plate, although the still pot itself furnishes one plate.

TABLE 2-5 NUMBER OF THEORETICAL PLATES
REQUIRED TO MAKE A GOOD SEPARATION

ΔT_b, ° C	No. of Plates
108	1
72	2
36	5
20	10
10	20
2	100

After K. B. Wiberg, *Laboratory Technique in Organic Chemistry*, McGraw-Hill, 1960, p. 44.

Types of Fractionating Columns. A few types of columns in common use will be described briefly (Figure 2-19).

A Vigreux column consists of a glass tube which has been indented in a regular fashion with projections extending inward and slightly downward. It may be insulated with asbestos tape or sealed in a vacuum jacket. It is inexpensive and permits a relatively high throughput with a low holdup. A Vigreux column is much better than a plain empty tube, but at best it is still rather inefficient.

A glass tube packed with irregularly shaped pieces of material is one of the most common forms of fractionating columns. Glass or metal helices offer a large surface for good equilibration between the vapor and liquid. Metal helices give more efficient columns than glass, but cannot be used with corrosive mix-

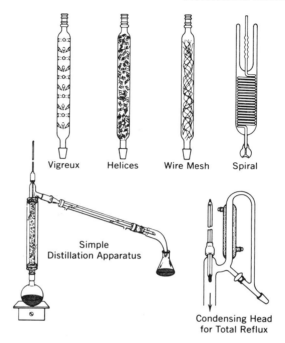

Vigreux Helices Wire Mesh Spiral

Simple
Distillation Apparatus

Condensing Head
for Total Reflux

FIGURE 2-19. Typical fractionation columns.

tures. A column packed with a copper or stainless steel sponge (scouring pad) is a surprisingly good and very inexpensive variation. It is adequate for many simple laboratory distillations.

A concentric tube column consists of a straight, uniform diameter inner tube exactly centered within a precision-bore outer tube. The vapors pass through the annular space ($\sim$0.75 mm) between the tubes while the descending liquid flows down the walls. The high area to volume ratio gives extremely good efficiency with a very low holdup.

The spinning-band column is designed for optimum performance. A twisted strip of wire gauze is inserted into a tube and spun at 2000–3500 r.p.m. A very low holdup is achieved because excess liquid is thrown against the wall of the tube, allowing it to drain freely.

Typical performance data are given in Table 2-6. The limits given are approximate for ordinary operation.

TABLE 2-6 PERFORMANCE DATA OF FRACTIONATING COLUMNS

Type	Throughput, ml/min.	Holdup, ml/plate	HETP, cm
Vigreux	5–10	0.5–2	7–12
Glass helices	2–7	0.7–1	3–5
Metal helices	1–5	0.2–0.5	1.0–1.5
Concentric-tube	0.5–2	0.02–0.03	0.5–1.0
Spinning-band	3–5	0.01–0.03	1–3

QUESTIONS AND PROBLEMS

2-1. The melting point of some impure camphor is observed to be $170.0°$ C. The stem of the thermometer reads $120°$ at the surface of the liquid. A second thermometer shows that the average temperature of the space above the liquid is $120°$. What is the corrected melting point of the mixture? If the melting point of pure camphor is $178.9°$, what is the molality of the impurity? The impurity is known to be naphthalene. Calculate the percent by weight of naphthalene in the impure camphor. *Ans.* $170.4°$ C, 0.224 m, 2.78% w/w.

2-2. Plot the stem correction as a function of observed reading for a thermometer which is always immersed to the $-10°$ mark, assuming that the average temperature of the exposed stem is $30°$ C.

2-3. Calculate the expected freezing point of an aqueous solution containing 10 g of glycerol in 50 g of water. *Ans.* $-4.0°$.

2-4. A 7.50-g sample of a paraffin hydrocarbon was dissolved in 50.0 g of benzene. The freezing point of the solution was $0.0°$ C. Identify the hydrocarbon. *Ans.* $C_{10}H_{22}$.

2-5. If you were to choose a solvent for the determination of molecular weight by the freezing point depression, which solvent (from those in Table 2-1) would you select for maximum accuracy? Why?

2-6. Describe the composition of the system containing an intimate mixture of 2 moles of naphthalene and 2 moles of camphor as it is heated from $0°$ to $200°$ C.

2-7. A 1.00-g sample of a polymer with the general formula $(CH_2)_n$ dissolved in 7.5 g of benzene depressed the freezing point of benzene by $0.50°$. What is the value of n?
Ans. 98.

2-8. Draw the temperature-composition curve for mixtures of cinnamic acid (m.p. $136.8°$) and benzoic acid (m.p. $121.5°$). The melting point of the eutectic mixture containing 57 mole % benzoic acid is $82°$. There are no solid solutions. Predict the shape of the cooling curve (temperature vs. time) for:
   A. pure benzoic acid;
   B. a mixture containing 20% cinnamic acid;
   C. a mixture containing 20% benzoic acid;
   D. the eutectic mixture.

2-9. The vapor pressure of ether is 442 torr at 20° C, 647 torr at 30°, 760 torr at 34.6°. What is its heat of vaporization? If the pressures are expressed in atmospheres, the value of R is 1.987 cal mole^{-1} deg^{-1}. *Ans.* 7000 cal/mole.

2-10. The heat of vaporization of water at its normal boiling point is 9718 cal mole^{-1}. What is its vapor pressure at 75°? *Ans.* 299 torr.

2-11. What is the vapor pressure of a benzene-toluene solution at 30°? State the answer in the form of an equation involving mole fraction of benzene, and the two vapor pressures of the pure compounds—118 torr for benzene and 36 torr for toluene, both at 30°. Assume Raoult's law is valid for this system.

2-12. From the data in Problem 2-11, calculate the mole fraction of benzene in the vapor which is in equilibrium with an equi-molar solution of benzene and toluene at 30° C. *Ans.* 0.765.

2-13. The vapor pressure of n-octane at 100° C is 351 torr, while that of *iso*-octane is 777 torr. If a fuel contains 90 mole % *iso*-octane and 10 mole % n-octane what is its vapor pressure at 100°? What is the composition of the vapor in equilibrium with the liquid at 100°? What additional information is needed in order to compute the boiling point of this fuel? *Ans.* 734 torr, $X_{iso}^{vap} = 0.952$.

2-14. The vapor pressures of some paraffins are given in Table 2-3.

    (*a*) What is the vapor pressure of a 1:1:1 (by moles) mixture of pentane, heptane, and octane at 30°? *Ans.* 229 torr.

    (*b*) What is the vapor pressure of a 1:1:1 (by weight) mixture of pentane, heptane, and octane at 30°? *Ans.* 282 torr.

    (*c*) What mixture of n-pentane and n-heptane boils at 90° under atmospheric pressure? *Ans.* 5.9 mole % pentane.

    (*d*) n-Heptane boils at 98°. What would be the composition of a mixture of n-pentane and n-octane which boils at the same temperature? How could you distinguish between these two liquids (heptane and the pentane-octane mixture) which have the same boiling point by distillation alone?

    (*e*) What is the composition of a mixture of hexane and heptane which boils at 80°? *Ans.* $X_{hex} = 0.535$.

    (*f*) What is the composition of the vapor over a mixture of hexane and heptane (mole fraction = 0.5) at 100°? *Ans.* $X_{hex}^{vap} = 0.70$.

    (*g*) Does the composition of the vapor calculated in (*f*) depend on temperature?

2-15. A liquid mixture of 3 moles of A and 2 moles of B boils freely at 100° C when atmospheric pressure is 760 torr. Calculate the vapor pressure of pure A if the vapor pressure of pure B is 400 torr (all at 100° C). *Ans.* 1000 torr.

2-16. Calculate the total pressure of the system and the mole fraction of A in the vapor of a mixture of A and B ($X_A = 0.3$) at a temperature where the vapor pressure of pure A is 700 torr and that of pure B is 300 torr. *Ans.* 420 torr, 0.5.

2-17. Show that the number of theoretical plates in a fractionation column depends on the type of mixture to be separated.

2-18. Why should the reflux ratio be increased when the number of plates in the column is increased?

2-19. Why is the effective number of plates in a bubble-cap column less than the actual number?

2-20. How would you expect HETP to vary with the reflux ratio? What factors must you consider when determining an optimum reflux ratio?

REFERENCES

G. R. Robertson and T. L. Jacobs, *Laboratory Practice in Organic Chemistry*, 4th ed., Macmillan, New York, 1962; Chapters 5, 6, and 7.

J. Cason and H. Rapoport, *Laboratory Text in Organic Chemistry*, 2nd ed., Prentice-Hall, Englewood Cliffs, N. J., 1962; pp. 9–17, 30–43, 270–311.

K. B. Wiberg, *Laboratory Technique in Organic Chemistry*, McGraw-Hill, New York, 1960; Chapters 1 and 2.

W. G. Pfann, *Zone Melting*, 2nd ed., Wiley, New York, 1966.

3 EXTRACTION

Extraction methods have much in common with distillation methods. In fractional distillation, a separation of components is possible because of the difference in vapor pressure or volatility of the components. At a given temperature and pressure, the equilibrium concentrations of a component in the liquid phase, C_l, and vapor phase, C_v, are expressed by the equation:

$$K = C_l/C_v \qquad (3\text{-}1)$$

where K is an equilibrium constant. For a two-component system, K is greater than unity for the less volatile component, and less than unity for the more volatile. Therefore, in the process of vaporization we have achieved a partial separation of the original mixture.

Extraction is an analogous separation process in which a solute is distributed between two immiscible solvents. A similar law defines the ratio of the concentrations of the solute in the two solvents, 1 and 2:

$$K = C_1/C_2 \qquad (3\text{-}2)$$

where K is the *distribution coefficient* or *partition coefficient*—a special type of equilibrium constant which is essentially equal to the relative solubilities of the solute in the two solvents. Often one solvent is water and the other is an organic solvent, so that inorganic ionic species as well as polar organic compounds are found largely in the aqueous phase while non-polar organic compounds are largely in the organic phase. This is another way of saying "like dissolves like." In dilute solution, to a first approximation, the distribution coefficient is independent of concentration.

example. Suppose that we wish to separate the excess fatty acids from a sample of toilet soap. A pair of solvents such as ether and water would be very effective because fatty acids are far more soluble in ether than in water, while the opposite is true for soap. If ether is arbitrarily defined as "solvent 1" in Equation 3-2, then K is very large for fatty acids and very small for soap.

SIMPLE EXTRACTION

Distribution Law. If the distribution coefficient is very large (> 100), a single extraction in a simple separatory funnel will probably be sufficient to remove a solute from one phase to another. However, it can be shown that with a given amount of extracting solvent, it is more effective to use it in several small portions rather than in a single large batch.

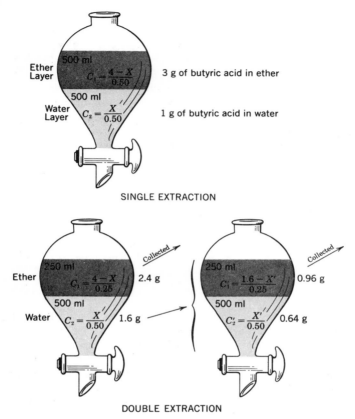

SINGLE EXTRACTION

DOUBLE EXTRACTION

FIGURE 3-1. Comparison of extraction procedures for butyric acid; 4 g of acid originally in 500 ml of water extracted with one 500 ml portion of ether (top), or two 250 ml portions of ether (bottom).

For example, assume that 4 g of butyric acid is to be extracted from 500 ml of water with 500 ml of ether. The distribution coefficient for this system is 3 at 25° C. If the ether is used in a single batch:

$$K = C_{et}/C_{aq} = 3 = \frac{(4 - X)/0.5}{X/0.5}$$

where X is the weight of butyric acid remaining in the water layer. Thus $X = 1$ and 3 g are extracted into the ether layer, as shown in Figure 3-1. However, if

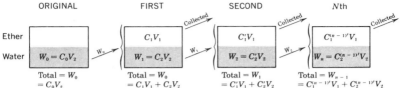

FIGURE 3-2. Successive extractions of sample of W_0 g originally in V_2 ml of water. Distributions are shown after several extractions with V_1 ml portions of ether.

the ether is used in two successive 250 ml portions, for the first one:

$$K = 3 = \frac{(4 - X)/0.25}{X/0.50}$$

In this case, $X = 1.6$ and 2.4 g are found in the ether layer, which is then removed. In the second extraction with the remaining 250 ml portion of ether:

$$K = 3 = \frac{(1.6 - X')/0.25}{X'/0.50}$$

An additional 0.96 g is extracted by the ether and 0.64 g remain in the water. Thus a total of 3.36 g have been extracted, a significant improvement.

A similar calculation shows that had the ether been divided into five 100-ml portions, only 0.23 g of the original 4 g of butyric acid would remain in the aqueous phase after the fifth extraction, and the combined ether extracts would contain 3.77 g.

For the general case, assume that W_0 g of a solute are originally contained in V_2 ml of solvent 2. This is to be extracted with equal portions of V_1 ml of solvent 1, as shown in Figure 3-2. The distribution coefficient is $K = C_1/C_2$. After the first equilibration, the solute is distributed as follows:

$$W_0 = \underset{\text{Top}}{C_1 V_1} + \underset{\text{Bottom}}{C_2 V_2} = (KV_1 + V_2)C_2 \qquad (3\text{-}3)$$

The top layer containing an amount of solute equal to $C_1 V_1$ is then withdrawn, leaving in the bottom layer an amount equal to W_1 or $C_2 V_2$ to be equilibrated in the second extraction:

$$W_1 = C_2 V_2 \qquad (3\text{-}4)$$

From Equation 3-3:

$$C_2 = W_0/(KV_1 + V_2) \qquad (3\text{-}5)$$

Substituting Equation 3-5 into Equation 3-4:

$$W_1 = W_0 \frac{V_2}{KV_1 + V_2} \tag{3-6}$$

In the second extraction, W_1 g of solute are equilibrated between the two phases:

$$W_1 = \underset{\text{Top}}{C_1'V_1} + \underset{\text{Bottom}}{C_2'V_2} \tag{3-7}$$

with the concentrations C_1' and C_2' satisfying the distribution coefficient, K. By analogy we define the amount of solute in the bottom layer as W_2

$$W_2 = C_2'V_2 \tag{3-8}$$

But from Equation 3-7 and the definition of K:

$$C_2' = W_1/(KV_1 + V_2) \tag{3-9}$$

And substituting Equation 3-9 into Equation 3-8, we obtain:

$$W_2 = W_1 \frac{V_2}{KV_1 + V_2} \tag{3-10}$$

and from Equation 3-6

$$W_2 = W_0 \left(\frac{V_2}{KV_1 + V_2}\right)^2 \tag{3-11}$$

Finally, by carrying on this process repeatedly, we arrive at the general equation:

$$W_n = W_0 \left(\frac{V_2}{KV_1 + V_2}\right)^n \tag{3-12}$$

where W_n is the amount remaining in the water layer after n extractions with n equal portions of extractant. As n increases, W_n decreases, but the relationship is exponential and diminishing returns soon set in, as shown in Figure 3-3.

More than five successive extractions are seldom worthwhile. If this number has not resulted in an adequate extraction, it is more practical to look for a better extractant (more favorable K). It should be noted that in deriving Equation 3-12, it was tacitly assumed that the two phases are completely separated after each equilibration.

Apparent Deviations from the Distribution Law. Equation 3-2 pertains only to ideal conditions—in practice there are many reasons for deviations. Like any other equilibrium constant, the distribution coefficient is valid only if activities rather than concentrations are used. Furthermore, the solute may dissociate, dimerize, or form complexes with some other component or with one of the solvents. The distribution coefficient is valid only for a single species and

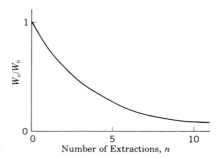

FIGURE 3-3. Fraction of solute remaining in water layer after a number of successive extractions with fresh portions of ether.

does not apply to the possible products of side reactions. On the other hand, in making an extraction we are more interested in the overall distribution rather than that of a single species. The side effects can be taken into account, but the result is a more complicated expression.

For example, undissociated benzoic acid has a distribution coefficient of K_D between ether and water:

$$K_D = (HB)_{et}/(HB)_{aq} \qquad (3\text{-}13)$$

In the water layer, the acid dissociates:

$$HB = H^+ + B^-; \qquad K_a = (H^+)_{aq}(B^-)_{aq}/(HB)_{aq} \qquad (3\text{-}14)$$

as illustrated in Figure 3-4. The total amount of benzoic acid in the water layer is equal to $(HB)_{aq} + (B^-)_{aq}$, and the distribution "quotient" which is of interest is:

$$K^* = \frac{(HB)_{et}}{(HB)_{aq} + (B^-)_{aq}} = \frac{(HB)_{et}}{(HB)_{aq} + K_a(HB)_{aq}/(H^+)_{aq}} \qquad (3\text{-}15)$$

Note that ether is a non-ionizing solvent; benzoic acid does not dissociate in ether and its ions are not extracted from the water layer. Upon rearrangement, Equation 3-15 gives:

$$K^* = \frac{(HB)_{et}}{(HB)_{aq}(1 + K_a/(H^+)_{aq})} = \frac{K_D}{1 + K_a/(H^+)_{aq}} \qquad (3\text{-}16)$$

Equation 3-16 shows that when $(H^+) \gg K_a$, K^* is nearly equal to K_D and the benzoic acid is extracted into the ether layer. When $(H^+) \ll K_a$, K^* approaches

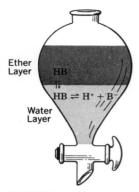

FIGURE 3-4. Distribution
of benzoic acid, HB, between
the ether and water layers in
an extraction.

$K_D(H^+)_{aq}/K_a$, a very small number because $(H^+)_{aq}$ is small, and the benzoic acid is extracted into the water. Thus the pH controls the direction of extraction because it controls the fraction of benzoic acid which exists as dissociated ions in the aqueous layer.

If benzoic acid is extracted from water with benzene, the acid dimerizes in the organic solvent, as shown in Figure 3-5. For a general reaction, we will write:

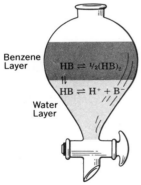

FIGURE 3-5. Distribution of
benzoic acid, HB, between the
benzene and water layers in an
extraction.

$$2A = A_2; \qquad K_d = (A_2)_{bz}/(A)_{bz}^2 \qquad (3\text{-}17)$$

Representing K_D and K^* as:

$$K_D = \frac{(A)_{bz}}{(A)_{aq}} \quad \text{and } K^* = \frac{(A)_{bz} + 2(A_2)_{bz}}{(A)_{aq}} \qquad (3\text{-}18)$$

it can be shown that:

$$K^* = K_D[1 + 2K_d(A)_{bz}] \qquad (3\text{-}19)$$

As the total amount of benzoic acid becomes less, a smaller fraction will be extracted into the benzene layer because a smaller fraction of it will dimerize in benzene. The two effects described by Equation 3-16 and Equation 3-19 may be combined, giving a distribution "quotient" which is even more complicated and of little value for practical use.

Separations by Extraction. The extraction of a single substance from one solvent to another is of little interest. The great value of extraction is the possibility of separating two or more substances based upon a difference in their distribution coefficients. If one solute has a K much greater than 1, and the other much less than 1, a single extraction will cause nearly complete separation. This fortunate circumstance will arise only if two solutes are very different chemically, in which case the pair could no doubt be separated easily in many other ways. If the two solutes have similar, but not identical, distribution coefficients, a single extraction will cause only a partial separation with an enrichment of one solute in one solvent and an enrichment of the other solute in the other solvent. If we are to make an adequate separation, we must repeat the process many times.

MULTIPLE EXTRACTION

After the first extraction, each phase may be further equilibrated with a fresh portion of the opposite solvent. By a systematic recycling of the various intermediate fractions, a satisfactory separation can eventually be achieved at a cost of considerable amounts of solvent and numerous manipulations. The Craig machine has been designed to perform these operations semiautomatically. The mathematical relations describing the Craig process are helpful in understanding many column operations. The distribution profile of a substance as it passes through this apparatus approximates that obtained in a chromatographic separation to be discussed in the following chapters.

Craig Apparatus. The apparatus consists of series of separatory vessels connected so that the outlet of one vessel flows into the inlet of the next. Each vessel consists of two chambers connected to each other as shown in Figure 3-6.

42

The operation is begun by introducing through inlet A an amount of the heavier solvent which will fill chamber B somewhat less than half full. Each of the vessels in the train is filled in a like manner. The sample to be separated is introduced as a solution in the lighter solvent into chamber B of the first vessel. The assembly is rocked back and forth through an angle of about 35° around pivot P. After equilibration has been achieved and the solvents separated into two layers, the assembly is rotated 90° clockwise. The lighter solvent flows through connecting tube C into chamber D while the heavier solvent is trapped in the lower part of chamber B. When the assembly is rotated back to its original position, the lighter solvent now in D flows through outlet E into chamber B of the *next* stage. Hundreds of these assemblies can be mounted side by side or in banks, and all of them rocked and rotated simultaneously by a motor timed to operate as indicated.

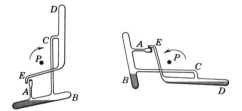

FIGURE 3-6. Extraction vessel of the Craig apparatus.

The Craig Process.   The Craig machine has been a very powerful and practical tool in biochemistry for extremely difficult separations of substances which are chemically very similar. In order to describe the operation mathematically, we will use a schematic representation of the machine shown in Figure 3-7. Consider a series of vessels numbered consecutively from 0. Each vessel is of the same size and is initially half filled with the heavier solvent to be used (solvent I). There is also a series of connecting tubes and valves so that the solvent to be contained in the upper half of the vessels can be transferred from one vessel to the next when desired. No mixing is allowed during the transfer. We will follow the course of a single solute, although whether or not it is present in a mixture is immaterial since each solute should behave independently of all others. The arithmetic will be greatly simplified if we assume that each phase occupies one-half the volume of the vessel and that the K of the solute is 1.

To start the operation, we introduce the sample dissolved in the first portion of the lighter solvent, II, into vessel 0. After equilibration (shaking and settling), one-half of the solute is in the upper phase and one-half in the lower phase. The

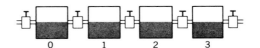

FIGURE 3-7. Apparatus for the ideal Craig process.

upper layer, solvent II, is then transferred to vessel 1 and a fresh portion of solvent II is added to vessel 0. After equilibration, one-quarter of the solute is now found in each phase of each vessel, 0 and 1. Next solvent II in vessels 0 and 1 is transferred to vessels 1 and 2, along with a fresh batch of solvent II to vessel 0. The pattern of the operation has now been established and the distribution of the solute develops as in Figure 3-8 in which the vessels are labeled across the

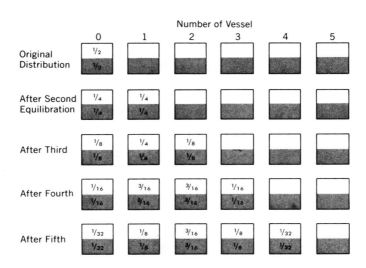

FIGURE 3-8. Successive distribution of solute in the Craig process. Fraction of total solute in each layer of each plate.

top and the number of transfers labeled down the side. To continue the process, it is easier to tabulate the fraction of the solute found in each vessel after n transfers and equilibrations as shown in Table 3-1.

TABLE 3-1   DISTRIBUTION OF SOLUTE IN THE CRAIG PROCESS–FRACTION IN EACH VESSEL

No. of Transfers	Vessel Number								
	0	1	2	3	4	5	6	7	
0	1								$\times 2^0$
1	1	1							$\times 2^{-1}$
2	1	2	1						$\times 2^{-2}$
3	1	3	3	1					$\times 2^{-3}$
4	1	4	6	4	1				$\times 2^{-4}$
5	1	5	10	10	5	1			$\times 2^{-5}$
6	1	6	15	20	15	6	1		$\times 2^{-6}$
7	1	7	21	35	35	21	7	1	$\times 2^{-7}$

The numbers in each row of the table are the coefficients of the terms in the binomial expansion of $(X + Y)^n$. For example, after 7 transfers, 1×2^{-7} or 1/128 of the material is in vessel 0, 7×2^{-7} or 7/128 of the material is in vessel 1, 21/128 of it is in vessel 2, etc. In the general case, the volumes occupied by the two solvents are not equal, and the distribution coefficient is not unity. By the same procedure, however, a table for the distribution of the solute can be generated from the expansion of the binomial expression:

$$\left(\frac{KV_{II}}{KV_{II} + V_I} + \frac{V_I}{KV_{II} + V_I}\right)^n \quad \text{or} \quad \left(\frac{C_{II}V_{II}}{C_{II}V_{II} + C_I V_I} + \frac{C_I V_I}{C_{II}V_{II} + C_I V_I}\right)^n \quad (3\text{-}20)$$

where V_I and V_{II} are the volumes occupied by the two phases in each vessel, and K is the distribution coefficient, $K = C_{II}/C_I$. The first term in each expression is the fraction of the component in phase II, and the second is the fraction of material in phase I. These fractions are the same of course in each vessel. The distribution after n transfers is a function of the K. This effect is shown dramatically in Figure 3-9, where the distribution of two solutes with K of 3/7 and 7/3 is shown after 5, 10, and 15 transfers.

Several conclusions are now apparent. The degree of separation increases with the number of transfers. The movement of the peak maximum is directly proportional to the number of transfers and to the distribution coefficient. As the number of transfers is increased, the solute is spread through more vessels, and becomes more dilute because of the increasing volume of solvent. In fact, the solute is never completely removed from even the first vessel, although after a few transfers the amount of solute remaining in the first vessel may be safely neglected. In principle, any two solutes can be separated by this technique.

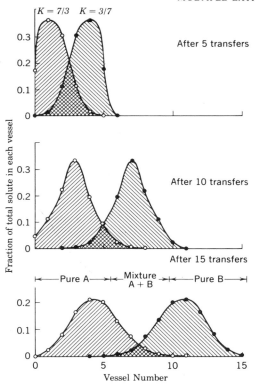

FIGURE 3-9. Distribution of two solutes, A and B, with $K = 7/3$ and $3/7$ respectively, as they travel through vessels of the Craig apparatus, showing that degree of separation increases with number of transfers. (From Purnell, *Gas Chromatography*, Wiley, 1962, p. 95).

For solutes with very similar K's, the number of transfers required increases rapidly as does the cost of apparatus, the amount of solvent, and time required. Nevertheless, all of these costs are within reason for important but very difficult separations.

The Craig apparatus was once a favorite tool of biochemists and is particularly effective in separating complex mixtures of fragile, heat-labile solutes such as hormones and vitamins. Because of its bulk and expense, and the time required for its operation, it has been largely replaced by various forms of chromatography.

46   *Continuous Countercurrent Extraction.* In the Craig apparatus, one solvent moves with respect to the other in a discontinuous fashion. Imagine now that the size of each equilibration vessel is reduced until the entire system becomes a single column, and that the extracting solvent is passed through the system continuously. If both solvents are restricted to thin layers, it is possible to approach an equilibrium state at all points in the apparatus even though it is not exactly attained anywhere. Instead of a series of discrete vessels, it is convenient to construct a column packed with some porous material which will hold one of the solvents stationary on its surface, while allowing the other solvent to percolate through it. The "stationary" solvent need not be fixed in position; it is only necessary that the two solvents "pass through each other," exposing a large interface. Thus the term "countercurrent" is appropriate. In this way an extremely large number of equilibrations can be achieved without expanding the apparatus unduly.

The relationship of continuous countercurrent extraction to the discontinuous Craig process is much the same as the relationship of continuous fractional distillation with a packed column to the ideal bubble-cap plate distillation. Hence, it is common to refer to "theoretical plates" in a continuous extraction column. Here this expression refers to the number of separate equilibrations and transfers which would have to be done in order to achieve the same degree of separation. Actually, countercurrent extraction is identical to one form of elution chromatography.

QUESTIONS AND PROBLEMS

3-1. What is the minimum value of K which would allow the extraction of 99.9% of a solute from 50 ml of water with five successive 50-ml portions of ether?   *Ans. $K = 3$.*

3-2. If five extractions with 100-ml portions of ether extract nine-tenths of a solute from an aqueous solution, what fraction of the solute will ten similar extractions remove?

Ans. 99%.

3-3. Derive an expression similar to Equation 3-16 for the distribution of pyridine between water and benzene:

$$C_5H_5N + H^+ = C_5H_5NH^+ \text{ (in water)}$$

3-4. In Equation 3-19, the dissociation of benzoic acid in the aqueous layer was ignored. Derive an expression for K^* for the distribution of benzoic acid between water and benzene taking into account both the dissociation and dimerization.

3-5. In the Craig process, some of the solute remains in the first vessel no matter how many transfers are made. Assuming that $V_I = V_{II}$, and that $K = 1$, what fraction of the solute will remain in the first two vessels after ten transfers?   *Ans. $1/1024 + 1/102 \approx 1\%$.*

3-6. Formaldehyde has a distribution ratio, $C_{et}/C_{aq} = 1/9$ at 25°. How many liters of water will be required to remove in one extraction 95% of the formaldehyde from 1 liter of ether containing 0.5 mole of formaldehyde? *Ans.* 2.1 liters.

3-7. How much formaldehyde would remain in 50 ml of ether initially containing 5 g of formaldehyde after five successive extractions with 25-ml portions of water? *Ans.* 1 mg.

3-8. Suppose you were given 100 ml of an aqueous solution containing 1 mg of LSD. You wish to extract the LSD into ether. The distribution coefficient is given by

$$K = \frac{\text{conc in ether}}{\text{conc in water}} = 10$$

(a) How much LSD would be extracted with one 150-ml portion of ether?
(b) How much LSD would be extracted with three successive 50-ml portions of ether? *Ans.* (a) 0.938 mg, (b) 0.995 mg.

3-9. The dissociation constant for propionic acid, HOPr, in water is $K_a = 1.00 \times 10^{-5}$, and its distribution coefficient between ether and water is $K_D = 2.85$. You are given a solution of 8.00 g of HOPr in 500 ml of water which has been adjusted to pH 4.00 by the addition of base. The HOPr is extracted from the aqueous solution with two 250-ml portions of ether. What is the pH of the water layer after the second extraction? *Ans.* 4.72.

3-10. Prove that the two expressions given in Equation 3-20 are equivalent.

REFERENCES

L. C. Craig and D. Craig, in *Technique of Organic Chemistry*, A. Weissberger, Editor, Vol. III, Part I, 2nd ed., Interscience, New York, 1956; pp. 150–392. A comprehensive and definitive discussion of extraction and distribution.

E. W. Berg, *Physical and Chemical Methods of Separation*, McGraw-Hill, New York, 1963; Chapter 3. Intermediate level discussion of extraction, probably more useful to the student than Weissberger.

4 CHROMATOGRAPHY

Chromatography embraces a variety of extremely powerful separation techniques. The common feature of them all is that the components of the sample mixture are distributed between two phases, one of which remains stationary while the other phase percolates through the interstices or over the surface of the fixed phase. The movement of the mobile phase results in a differential migration of the sample components. The diverse mechanisms which cause the differential migration are the subjects of the following chapters.

The first detailed description of chromatography is generally credited to Michael Tswett, a Russian biochemist, who separated chlorophyll from a mixture of plant pigments in 1906. He placed a small sample at the top of a column filled with powdered calcium carbonate and then washed the sample through with petroleum ether. As the sample moved down the column, it separated into distinct bands, each one moving at a different rate. Because of the nature of the pigments in the sample, each band had a distinctive color—thus the name for the process was coined from the Greek words for "color" and "to write", although the colors are incidental and have no bearing on the principles of the method.

We have made no restrictions on the nature of the two phases. The stationary phase can be either a solid or a liquid, and the mobile phase can be either a liquid or a gas—thus several combinations are possible. The two combinations which are not possible are gas-gas and solid-solid.

TABLE 4-1 TYPES OF CHROMATOGRAPHY

Mobile Phase	Stationary Phase	Abbrev.
Liquid	Solid	LSC
Gas	Solid	GSC
Liquid	Liquid	LLC
Gas	Liquid	GLC

Likewise, there are no restrictions on the mechanism of the distribution of sample components between the two phases. In LSC it is usually adsorption on the surface of the solid, or a reversible chemical reaction resulting from exchange of ions, or the formation of complexes or other adducts. In GSC it is usually adsorption, but might also be entrapment within the microscopic structure of the solid or a reversible chemical reaction with the solid. In LLC it is a partitioning

49

of the solute defined by the relative solubility in the two liquids. In GLC it is a partitioning of the solute defined by the partial vapor pressure of the solute in solution. Often two or more mechanisms may operate simultaneously, as in electrophoresis, where an electrical force is superimposed on the migration of ionic species.

TYPES OF OPERATION

There are several ways to carry out a chromatographic process depending on how the sample is introduced and moved through the stationary phase. The common methods are elution, displacement, and frontal analysis, which are represented schematically in Figures 4-1, 4-2, and 4-3.

Elution. The sample is introduced as a thin layer at the top of the column as in Figure 4-1a. An inert mobile phase (gas or liquid) flows through the column carrying the sample components with it. The sample molecules, however, distribute themselves between the two phases with each molecule spending a certain fraction of the time in each phase as defined by the appropriate distribution coefficient. While on or in the stationary phase, these molecules do not progress down the column. Thus, the average rate of travel of all molecules of the same kind is a function of the distribution coefficient and the velocity of the mobile phase. In Figure 4-1b and 4-1c this behavior is illustrated at two different times during the elution. A plot of the concentration of the components in the eluent as it emerges from the end of the column is known as a "chromatogram," Figure 4-1d. The time or volume of eluent required to reach the peak maximum is related to the identity of the component, and the area under the peak is related to the amount of the component. Elution is by far the

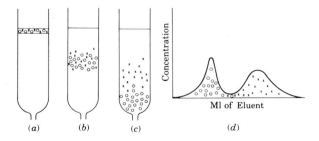

FIGURE 4-1. Schematic representation of elution chromatography, showing the distribution in the column of two components, o and x, after several times a, b and c; and the chromatogram obtained as the components leave the end of the column.

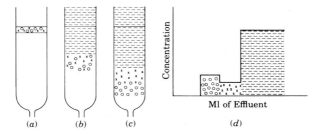

FIGURE 4-2. Schematic representation of displacement chromatography, showing the distribution in the column of two components, o and x, and the displacing agent, –, after several times, *a*, *b* and *c*; and the chromatogram obtained as the components leave the end of the column.

most widely used chromatographic technique and will be discussed in detail under gas chromatography in the next chapter.

Displacement. The sample is introduced as a thin layer at the top of the column as in Figure 4-2*a*. In contrast to the inert mobile phase used in elution, an active mobile phase (or one containing an active ingredient) is used to displace the sample essentially completely from the stationary phase. The more tightly held sample components likewise tend to displace the less tightly held components. Zones of the components develop in the order of decreasing distribution coefficients, each zone displacing the one immediately preceding it until they are all forced out the end of the column. Figures 4-2*b* and 4-2*c* show the development of zones and Figure 4-2*d* shows how the concentration profile appears as the effluent emerges from the column. Each step indicates a new substance. The

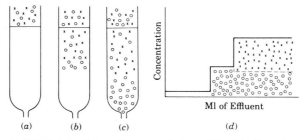

FIGURE 4-3. Schematic representation of frontal chromatography, showing the distribution in the column of two components, o and x, after several times, *a*, *b*, and *c*; and the chromatogram obtained as the components leave the end of the column.

horizontal distance of the step is related to the amount of material, and the step height is related to its identity.

The important advantages of displacement are that the sample is not diluted in large quantities of effluent and the column is used to its full capacity. On the other hand, the zones tend to overlap to some extent, and at the end of the run the column is loaded with the displacing agent which may be difficult to remove. For these reasons, it is not a popular technique.

Frontal Analysis. The sample is continuously introduced as a mixture with the mobile phase, as shown in Figure 4-3a. Each component has a different distribution coefficient, so the column has a different capacity for each one. Unfortunately, the capacity for a given component is not independent of the presence of other substances. The one least tightly held will be the first to emerge, but it will not do so until the column is saturated with respect to it. After its breakthrough, the first component will continue to emerge at a constant concentration until the column also becomes saturated with the second component. After this, both components will continue to emerge unseparated. Only the first component can be obtained in a pure state. However, each additional component will be observed as another breakthrough step in the chromatogram. The time required to reach the step is related to the identity of the component and the height of the step is related to the amount, but not in a simple fashion. Frontal analysis is used primarily to obtain thermodynamic data.

SURVEY OF CHROMATOGRAPHIC PROCEDURES

Of the many possible combinations of materials, mechanisms of distribution and modes of operation, several are of current importance and will be discussed in detail in the next few chapters.

Liquid-solid or adsorption chromatography, discovered by Tswett and reintroduced by Kuhn and Lederer in 1931, has been used extensively for organic and biochemical analysis. Typically, silica gel or alumina, which have a very large ratio of surface area to volume as well as chemically active surfaces, are used as column-packing materials. Unfortunately there are only a few suitable adsorbents, so the choice is limited. An even more serious limitation is the fact that the distribution coefficient for adsorption often depends on the total concentration. It will be shown that this behaviour results in skewed peaks with long tails giving incomplete separations.

Liquid-liquid or partition chromatography was a major advance when introduced by Martin and Synge in 1941; in fact, they were later awarded the Nobel Prize for this work. The stationary phase consists of a thin layer of liquid held in place on the surface of a porous inert solid. A wide variety of liquid combinations are suitable so that this method is very versatile. Furthermore, the distribution coefficient for these systems is more likely to be a constant, giving symmetric sharp elution bands.

Gas-solid chromatography was used before 1800 to purify gases, but not as a true separating tool until much later. Hesse, Claesson, and Phillips made major contributions in the 1940's. In the past it has suffered from the same defects as liquid adsorption chromatography, but current research with new types of solid phases is extending the technique rapidly.

Gas-liquid chromatography (commonly called vapor-phase chromatography or VPC by organic chemists) is perhaps the most powerful and most versatile of all forms. It has caused a revolution in organic chemistry since it was first introduced by James and Martin in 1952. At the moment, the only serious remaining obstacle seems to be that the sample components must have a vapor pressure of at least a few torr at the temperature of the column. Sample sizes from less than a microgram to more than 100 g can be handled, and traces of the order of 10^{-15} g have been detected. There are problems still to be solved, but Nobel Laureate A. J. P. Martin has predicted that the day will come when the analytical laboratory will consist of a master gas chromatograph which can separate any sample automatically and send the various components to the appropriate slave device for identification and measurement.

Ion exchange chromatography is a special field of liquid-solid chromatography. As the name implies, it is specifically applicable to ionic species—not the case with most other forms of chromatography. The introduction of synthetic resins with ion exchange properties just before World War II has revolutionized the difficult separations of rare earth metals and amino acids. At one time, the entire world's supply of mendelevium (about 17 atoms) was concentrated in a single bead of an ion exchange resin.

Paper chromatography is a special field of liquid-liquid chromatography in which the stationary liquid is an adsorbed film of moisture on a paper mat. Other stationary liquids can be used as well. This technique is the ultimate in simplicity. All one needs to do is to spot the sample near the edge of a piece of paper, and dip the edge of the paper into the eluting solvent. With sensitive developing reagents, it is particularly suited to separating and identifying traces of components.

Thin-layer chromatography is similar to paper chromatography except that the paper is replaced by a glass plate coated with a thin layer of alumina, silica gel, or other powdered material. The properties of this "thin layer" are far more reproducible than for paper.

Gel filtration is a separation process performed with a gel consisting of modified dextran—a three-dimensional network of linear polysaccharide molecules which have been cross-linked. The material swells in water to form a sieve-like structure which can sort out molecules by their size. In addition to

54 geometrical effects, some surface effects are involved. Molecules in the molecular weight range from 100 to several million can be concentrated and separated.

Continuous-zone electrophoresis consists of a double-barreled approach. During the course of an elution by paper chromatography, an electrical field is applied across the paper perpendicular to the flow of solvent. Thus ionic species are deflected at an angle from the mainstream, depending on their charge and mobility. This procedure, using crossed gradients, makes continuous chromatography possible. Otherwise, elution chromatography is essentially a batch process.

For the most part, the practice of chromatography is highly empirical. The theory of chromatography has been developed to the greatest extent for gas-liquid chromatography for many reasons. In GLC, there is a large number of useful stationary phases available, and very wide variations in temperature, pressure, and flow rate are attainable. Data can be acquired easily and rapidly. This great flexibility leads to a greater need for an understanding of the process so that experimental conditions can be selected wisely. Furthermore, suggested theories can be tested conveniently over a range of conditions. Therefore, we shall examine GLC first and then apply the concepts to other forms of chromatography.

REFERENCES

A. H. Gordon and J. E. Eastoe, *Practical Chromatographic Techniques*, G. Newnes, London, 1964. Condensed version of theory, written for the working chromatographer.

L. Lederer and M. Lederer, *Chromatography*, 2nd ed., Elsevier, New York, 1957. A classic, now somewhat out of date.

E. Heftmann, *Chromatography*, 2nd ed., Reinhold, New York, 1967.

5 GAS CHROMATOGRAPHY

The separation of benzene (b.p. 80.1° C) from cy-clohexane (b.p. 80.8° C) by fractional distillation is virtually impossible, yet it can be accomplished with the simplest of GLC equipment by an unskilled technician in a few minutes. The more difficult separations—for example, the detection of a hundred or more hydrocarbons in gasoline, the analysis of a fruit skin for traces of pesticide residues, or the separation of steroids at 100° below their boiling points—push the GLC method to its limits, and require an understanding of the details of the process. There is always a delicate compromise among speed, completeness of separation, and the size of sample that can be handled, not to mention the cost and complexity of the apparatus required. As with most instruments, the time spent examining "what's inside the black box" will be well repaid. In this chapter we emphasize fundamental principles that underlie all chromatographic methods. Although the concepts and equations are developed for gas-liquid chromatography, the same ideas apply to all other forms with minor modifications.

GAS-LIQUID CHROMATOGRAPHY

Basic GLC Apparatus. The essential components are shown in Figure 5-1. The inert carrier gas passes through a pressure regulator into a sample injection

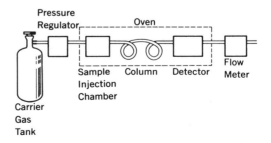

FIGURE 5-1. Essential features of a gas chromatograph.

55

and mixing chamber. From here the carrier gas carries the sample into the column. The column may be packed with a porous solid coated with a thin film of a non-volatile liquid (stationary) phase, or it may be a long capillary tube with a thin coating of liquid on its wall. The sample components are separated as they pass through the column, and one after the other pass through a detector which sends a signal to a recorder. Finally, the gas passes through a flow meter and is exhausted to the atmosphere. A thermostatted oven is provided for the the column, injector, and detector, although the last two may be heated separately.

There are innumerable variations of each of the basic components of a gas chromatograph, and scores of commercial models are available. We will first examine the one most important part common to all—namely, the column itself and its mode of separation.

THEORETICAL PRINCIPLES OF GLC

Linear Ideal Chromatography. We have already implied in Chapter 3 that the Craig extraction technique, if it could be operated in a continuous fashion with very small vessels, has much in common with elution chromatography. In GLC, the sample is introduced in a small volume at the head of the column. The components are immediately distributed between the gas and liquid phases according to a partition coefficient:

$$K = C_L/C_G \qquad (5\text{-}1)$$

If the value of K is truly constant over a wide range of concentrations, then a plot of C_L vs. C_G will be a straight line and we have "linear" chromatography. If, in addition, the following conditions prevail, we have "linear ideal" chromatography:

1. Instant equilibrium is maintained throughout the column at all times.

2. The molecules of the sample are transported through the column only by the motion of the carrier gas. There is no diffusion in either direction along the length of the column, in either gas or liquid phases.

3. The column is packed uniformly so that the ratio of gas to liquid is the same for any cross section of the column.

Thus the fraction of the number of molecules of a given component which are in the gas phase is always the same regardless of where the component is located within the column. This distribution for a three-component mixture is illustrated in Figure 5-2. As a consequence, each component travels through the column at a rate determined by the relation:

Rate = velocity of carrier gas × fraction of time spent in gas phase   (5-2)

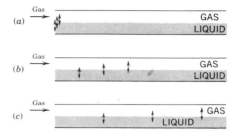

FIGURE 5-2. Linear ideal gas-liquid chromatography, showing the distribution of three components in the column after several times, *a*, *b* and *c*. Vertical position of arrows represents the distribution coefficient. In this schematic column, the solid support is omitted and the entire liquid phase is collected in the bottom half of column.

In this idealized version, the several components should be separated from each other very quickly and emerge as sharp zones or peaks as depicted in the chromatogram in Figure 5-3. No one has yet constructed an ideal column, and some of the requirements for its operation are incompatible with each other. Instant equilibrium implies infinitely fast lateral diffusion across the column, yet there must be infinitely slow longitudinal diffusion along the column. In practice, there is always some broadening of the peaks which is indicative of non-ideal processes.

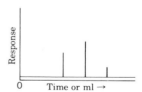

FIGURE 5-3. Ideal gas chromatogram.

Linear Non-Ideal Chromatography. Gas-liquid chromatography in most applications is a form of linear non-ideal chromatography. Non-ideal diffusion processes, illustrated schematically in Figure 5-4, cause the peaks to broaden as they pass down the column. Broad peaks are likely to overlap if they occur too

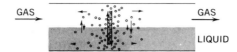

GAS   GAS

LIQUID

FIGURE 5-4. Non-ideal diffusion processes which lead to band broadening in a gas-liquid column. Length of arrows represents rate of diffusion at various points.

close together. In principle, overlapping peaks can eventually be separated if a long enough column is employed, but this is not the only approach to be considered. The separation of two components is a function of the ratio of their retention times (*the separation factor*). The *resolution* of two components (the degree of separation) can be improved, as shown in Figure 5-5, by employing a

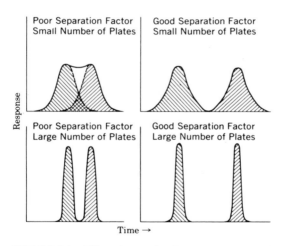

FIGURE 5-5. Effect of separation factor and number of plates in column on the resolution of two peaks.

column having more theoretical plates (see also Figure 5-6), or by choosing a better liquid phase giving a more favorable separation factor, or by a combination of both.

If we are to make the best use of our chromatographic column, we must have some understanding of the factors that determine retention times and the factors that determine the band broadening. The first problem is largely in the realm

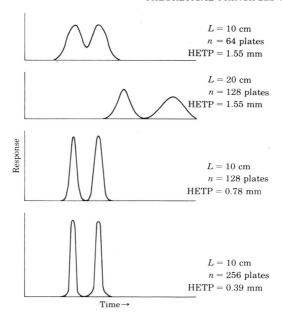

FIGURE 5-6.   Separation of hexane and benzene on four columns. Each column is packed with a Silicone oil liquid phase and is operated at the same flow rate and temperature.

of thermodynamics and the second is in the realm of kinetics. We shall consider the kinetic problem first.

The complete mathematical description of the non-ideal processes which occur in a column and lead to band spreading is far too complex to be treated here. However, two general approaches have been very fruitful—indeed, the so-called "Plate Theory" and "Rate Theory" have been indispensable to the rapid advance of GLC.

Plate Theory.   Let us assume that the column can be divided by hypothetical cross sections into identical segments, of such a length that within each segment an "average" equilibrium distribution is achieved during the passage of carrier gas. Each of these segments is called a "theoretical plate." Then, with a knowl-edge of the K and the carrier gas flow rate, it should be possible to predict the distribution of a solute along the column at any time, or the concentration at a given point as a function of time and, in particular, the shape of the emergent peak. All this can be done from considerations analogous to the operation of the

Craig process. Conversely, from the experimentally observed elution curve (*chromatogram*), we can reverse our thinking and compute the number of theoretical plates in the column. Several equations have been derived for this purpose but perhaps the most useful is:

$$n = 16(t_R/\Delta t)^2 \tag{5-3}$$

where the symbols are defined in Figure 5-7. In applying Equation 5-3, retention and peak width can be measured in any unit (sec, min., cm of chart paper; ml of carrier gas) as long as the same unit is used for both.

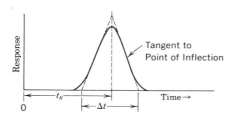

FIGURE 5-7.   Schematic chromatogram.

The number of theoretical plates computed by Equation 5-3 is not solely a function of how the column is built, but also of the nature of the solute, flow rate, temperature, method of sample introduction, and many other variables. Therefore, the number of plates, or the height equivalent to a theoretical plate, HETP (column length/number of plates), is only an approximate number useful for rough comparative purposes as a description of the efficiency of a column.

There are two ways of increasing the number of plates in a column. First, we can lengthen the column, and we find that the number of plates is nearly proportional to the column length, L, as shown in Figure 5-6. In this case, the band width increases as the square root of the column length, but the actual distance between the two peak maxima increases directly with the column length. That is to say, the *ratio* of retention times is constant and independent of column length. Second, we can presumably make a better column without increasing its length, and operate it more favorably so that there are actually more plates in the same column length, as shown in Figure 5-6. The second approach is obviously the better one because retention times are not increased and the peaks actually do become narrower. In fact, the operation described above as linear ideal chromatography, and depicted in Figure 5-3, must involve a column with an infinite number of theoretical plates, or an HETP of zero. The major shortcoming of the plate theory is that it does not treat the experimental factors that actually determine HETP; therefore, it does not indicate how to improve column performance.

Rate Theory. The most important, and unavoidable, causes of non-ideal behavior are considered to be: (*a*) the unequal path lengths of different molecules as they pass through the column due to the variety of tortuous pathways available, (*b*) longitudinal diffusion of the sample components due to concentration gradients within the column, and (*c*) imperfect equilibrium due to the finite time required for mass transfer between the two phases. The detailed mathematical formulation and derivation is beyond the scope of this discussion and only the result, known as the (abbreviated) *Van Deemter equation*, will be presented here:

$$\text{HETP} = A + B/u + Cu \tag{5-4}$$

where A, B, and C are constants related to the three non-ideal effects listed above, and u is the linear velocity of the carrier gas.

The three terms of the Van Deemter equation are often called the A, B, and C terms, or the Eddy Diffusion, Longitudinal Diffusion, and Mass Transfer terms, respectively. In the abbreviated form (Equation 5-4), the role of the gas velocity is emphasized, for this is the factor most easily varied once the column is constructed. As the velocity is *increased*, elution will be faster, there will be less time available for longitudinal diffusion to spread the band, but there will be less time to achieve equilibrium (fewer transfers between the phases). Thus the B term will contribute less and the C term more to the plate height. Conversely, as the velocity is *decreased*, the opposite argument holds—the B term contributes more and the C term less to the plate height. The A term appears to be independent of gas velocity.

It is instructive to plot HETP as a function of u, as in Figure 5-8. Curves of this type are determined experimentally, because many of the data required in the Van Deemter equation are not available. In order to get the HETP vs. u curve, it is necessary to determine HETP with Equation 5-3 for at least three

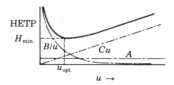

FIGURE 5-8. Van Deemter plot of column efficiency. Each of the terms is plotted separately *vs.* velocity of the carrier gas. The sum of the three terms at any velocity gives the HETP.

different values of u. These values of HETP are then inserted into Equation 5-4 giving a system of three simultaneous equations in three unknowns, A, B and C. The construction of the curve in Figure 5-8 is then obvious. The minimum in the curve shows that there is an optimum gas velocity for best efficiency.

We shall next examine each of the terms in the Van Deemter equation individually. The A term will be decreased if the path lengths through the column of all molecules are made more uniform. This can be achieved by using smaller particles and also by selecting more uniformly sized particles. It is most important to pack the column carefully to avoid vacant channels.

The B term will be decreased if we can reduce longitudinal diffusion. We can reduce the rate of diffusion somewhat by using a denser carrier gas (higher molecular weight, lower temperature, or higher pressure).

The C term results from our inability to achieve instant equilibrium. The most important factor in this regard is the thickness of the liquid layer. Other factors must also be considered; for example, equilibrium can be achieved faster at a higher temperature.

There are numerous assumptions in the Van Deemter treatment. All of the sample must be introduced simultaneously into the first plate of the column. The solid support must be inert and have a constant specific surface throughout the column. The liquid phase must be distributed evenly as a layer of uniform thickness over the entire surface of the solid support. The sample size must be small enough so that a saturated solution is never reached. Diffusion in the gas phase is assumed to be fast relative to that in the liquid phase. Finally, it is assumed that all processes which contribute to band broadening operate independently of one another. In general, most of these assumptions are reasonably close to the truth under normal operating conditions, but careful studies have resulted in numerous modifications and extensions of the original Van Deemter equation. Even the simplified version (Equation 5-4), however, tells us a great deal about the factors which determine the efficiency of the column, and what should be done to make and operate it better.

Factors Determining Retention. The retention time, t_R, is defined as the time measured from the injection of the sample to the maximum of the elution peak, as shown in Figure 5-7. Our objective here is to relate the retention time to the distribution coefficient, K; and in order to do so, it is easier to work with the retention volume, V_R, which should be measured at the column temperature, T_c. The *retention volume* is proportional to the retention time and to the flow rate. The latter, however, is normally measured at the end of the column with a soap-bubble flow meter. Thus the carrier gas at that point is at room temperature and presumably is saturated with water vapor. Therefore, the true flow rate at column temperature, F_c, is

$$F_c = F_{meas} \times \frac{T_c}{T_{room}} \times \frac{p_o - p_{H_2O}}{p_o}$$

where p_o is the outlet pressure (atmospheric) and p_{H_2O} is the vapor pressure of water at the temperature of the flow meter. The retention volume, V_R, at column temperature and atmospheric pressure is then:

$$V_R = t_R F_c \tag{5-5}$$

The retention volume defined by Equation 5-5 must be further corrected to the *average* pressure in the column. The pressure at the inlet, p_i, must always be higher than the pressure at the outlet, p_o, if there is to be flow through the column. From the gas law and the requirement of a constant volume throughput at all points in the column, it is possible to derive a pressure drop correction factor, j, which relates the average pressure to the inlet and outlet pressures:

$$p_{av} = p_o \times \frac{2[(p_i/p_o)^3 - 1]}{3[(p_i/p_o)^2 - 1]} = p_o/j \tag{5-6}$$

Selected values of j are given in Table 5-1.

TABLE 5-1 VALUES OF THE PRESSURE DROP CORRECTION FACTOR

p_i/p_o	j	p_i/p_o	j
1.00	1.000	1.80	0.695
1.10	0.952	1.90	0.668
1.20	0.907	2.00	0.643
1.30	0.865	2.10	0.619
1.40	0.826	2.20	0.597
1.50	0.790	2.30	0.576
1.60	0.756	2.40	0.557
1.70	0.725	2.50	0.539

The "corrected" retention volume, V_R°, is thus:

$$V_R^\circ = t_R F_c j \tag{5-7}$$

There is one more correction to be considered. In order to transport a non-absorbed solute through the column, it is necessary to use a volume of carrier gas equal to the free gas space in the column, V_G. Any solute which is partially absorbed (retained) will require a volume of carrier gas in excess of V_G. Clearly, V_G is a property of the column and the way it is packed. It has nothing to do with retention, and should be subtracted from the measured retention volume. V_G is easily determined by noting the time (volume) required for a trace of air injected along with the sample to reach the end of the column and make a small pip in the recorder signal.

In Equation 5-2 it was shown that the rate of travel of a component (inversely related to retention) was determined by the fraction of time spent in the liquid phase, and this in turn depends on the total amount of liquid phase present, W_L. Therefore, it is desirable to compute the retention volume *per gram of solvent* in the column—a quantity known as the *specific retention volume*, V_g. Conventionally, V_g is corrected to $0°$ C.

Finally, we note that the raw data are taken from a recorder chart paper on which we measure distance, d_R, from the injection to the peak maximum, and a corresponding d_A for the air peak. All of these concepts can be summarized in a single equation defining V_g:

$$V_g = \underbrace{\underbrace{\frac{d_R - d_A}{\text{chart speed}} \times F_c}_{\text{retention volume}} \times \frac{3[(p_i/p_o)^2 - 1]}{2[(p_i/p_o)^3 - 1]} \times \frac{273}{T_c} \times \frac{1}{W_L}}_{\text{corrected retention volume}} \qquad (5\text{-}8)$$

where $\frac{d_R - d_A}{\text{chart speed}}$ is retention time.

V_g, like K, is a true equilibrium constant, dependent only on the nature of the solute and solvent, and the temperature of the column. The two constants differ only because of the different units used:

$$V_g = \frac{\text{corrected retention volume}}{\text{weight of liquid in column}} \times \frac{273}{T_c}$$

$$K = \frac{\text{conc of solute in liquid phase}}{\text{conc of solute in gas phase}}$$

One method of relating the two is as follows. At the maximum of the peak, half of the solute has been eluted in a volume $V_R^\circ - V_G$, and the other half remains in the column, distributed between the gas and liquid phases V_G and V_L. In terms of amounts of solute:

$$\underbrace{C_G V_G}_{\substack{\text{amt in} \\ \text{gas}}} + \underbrace{C_L V_L}_{\substack{\text{amt in} \\ \text{liquid}}} = \underbrace{C_G(V_R^\circ - V_G)}_{\substack{\text{amt already eluted} \\ \text{at the peak max}}} \qquad (5\text{-}9)$$

In GLC, the distribution coefficients are usually much larger than unity, and therefore the first term in Equation 5-9 is much smaller than the second. Neglecting the first term, dividing by C_G, and employing the definition of $K = C_L/C_G$, we arrive at the *basic equation for retention*:

$$V_R^\circ = V_G + KV_L \qquad (5\text{-}10)$$

From the relations contained in Equations 5-7, 5-8, and 5-10, it follows that:

$$V_g = \frac{273K}{T_c \rho_L} \tag{5-11}$$

where ρ_L is the density of the liquid phase at column temperature.

example / problem 5-1: Some typical retention data are listed below. Calculate the specific retention volume and the partition coefficient.

Retention time, t_R	3.5 min.
Air peak time, t_A	0.5 min.
Flow rate (25°, 1 atm), F_{meas}	60 ml/min.
Column temp., T_c	150° C
Inlet pressure, p_i	1000 torr
Outlet pressure, p_o	760 torr
Vapor pressure of water at 25°	24 torr
Weight of liquid phase, W_L	2.5 g
Density of liquid phase at 150°, ρ_L	0.95 g/ml

The flow rate at column temperature and 760 torr is

$$F_c = 60 \times \frac{423}{298} \times \frac{760\text{-}24}{760} = 82.5 \text{ ml/min.}$$

The ratio of inlet to outlet pressures is $1000/760 = 1.32$.

The pressure drop correction factor, j, is 0.857 (Table 5-1). Therefore, from Equation 5-8:

$$V_g = (t_R - t_A) \times F_c \times j \times \frac{273}{T_c} \times \frac{1}{W_L}$$

$$= (3.5\text{-}0.5) \times 82.5 \times 0.857 \times \frac{273}{423} \times \frac{1}{2.5} = 55.0 \text{ ml/g}$$

And from Equation 5-11

$$K = \frac{T_c \rho_L V_g}{273} = \frac{423 \times 0.95 \times 55.0}{273} = 81.0$$

The factors which determine K, and thus indirectly influence the retention time, are not completely understood. The kinds of solutions used in gas chromatography often involve solutes and solvents of widely different chemical properties, and always of different molecular dimensions. Such solutions rarely obey Raoult's law, but often obey Henry's law provided they are highly dilute. The distribution coefficient is directly related to the Henry's law constant, or the volatility of the solute. The volatility, in turn, is a function of the cohesive forces acting between the molecules of the solute and solvent. In this regard, some qualitative concepts will help us to understand the factors which determine retention at the molecular level.

1. *Dipole-Dipole Interactions.* Molecules containing electronegative or electropositive atoms possess a permanent electrical dipole, and will interact

66

strongly with other molecules possessing a dipole. Thus a polar solute will have an abnormally low volatility (high solubility) in a polar solvent. On the other hand, in a non-polar solvent, the dipole-dipole interactions between the polar solute molecules themselves are decreased by dilution, resulting in an abnormally high volatility (low solubility). Dipole-dipole interactions are decreased as the temperature is increased.

2. *Induction Forces.* If either the solvent or solute contains a permanent dipole, it can induce a temporary dipole in the other. The magnitude of the force depends on the polarizability of the other molecule and is generally rather small.

3. *Dispersion Forces.* The vibrations of non-polar molecules often produce temporary dipoles by slight separation of the electrical charges within the molecules. The oscillating dipoles can induce similar temporary dipoles in neighboring polarizable molecules. A small force of attraction is thus generated. These forces are present in all solutions.

4. *Hydrogen Bonds.* An especially strong dipole-dipole interaction is possible when one molecule contains a polarized hydrogen atom and the other a strong electronegative atom, such as a fluorine or oxygen atom. The extra strength results from the closeness of approach afforded by the small size of the proton.

5. *Formation of Metal Complexes.* Solutions of silver nitrate in glycols or benzyl cyanide selectively absorb olefins because of the weak organo-metallic complexes formed. Thus the olefins are retained far longer than corresponding paraffins in these columns. Similarly, heavy metal salts of fatty acids retard amines because of complex formation.

In general, non-polar liquid phases are non-selective; that is, in the absence of special forces between solute and solvent, the volatility of the solute is determined primarily by its vapor pressure. Thus separations will be in the order of increasing boiling points of the solutes. On the other hand, with polar liquid phases, the volatility is not so simply determined because of the complicating factors just mentioned.

Obviously, the polarity of the liquid phase is the primary concern. Rohrschneider has proposed a relative polarity scale for solvents based on the relative retention of butadiene vs. butane, which would be large for polar solvents and small for non-polar solvents. The polarity of squalane is arbitrarily assigned a value of zero, and the polarity of oxydipropionitrile is fixed at 100. The relative polarity, P, of any solvent then is determined from the expression:

$$P = 100 - 100(q_1 - q_x)/(q_1 - q_2) \qquad (5-12)$$

where q_1 is log $(V^\circ_{butadiene}/V^\circ_{butane})$ measured on oxydipropionitrile, q_2 is that measured on squalane and q_x is that measured on the given solvent. The polarities of a few liquid phases are given in Table 5-2.

TABLE 5-2 RELATIVE POLARITIES OF SOME LIQUID PHASES

β,β'-Oxydipropionitrile	O with CH$_2$—CH$_2$—CN and CH$_2$—CH$_2$—CN	100
Propylene glycol carbonate	H$_2$C—O, HC—O with C=O, CH$_3$	83
Acetylacetone	CH$_3$COCH$_2$COCH$_3$	73
Diethyl formamide	HCON with C$_2$H$_5$ and C$_2$H$_5$	62
Dibenzyl ether	C$_6$H$_5$CH$_2$OCH$_2$C$_6$H$_5$	44
Chlorooctadecane	ClCH$_2$(CH$_2$)$_{16}$CH$_3$	13
Silicone oil		7
2, 6, 10, 15, 19, 23-Hexamethyl-tetracosane (squalane)		0

[After L. Rohrschneider, *Z. Anal. Chem.*, **170**, 256 (1959).]

CARRIER GAS

In GLC, the carrier gas provides transportation for the sample components through the apparatus. It must be chemically inert and available in pure form at reasonable cost. The most commonly used gases are helium, nitrogen, argon, hydrogen, and carbon dioxide, although others, such as steam, are used for special purposes. A high density is preferred for best efficiency, and a low density for maximum speed; but the choice is usually based on the specific requirements of the detector and the availability of the gas (e.g., helium is seldom used outside the U.S.).

68   Since even trace impurities in the carrier gas can cause noise in the detector signal, the purity is critical. Passage through a cold molecular sieve trap is very effective for removing the last traces of water vapor.

Adequate flow control is obtained from standard two-stage diaphragm reducing valves. Some chromatographs have a constriction at the head or at the end of the column to help reduce pressure fluctuations. The pressure drop in the column itself evens out most fluctuations. Long-term drifts in the inlet pressure must be avoided.

A soap film flowmeter is used almost exclusively to measure the flow rate. It can be a simple side-arm buret with a rubber bulb filled with soap solution connected to the bottom outlet. The time required for a film (bubble) to pass between two marks on the buret is easily converted to flow rate as discussed previously.

COLUMNS

There are two distinct types of columns in common use, packed and open tubular (capillary). The packed columns are easier to fabricate, less expensive, last longer, have a higher capacity, and suffice for all but the most difficult separations. The open tubular columns have less pressure drop and therefore can be made much longer (more plates).

Packed columns are usually 3 to 50 feet long and 1/8 inch to 3/8 inch in diameter, although columns up to several inches in diameter are used for preparative scale work. Open tubular columns are usually 50 to 100 feet long and 0.01 inch to 0.05 inch in diameter. The geometrical configuration of the column is of little concern as long as the bends are not sharp. Columns are bent in a U or W shape or coiled to fit the oven. Short columns are often made of glass, but longer columns are made of copper, aluminum, or stainless steel tubing to facilitate bending which must be done after the column is filled. It is possible to draw glass capillary tubing in lengths of several hundred feet— capillary columns up to a mile in length have been fabricated.

SOLID SUPPORT

The ideal solid support is not yet available. It should have a high specific surface ($1 \ m^2/g$), and the surface must be chemically inert although wettable by the liquid phase so that it will spread in a thin layer of uniform thickness. In addition it must have thermal stability, mechanical strength, and be available in uniformly sized, near-spherically shaped particles.

The most commonly used supports are derived from diatomaceous earth, a spongy siliceous material sold under many trade-names depending on the supplier and pre-treatment. Chromosorb-P is a form of crushed commercial firebrick. Chromosorb-W is a form of diatomaceous earth which has been heated with an alkaline flux. The latter is less acidic and lighter in color. These materials are interlaced with a network of fine pores, requiring about 0.5% (by weight) of a liquid to cover the entire surface with a monolayer. As a heavier coating is applied, the finer pores fill up first, but even with a 20% coating many free passage-ways still exist, and the average thickness of the layer is still only a few hundred angstroms.

The surface of commercial firebrick (Chromosorb-P) has the general structure:

$$\begin{array}{ccc} \text{OH} & & \text{OH} \\ | & & | \\ -\,\text{Si} & -\,\text{O}\,- & \text{Si}\,- \\ | & & | \end{array}$$

The –OH groups are acidic and somewhat polar, and tend to react with polar solutes, especially those with basic functional groups. Chromosorb-W is much less acidic, but has a lower specific surface. The surface activity can be partially reduced and some impurities removed by washing in acids or bases. For the separation of amines, it is desirable to leave a thin coating of sodium hydroxide on the surface. A very effective treatment consists of silanizing the surface with hexamethyldisilazane (HMDS):

$$\begin{array}{ccc} \text{OH} & & \text{OH} \\ | & & | \\ -\,\text{Si} & -\,\text{O}\,- & \text{Si}\,- \qquad +\ (\text{Me}_3\text{Si})_2\text{NH}\ \longrightarrow \\ | & & | \end{array}$$

$$\begin{array}{ccc} \text{Me} & & \text{Me} \\ | & & | \\ \text{Me}\,-\,\text{Si}\,-\,\text{Me} & \quad & \text{Me}\,-\,\text{Si}\,-\,\text{Me} \\ | & & | \\ \text{O} & & \text{O} \\ | & & | \\ -\,\text{Si} & -\ \text{O}\ - & \text{Si}\,- \\ | & & | \end{array}$$

In this way the polar –O–H is replaced by a relatively inert trimethyl silyl group.

Powdered Teflon is useful as a support for very polar solutes, but it has a low surface area. It is so inert that it is difficult to coat evenly. It is more easily handled if first cooled in a refrigerator. Some other supports which have been suggested are micro glass beads, graphitized carbon, and carborundum.

Coating the Support. The column packing is prepared by mixing the solid with the correct amount of liquid phase dissolved in a suitable low-boiling solvent such as pentane, dichloromethane, or acetone. The solvent is then evaporated with judicious heating; stirring as necessary to obtain a uniform coating. The last traces of solvent may be removed under vacuum. Columns are usually filled by pouring the packing into the straight tube with gentle shaking or tapping. Both ends are plugged with glass wool and the column bent to the appropriate shape to fit the oven. Great care is necessary in packing large columns to avoid channeling and segregation of the particles according to size. A newly packed column must be conditioned by passing carrier gas through it at elevated temperature for several hours.

Open tubular columns, of course, contain no packing. The thin coat of liquid phase is applied by forcing a dilute solution through the column at a slow rate. The solution remaining on the wall is evaporated by passing through carrier gas, leaving a layer of liquid phase. Experience helps in getting a satisfactory coating.

LIQUID PHASE

The versatility of GLC is in large part due to the wide variety of liquid phases available. Hundreds of liquids have been tried, but perhaps a dozen or so will suffice for most purposes.

The requirements for a good liquid phase are: (1) it should be essentially non-volatile (vapor pressure < 0.1 torr) at the temperature it is to be used; (2) it must be thermally stable; (3) it should yield appropriate K values for the components to be studied—neither too small nor too large; (4) it should be readily available in a reproducible form, preferably as a single pure compound of known molecular weight; and (5) it should be inert toward the solutes, or if it reacts, it should do so fast and reversibly.

No single liquid meets all requirements for all possible solutes. Some are needed for low temperatures, others for high temperatures. For some studies a non-selective liquid is desirable, for others a highly selective phase is needed. A few liquids commonly used are listed in Table 5-3. The choice is often based on availability and/or habit, but the difference between a successful and a poor separation may well lie in the choice of the best liquid phase.

SAMPLE INTRODUCTION

A consideration of the ideal chromatographic process requires that the sample should be introduced into the first theoretical plate in a near instantaneous fashion. If the sample is not already a vapor, enough heat must be supplied to establish equilibrium immediately. If these requirements are not met, the sample will be unnecessarily spread out before the separation process has begun.

The size of the sample is dictated by several factors: the amount available, the capacity of the column and the sensitivity of the detector. The ordinary laboratory chromatograph with a $\frac{1}{4}$-inch packed column and a thermal conductivity detector utilizes a sample of 1 to 50 μl or less. An open tubular column can handle only a much smaller sample, of the order of 10^{-3} to 10^{-2} μl. Samples

***TABLE* 5-3** COMMON LIQUID PHASES

Liquid Phase	Typical Samples	Max. Temp, °C
Inorganic eutectic mixtures	Volatile inorganic cpds.	
Silicone rubber gum (SE-30)	Steroids, alkaloids, pesticides, acids, methyl esters	350
Apiezon L (a high molecular weight paraffin)	High boiling hydrocarbons, esters, ethers, boranes	300
Carbowax 20 M (polyethylene glycol)	Aromatics, alcohols, amines, ketones, essential oils	250
Silicone oil (DC-550)	All types	200
Dinonyl phthalate	All types	150
Squalane (hexamethyl tetracosane)	Hydrocarbons	140
β,β'-Oxydipropionitrile	Olefins, alcohols, aldehydes	100
Hexadecane	Hydrocarbons, fluorides	60
Silver nitrate in propylene glycol	Olefins, cyclic hydrocarbons	50

of this size must be introduced by a splitting technique, as indicated in Figure 5-9. In this way only a small fraction of the measured sample is used, the remainder is exhausted to the atmosphere. The sample must be quickly vaporized and

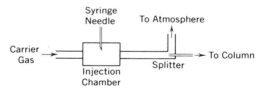

FIGURE 5-9. Splitter for obtaining very small samples.

mixed with the carrier gas to avoid fractionation before it enters the column. The accurate measurement of samples of this size is questionable and may account for much of the error in quantitative analysis. For reliable thermodynamic data, retention values should be obtained with several sample sizes and extrapolated to zero sample (infinite dilution).

Liquid samples are injected from a syringe of appropriate capacity through a rubber septum into a small heated chamber immediately preceding the column. A swift, neat motion of the plunger is necessary, and due care must be exercised in manipulating the plunger because this part of the apparatus is under pressure. Gas samples are much easier to measure accurately because of their larger volume. Solid samples are more difficult to introduce, but can be sealed into a thin-walled glass vial which is inserted into the injector port and then crushed from the outside.

The sample inlet should be as close as possible to the head of the column so that unnecessary spreading will be avoided.

DETECTORS

The remarkable separations performed in the column must somehow be sensed and recorded. All of the components are highly diluted in the carrier gas with concentrations of 1 part per thousand at best, ranging down to zero. Furthermore, sharp peaks may pass through the detector in less than a second, while the last peaks may not emerge for hours and be barely discernible above the base line. Somehow the detector must ignore the large amount of carrier gas and find the trace amounts of sample components contained therein.

The universal detector has not yet been invented, for it must meet all of the following requirements: low limit of detection, linear response over an extreme range of concentrations, uniform response to all possible substances, simple calibration, short response time, small internal volume, low noise, long term stability; and it must be simple, inexpensive, robust, and safe to operate. There may be some occasions when selective response to a few components is desirable as an aid to identification, or as a means of finding a trace component which is incompletely separated from a major component.

Detector Evaluation. Comparison of detectors is not always meaningful because their performance may depend on how it is measured. In general terms, it is useful to plot the response or signal, R, vs. the quantity measured, Q, as in Figure 5-10. The *ultimate limit of detection*, Q_0, is determined by the noise level,

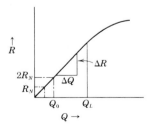

FIGURE 5-10. Sensitvity curve of a detector.

R_N, of the detector, and it is assumed that a signal equal to $2R_N$ can be distinguished from the background noise. Q_0 corresponds to $2R_N$. The slope of the curve, $\Delta R/\Delta Q$, defines the *sensitivity*. The region where the curve begins to deviate from a straight line defines the *limit of linear response*, with Q_L being the upper limit. The measurements are a function of the construction of the detector, but also of the way it is operated.

Types of Detectors. Scores of types of detectors have been proposed, and we could classify them ad infinitum. Differential detectors measure instantaneous concentration or instantaneous rate of emergence of the component. Integral detectors accumulate the sample components and the signal gives the total amount which has emerged up to a given instant. Signals from differential detectors are usually integrated for quantitative analysis, and signals from integral detectors are often differentiated to make them easier to interpret for qualitative analysis. Either signal in Figure 5-11 can be derived from the other.

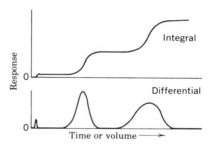

FIGURE 5-11. Differential and integral response for the same chromatogram.

Detectors can also be classified as destructive or non-destructive, depending on whether or not the sample components can be collected unchanged for further study.

Hydrogen Flame Detector. One of the simplest detectors is the hydrogen-flame detector, shown in Figure 5-12 with an exquisitely simple chromatograph. Hydrogen must be used as a carrier gas. It is burned as it emerges from the column through a hollow needle, yielding a nearly colorless flame. When an organic component emerges, the flame becomes yellow. The retention time can be measured with a stopwatch. The amount of the component is roughly proportional to the height and/or luminosity of the flame. This may sound very crude, yet it is not difficult to install a thermocouple to measure the flame temperature or a photocell to measure the luminosity and increase the accuracy

74

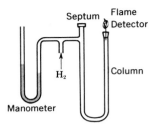

FIGURE 5-12. Simple chromatograph with hydrogen flame detector. (After Cowan and Sugihara, *J. Chem. Ed.*, **36**, 246 (1959).)

manyfold. Better still, since most organic compounds are ionized in the flame, an ion current can be collected between two oppositely charged electrodes, as in Figure 5-13. This is the principle of the *flame ionization detector*, one of the most sensitive and popular detectors in current use. The ions produced are collected

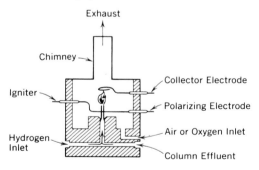

FIGURE 5-13. Hydrogen flame ionization detector.

between two electrodes, one of which may be the jet itself. Because the electrical resistance of the flame is very high (about 10^{12} ohms) and the current is extremely small (about 10^{-14} amp), the associated electronics are complicated and moderately expensive.

The ionization processes occurring in the flame are not completely understood. The ion current, however, is approximately proportional to the number of carbon atoms entering the flame. More precisely, the response depends also on the state of oxidation of the carbon atom—those which are already completely oxidized do not lead to ion formation. The relative response per carbon atom, or "effective carbon number," of several organic functional groups are listed in Table 5-4. The detector is insensitive to most inorganic compounds. It is especially worth noting that it does not "see" water vapor or air.

The flame ionization detector is relatively simple, extremely sensitive, and has a wide range of linear response. It is more difficult to operate than the thermal conductivity detector, and, of course, destroys the sample.

TABLE 5-4   CONTRIBUTIONS TO EFFECTIVE CARBON NUMBERS

C-aliphatic, aromatic, olefinic	1.0
C-acetylenic	1.3
C-carbonyl	0
C-nitrate	0.3
O-ether	−1.0
O-primary alcohol	−0.6
O-secondary alcohol	−0.75
O-tertiary alcohol, esters.	−0.25
N-amines	(same as O in alcohols)

[After J. C. Sternberg, W. S. Gallaway, and D. T. L. Jones, *Gas Chromatography* (Edited by Brenner, Callen, and Wiess), Academic Press, 1962; p. 265.]

Thermal Conductivity Detector. The measurement of the thermal conductivity of a gas is based on the transfer of heat from a hot filament to a cooler surface. Thus the gas conducts heat from the filament to the wall. If a constant amount of electrical energy is supplied to the filament, its temperature will be a function of the thermal conductivity of the gas. Rather than determining the temperature of the filament, it is easier to determine its electrical resistance which increases with temperature. As applied to gas chromatography, a double detector is used to cancel out the thermal conductivity of the carrier gas and to minimize fluctuations in the temperature, pressure and power supply. A schematic diagram of the detector is shown in Figure 5-14, and the associated electrical circuit in Figure 5-15. In some detectors, thermistors are used in place of filaments. Thermistors are somewhat more sensitive than filaments below about $100°$ C, but the reverse is true above about $150°$ C.

The temperature of the filament (and thus the signal) is a function of the bridge current, the geometry of the cell, and the thermal conductivity and flow rate of the gas. Increasing the bridge current will increase the running temperature of the filaments, and increase the sensitivity, but the filaments will burn out sooner. The quickest way to burn out the filaments is to leave the bridge current

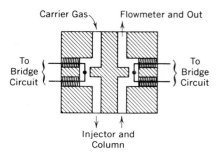

FIGURE 5-14. Typical thermal conductivity detector.

on with no carrier gas flowing to remove heat. Since the detector is measuring thermal conductivity, it is very important to keep the temperature of the detector walls constant; often this is the limiting factor in quantitative analysis.

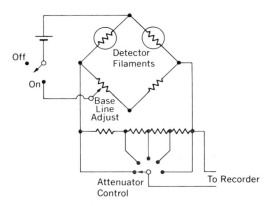

FIGURE 5-15. Circuitry required for thermal conductivity detector.

The thermal conductivities of a number of vapors are listed in Table 5-5, from which it is seen that both hydrogen and helium have very high thermal conductivities relative to most organic compounds. If either of these gases is used as a carrier gas, there will be a decrease in the thermal conductivity of the gas mixture whenever an organic compound is eluted. The temperature of the filament and its electrical resistance increase. The bridge circuit becomes un-

TABLE 5-5 THERMAL CONDUCTIVITIES OF SUBSTANCES AT 100° C

Substance	$k \times 10^5$, cal/° C/mole
Hydrogen, H_2 (Mol. Wt. = 2)	53.4
Helium, He (At. Wt. = 4)	41.6
Methane, CH_4 (Mol. Wt. = 16)	10.9
Ammonia, NH_3 (Mol. Wt. = 17)	7.8
Nitrogen, N_2 (Mol. Wt. = 28)	7.5
Ethane, C_2H_6 (Mol. Wt. = 30)	7.3
Acetylene, C_2H_2 (Mol. Wt. = 26)	6.8
Propane, C_3H_8 (Mol. Wt. = 44)	6.3
Ethyl propyl ether, $C_2H_5OC_3H_7$ (Mol. Wt. = 88)	5.4
Carbon dioxide, CO_2 (Mol. Wt. = 44)	5.3
Ethanol, C_2H_5OH (Mol. Wt. = 46)	5.3
Argon, Ar (At. Wt. = 40)	5.2
n-Hexane, C_6H_{14} (Mol. Wt. = 86)	5.0
Benzene, C_6H_6 (Mol. Wt. = 78)	4.4
Ethyl acetate, $CH_3COOC_2H_5$ (Mol. Wt. = 88)	4.1
Ethyl chloride, C_2H_5Cl (Mol. Wt. = 64.5)	4.1
Carbon tetrachloride, CCl_4 (Mol. Wt. = 154)	2.2

balanced and a signal is sent to the recorder. Nitrogen is often used as a carrier gas because helium is expensive and hydrogen is dangerous. With nitrogen, the sensitivity is reduced and the signal may be negative (inverse peak) because its thermal conductivity is closer to that of organic compounds.

The thermal conductivity of a mixture of gases is not easy to calculate, and this detector must be calibrated for each compound for highest accuracy. Some generalizations have been observed; for example, the *relative* response (signal per mole of compound/signal per mole of standard, in this case, benzene) for many compounds follows the relation

$$\text{Relative Response} = A + BM \qquad (\text{benzene} = 100) \qquad (5\text{-}13)$$

where M is the molecular weight, and A and B are constants for a given homologous series of compounds, a series in which a member is derived from the previous member by the insertion of a CH_2 group. Some values of A and B are listed in Table 5-6.

Many forms of geometry of the cell cavities have been proposed to reduce the effects of flow fluctuations without decreasing the sensitivity or increasing the time constant unduly. The internal volume of the detector, and especially the dead space, should be at a minimum in order not to remix the components. The thermal conductivity detector is simple, rugged, inexpensive, moderately

GAS CHROMATOGRAPHY

78

TABLE 5-6 VALUES OF A AND B IN EQUATION 5-13, WITH HELIUM CARRIER GAS IN THE TEMPERATURE RANGE 30°–160° C.

Type	Carbon No.	A	B
n-Alkanes	1–3	20.6	1.04
n-Alkanes	3–10	6.7	1.35
Methyl alkanes	4–7	10.8	1.25
Olefins	2–4	13.0	1.20
Methyl benzenes	7–9	9.7	1.16
n-Ketones	3–8	35.9	0.86
Primary alcohols	2–7	34.9	0.81
n-Ethers	4–10	43.3	0.89

[After A. E. Messner, D. M. Rosie and P. A. Argabright, *Anal. Chem.*, **31**, 230 (1959).]

sensitive, non-selective, essentially non-destructive, very accurate if properly calibrated, and more widely used than any other.

β-Ray Detector. The principle of operation is the same as that of the hydrogen flame ionization detector, except that ionization of the sample molecule is produced by another mechanism. Argon is used as the carrier gas. In the detector, a radioactive source emits β-Rays which excite some of the argon atoms to a metastable energy level. The sample molecules are then ionized by collisions with the excited argon atoms, and the resultant ion current collected by a pair of electrodes. The associated electronic circuitry is much the same as for the flame ionization detector.

The modern miniature version of this detector is extremely sensitive, but it is less accurate than other popular detectors and requires shielding of the β source (radium, strontium-90, or tritium).

Other Detectors. Of the many other detectors proposed, some of the more important are: (a) the gas density balance for which the response is a precise function of molecular weight; (b) the electron capture detector which is selective and extremely sensitive for substances containing electronegative atoms like the halogens; (c) coulometric titrator in which the column effluent is burned to give HCl, H_2S, etc., and then passed through a solution to be titrated with electrolytically generated silver ion (specific for halogens and sulfur); (d) thermionic ionization gauge, often used in connection with a mass spectrometer; and (e) a gas volume collector in which a carbon dioxide carrier gas is absorbed in sodium hydroxide solution contained in an inverted buret.

QUALITATIVE ANALYSIS

The gas chromatograph, as a separator, has no equal, but as an analytical tool it leaves much to be desired. It is easy to find impurities in a supposedly chemically pure reagent, or to detect 200 constituents in petroleum, but the identification is left to the ingenuity of the analyst.

Comparison of retention behavior with a known sample using several columns at more than one temperature is almost certain proof of identity. But this method would, in general, require infinite patience if not an infinite supply of pure chemicals. In a negative sense, the absence of extraneous peaks is now considered to be one of the best indications of purity of a reagent.

Ideally, it should be possible to identify a compound from the retention time; however, the retention time alone is of little value because it depends on so many other factors in addition to the nature of the compound. The *specific retention volume*, or the partition coefficient, is a reliable means of identification, but vast tables of data are required for the innumerable combinations of compounds, liquid phases, and temperatures. Many of these data are available, but are well scattered in the literature. A large fraction of the data is unreliable, or important details are missing. There are, however, some useful theoretical considerations and empirical observations which remove some of the witchcraft from the problem of identification.

Relative Retention. A re-examination of Equation 5-8 will show that in the course of running a chromatogram with several components, if all experimental conditions remain the same, then:

$$\frac{d_1 - d_A}{d_2 - d_A} = \frac{t_1 - t_A}{t_2 - t_A} = \frac{V_{R_1} - V_A}{V_{R_2} - V_A} = \frac{V_{g_1}}{V_{g_2}} = \frac{K_1}{K_2} = \alpha_{1,2} \qquad (5\text{-}14)$$

where the subscripts refer to the two components and air, and $\alpha_{1,2}$ is the *relative retention* of a component 1 with respect to component 2. The latter may be a standard compound to which all others are referred. Like K, α is a form of equilibrium constant, but is readily determined from two measurements of distance on the chart. No other measurements need be made—they all cancel out. This highly delightful situation is marred by the fact that we must choose and agree upon a standard substance. The standard should be readily available, should have a retention time close to (but easily resolved from) the sample components, and be chemically compatible with the sample. Obviously, no single substance will meet all requirements.

Retention Index. In this system, introduced by Kovats, the relative retention is referred to the series of normal paraffin hydrocarbons as standard substances. The Retention Index, I, is defined as:

$$I = 100 \frac{\log \alpha_{i, p_z}}{\log \alpha_{p_{z+1}, p_z}} + 100 z \qquad (5\text{-}15)$$

where α_{i, p_z} is the relative retention of compound i compared to the n-paraffin with z carbon atoms, and α_{p_{z+1}, p_z} is the relative retention of the two n-paraffins with $z + 1$ and z carbon atoms. By definition, I for the series of n-paraffins is $100 z$ for all liquid phases at all temperatures. The I value for all other compounds depends on the nature of the liquid phase as well as the nature of the compound. This system has a number of advantages: (1) a series of well-defined, readily available compounds having a wide boiling range is used; (2) the I values are relatively insensitive to temperature; and (3) additional structural information can be obtained by noting the *change* in retention index, ΔI, when a compound is measured on a very polar and a non-polar phase. ΔI values are determined by structure (nature of functional groups and their positions). Kovats has prepared tables giving ΔI values for common functional groups and positional features. The individual ΔI values appear to be additive for the molecule as a whole.

QUANTITATIVE ANALYSIS

Integral detectors give a signal which is directly proportional to some bulk property of the amount of a component which has been eluted, for example, a gas volume or titrant volume. Calibration presents no problem for this type of detector. With differential detectors, the interpretation is not so simple.

For those detectors which give a signal proportional to the instantaneous concentration, we must sum the amount found in each volume increment, or, in other words, we must find the area under the peak—more precisely the area between the curve and the hypothetical baseline.

$$\text{Amount} = \int C \, dV = f \int mV \, dt \qquad (5\text{-}16)$$

where f is the *calibration factor* (amount/unit area). Note that the area can be determined in any units (squares of any dimension on the chart paper, weight of the chart paper, millivolts × time, millivolts × distance, millivolts × volume, etc.), provided that the calibration factor is determined in the same units.

Measurement of Area. In practice, the area is measured by any of several techniques:

1. Cut out the peak with a scissors and weigh the paper. Determine the weight of paper per unit area in a separate experiment.

2. Use a planimeter.

3. Estimate the area by triangulation. Draw tangents to the points of inflection on the peak sides, and compute the area of the triangle formed with the base line, as in Figure 5-16.

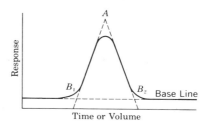

FIGURE 5-16. Measurement of peak area by triangulation. $A \approx B_1 + B_2$.

4. Use a mechanical or electronic accessory to the recorder which will automatically integrate the area. (Some devices operate directly from the detector.)

Any of these methods is satisfactory, provided the calibration factor is determined in the same way. The choice is determined by the convenience desired and the price we are willing to pay. Incompletely resolved (overlapping) peaks are usually treated by dropping a perpendicular from the minimum signal to the base line and dividing the area accordingly.

It is probably more difficult to determine the proper calibration factor than the peak area. From the discussion of detectors, it is evident that a different factor is required for each component and that the conditions for operating the detector must remain constant. Absolute calibration of a detector is indeed difficult and requires carefully prepared samples of known composition or precisely measured amounts of pure substances.

For some purposes, a normalization method is satisfactory. The fraction of the total area under each peak is assumed to be the same as the fractional composition, and if the calibration factors are known, these can be taken into account.

$$\% \text{ of component A} = \frac{f_A A_A}{\Sigma f_i A_i} \times 100 \qquad (5\text{-}17)$$

where f_i and A_i represent the calibration factor (amount per unit area) and area of the i-th component. Calibration factors given in weight/unit area or moles/unit area are equally satisfactory.

example/problem 5-2: A sample containing benzene, heptane, and 2-methylhexane gives a three-peak chromatogram with areas of 35, 58, and 13 "squares" for the respective peaks. Calculate the percentage composition.

Compound	Area	Response Factor, area/mole, (Table 5-6)	Cal. Factor, mole/area, relative	Weighted area, $f_i A_i$	Mole %
Benzene	35	100	1.00	35.0	41.1
Heptane	58	143	0.70	40.6	47.8
2-Methylhexane	13	136	0.735	9.5	11.1

Another problem arises if the peak is so sharp (narrow) that the area cannot be measured accurately. In this case, it is permissible to use the peak height as a measure of the amount, provided a proper calibration factor is determined. This technique is obviously applicable to repetitive analyses such as are required for process control.

TEMPERATURE EFFECTS

There are three important parts of the chromatograph in which the temperature must be controlled. First, the injector temperature determines the rate at which the sample is vaporized. Since the fastest rate possible is desired in order to get the sample into the column in a very small volume, the injector is kept at a relatively high temperature consistent with the thermal stability of the sample. Second, the detector must be hot enough so that the constituents do not condense in it. On the other hand, the sensitivity of a thermal conductivity detector decreases with temperature, so that some optimum temperature is selected just above the boiling point of the highest boiling sample component. The thermal stability of the electrical insulation must also be considered.

Finally, the temperature of the column itself is an important factor in determining retention and resolution. At high temperatures, components will tend to spend most of the time in the gas phase, thus will elute quickly and close together—resolution is poor. At low temperatures, components will spend most of the time in the liquid phase, thus will elute slowly and usually farther apart—resolution is improved at the expense of time.

APPLICATIONS

In the short space of about fifteen years, the literature of gas-liquid chromatography has jumped from one paper in 1952 to nearly 2,000 per year. It would be hopeless to attempt to list all the areas of applications which by now have reached into all branches of chemistry. It is perhaps better to recount some of the limitations:

1. The sample must have an appreciable vapor pressure (several torr) at the column temperature. Currently columns can be easily operated at 350° C, and

this is not an upper limit if one can use inorganic eutectic mixtures as liquid phases.

2. The chromatograph provides a limited amount of data—retention time, peak size and peak shape. This is to be compared with a wealth of information given by the various forms of spectroscopy.

3. One must compromise among speed, resolution and capacity—all three cannot be optimized at the same time.

Within these limitations, its versatility, speed, simplicity, and low cost have made it the most useful and popular analytical tool that has appeared in recent years.

GAS-SOLID CHROMATOGRAPHY

Historically, gas-solid chromatography (GSC) preceded gas-liquid chromatography (GLC) by many years. Charcoal filters to purify air have long been in common use. This is a form of GSC, but the development of the technique as a scientific method of separation was plagued by a number of difficulties.

Separation by GSC is very similar to that by GLC: the primary difference is that the partition within the column is caused by partial and selective adsorption on a solid surface rather than solubility in a liquid phase. The apparatus required is identical to that for GLC except for the column packing which is a finely divided, porous solid with a high specific surface.

Comparison of GSC and GLC.   Although there are many similarities between the two techniques, GSC has some unique advantages as well as some problems not associated with GLC.

1. GSC distribution coefficients, K, relating amount of component adsorbed per unit area of solid surface or per gram of packing to the concentration or partial pressure in the gas phase tend to be much larger than the partition coefficients for GLC. Thus retention times will be inconveniently long, except for the "fixed" gases like hydrogen, nitrogen, argon, oxygen, etc., which give retention times too short to be resolved by GLC.

2. Since there is no liquid phase to be retained in the column, the upper temperature limit of operation can be higher in GSC than in GLC. At higher temperatures, K values are lower and retention times shorter, but the temperature limit may be determined by thermal instability of the sample or the materials of construction of the apparatus itself.

3. Adsorption isotherms (a plot of amount adsorbed vs. partial pressure at constant temperature) are generally curved. In other words, the distribution coefficient is not independent of concentration. Curved isotherms result in

skewed peaks. Most isotherms, however, tend toward linearity at very low concentrations, indicating that extremely small samples are to be preferred.

4. Useful solid adsorbents have areas of about 100 m²/g, nearly 100 times that of solid supports most often used for GLC. Solids with such large surfaces are generally very effective catalysts whether or not they are chemically reactive in bulk. Thus samples may be readily pyrolyzed or otherwise converted into other substances, or even irreversibly adsorbed never to be seen again.

5. Solid surfaces are very difficult to reproduce—the size and shape of the area are certain to vary as well as the exact and detailed composition of the surface layer. Thus retention behavior is difficult to reproduce and a theoretical interpretation can be only approximate.

Adsorption Isotherms. The consequence of a non-linear isotherm is best illustrated by the diagrams in Figure 5-17. Figure 5-17*b* represents the linear

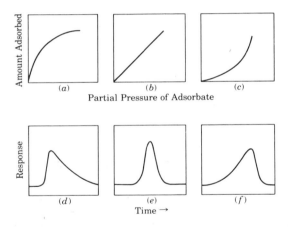

FIGURE 5-17. Typical isotherms for adsorption and their effect on peak shape.

behavior usually associated with GLC and a symmetric elution peak is observed (Figure 5-17*e*). Figure 5-17*a* illustrates the type of isotherm often found for GSC. The curvature is such that at high concentrations the fraction of component in the gas phase will be greater than that at low concentrations. As a result, the portion of the component at the peak maximum (high concentration) will move through the column at a faster rate than the rest of the component in the band edges. The peak maximum will catch up to the leading edge, leaving a long tail at the trailing edge as depicted in Figure 5-17*d*. The opposite behavior is observed in Figures 5-17*c* and 5-17*f*. Clearly a linear isotherm yields a peak of minimum width, a very desirable feature for optimum resolution. Linear isotherms, so common in GLC, can be obtained in GSC by using only a small portion of the (nearly straight) curve close to the origin (very small sample size) or by raising the temperature.

Some Common Adsorbents. Compared to the vast number of liquid phases used in GLC, relatively few adsorbents are available for GSC.

Carbon. There are many varieties available, differing in surface area, porosity, and surface activity. The surface can be treated either chemically or physically to make it more or less reactive. Carbon columns are commonly used in permanent gas analysis and for separations of the low boiling hydrocarbons.

Alumina. This is one of the most versatile and reproducible adsorbents, since the activity of its surface can be controlled by hydration or reaction with inorganic bases. Suitably modified alumina is useful for hydrocarbon analysis at high temperatures.

Silica gel. Like alumina, the surface activity of silica gel can be modified by controlled hydration. These columns are used for the same kinds of problems as carbon columns, and are more reproducible than the latter.

Molecular sieves. Some compounds, such as the calcium zeolites, have a well-defined, open structure with holes of molecular dimensions. Molecules having dimensions less than a critical size, depending on the size of the holes, are able to penetrate the interior of the porous structure and may be adsorbed on the interior surfaces or effectively "trapped." Larger molecules which do not penetrate the porous structures may pass through the column without significant retention. The size of the holes is carefully controlled in commercial preparations such as Linde sieves 4A, 5A, and 13X. Again, the surface activity is a function of adsorbed water and, in fact, molecular sieves are very effective drying agents for gas streams. In addition to their advantageous use for the analysis of the permanent and other inorganic gases, molecular sieves exhibit unusual behavior toward hydrocarbons. Linde 5A sieve retains *normal*-paraffins which are able to penetrate the holes, but not branched or cyclic hydrocarbons.

Porapak. Porous polymer beads fabricated from the polymerization of styrene cross-linked with divinylbenzene have an open structure much like molecular sieves. In gas chromatography, they serve both as solid support and as the liquid phase, so they combine the advantages of GLC and GSC. They are especially useful for polar compounds such as water, amines, acids, and alcohols.

Inorganic salts. Some complex inorganic salts, e.g., hydrates or ammoniates, can be decomposed thermally to yield open structures with very polar and often very selective adsorbing surfaces. Other salts can be deposited by evaporation from solution onto the surface of Chromosorb, silica gel, or alumina giving the characteristic adsorbing properties of the salt used. These techniques are relatively new, but would seem to add greatly to the versatility of GSC.

Up to the present, GSC has been used mostly for the separation of permanent gases at low temperatures and the separation of hydrocarbons at high temperatures. However, with the development of more sensitive detectors, so that smaller samples can be handled, and the development of modified adsorbents, the versatility of the method is enormously extended.

QUESTIONS AND PROBLEMS

5-1.   At the beginning of this chapter is a statement that the separation of benzene and cyclohexane, which have almost identical boiling points, is easy. How would you do it?

5-2.   The retention times of several compounds, measured from sample injection, are: air, 45 sec; propane, 1.5 min.; pentane, 2.35 min.; acetone, 2.45 min.; butyraldehyde, 3.95 min.; xylene, 15.0 min. What is the relative retention time of the organic compounds using pentane as the standard?   *Ans.* α for acetone = 1.06.

5-3.   Predict the effect on peak shape of:
  (*a*) Introducing the sample over a long period of time (say, 10 sec) rather than as a sharp plug.
  (*b*) Using too low a temperature at the injector so that the sample did not vaporize quickly.
  (*c*) Increasing the temperature of the column.
  (*d*) Increasing the flow rate.
  (*e*) Doubling the length of the column.
  (*f*) Doubling the recorder chart speed.

5-4.   For a particular experiment the column inlet pressure is held at 5 atm with the outlet at 1 atm. What is the average pressure in the column?   *Ans.* 3.44 atm.

5-5.   A certain thermal conductivity detector gave a response of 350 square units for 1.00 mg of *n*-pentane. What would be the response, in the same units, for 2.00 mg of *iso*-butane if all conditions were constant?   *Ans.* 563 units^2.

5-6.   The relative retention volume of butadiene versus *n*-butane is 5.93 on oxydipropionitrile (polarity = 100) and 0.964 on squalane (polarity = 0). What would the relative retention of this pair be on dibenzyl ether (polarity = 44)?   *Ans.* 2.14.

5-7.   Using the data in Problem 5-6, compute the polarity of a liquid phase that would give no separation of butadiene and *n*-butane.   *Ans.* 3.6.

5-8.   Retention times (corrected for the air peak) are given for the following compounds on a particular column. What is the retention index of each of these compounds on this column?

Ethane	0.25 min.	2-Methylbutane	1.20 min.
Propane	0.45	Butene-1	0.80
n-Butane	0.95	Hexene-1	2.95
n-Pentane	1.80	Ethylene	0.15
n-Hexane	3.50	Benzene	3.75
n-Heptane	6.95	*n*-Butanol	8.4
n-Octane	13.7	Water	3.50

Ans. Ethane, 200; Hexene-1, 574.

5-9. Retention times in minutes (corrected for air peak) for several straight-chain paraffin hydrocarbons on a silicone oil column at $90°\,C$ are given below. The flow rate was 85 ml/min.

C_1	C_2	C_3	C_4	C_5	C_6	C_7	C_8
0.00	0.12	0.60	1.44	2.80	5.90	11.6	22.8

(a) Calculate the retention volume for each paraffin.

(b) Calculate the relative retention volume for each paraffin (pentane = 100).

(c) Plot log relative retention time vs. carbon number.

5-10. The constants in the Van Deemter equation 5-4 for a particular column at $150°\,C$ were found to be $A = 0.08$ cm, $B = 0.15$ cm^2/sec, and $C = 0.03$ sec. What is the optimum gas velocity under these conditions? What is the corresponding minimum HETP?

Ans. 2.24 cm/sec, 2.14 mm.

5-11. A 2.00-mg sample gave the following peaks with areas given in parentheses: hexane (35), 1-heptanol (20), methyl butyl ketone (15), toluene (80). A thermal conductivity detector was employed. Calculate the mole percent composition of the sample.

Ans. 22.8% hexane, 12.5% 1-heptanol, 9.9% methyl butyl ketone, 54.9% toluene.

5-12. Describe how you could use a table of V_g values to identify the unknown compounds in a sample.

5-13. Glass micro-beads pack very uniformly in a column, but they have a small surface area relative to Chromosorb. Considering these two properties of glass beads, compare the efficacy of glass beads vs. Chromosorb as a solid support.

5-14. For propanol on a silicone oil column, the specific retention volume, V_g, varies with temperature as follows:

$T,°\,C.$	40	60	72	84	97	111
V_g, ml/g	169	85.0	64.6	44.5	31.6	22.0

(a) Plot both V_g and log V_g vs. both T and $1/T$ (in absolute degrees).

(b) What conclusion can you draw from these curves?

REFERENCES

J. H. Purnell, *Gas Chromatography*, Wiley, New York, 1962. Comprehensive and stimulating discussion with a definitive discussion of principles.

S. Dal Nogare and R. S. Juvet, Jr., *Gas-Liquid Chromatography*, Interscience, New York, 1962. Comprehensive review of important developments. Most useful source of information.

H. P. Burchfield and E. E. Storss, *Biochemical Applications of Gas Chromatography*, Academic Press, New York, 1962.

6 LIQUID COLUMN CHROMATOGRAPHY

Most of the principles we have developed for gas chromatography apply with only minor modifications to liquid chromatography as well. Retention time or volume is directly related to a distribution coefficient, and the same processes cause band broadening in the column.

On the other hand, there are many differences in the practical aspects of the two kinds of chromatography. The fundamental difference is, of course, that a liquid serves as the mobile phase. In gas chromatography, the carrier gas is usually chemically inert, and the vapor pressures of the solutes are independent of the nature of the gas used. Liquid eluents are seldom inert, and the solubilities of the solutes and their distribution coefficients do depend on the nature of the eluent used. Also, liquid eluents may become adsorbed on or dissolved in the stationary phase to a considerable extent, thus competing for the available adsorption sites, or changing the nature of the stationary liquid phase as the case may be. Liquids are essentially incompressible, and have a higher viscosity or resistance to flow than a gas, so the process will be much slower. Likewise, rates of diffusion of solutes are slower in liquids than in gases.

Gas and liquid chromatography complement each other—both have distinct areas of application. For example, if the sample is non-volatile, thermally unstable, or if its solutions are ionic, liquid chromatography is the choice. Furthermore, it is easier to scale up the procedures to handle large samples if the method is to be used as a preparative technique. Finally, a procedure known as "gradient elution" offers another variation with liquid eluents. In this method the composition of the eluent is changed gradually or stepwise by the addition of other constituents, or by mixing in a second solvent.

The common features of the kinds of chromatography to be discussed in this chapter are: (*a*) a column packed with a porous stationary phase is employed, and (*b*) a liquid mobile phase is used to elute the sample components through the column. Four kinds of chromatography are studied: (1) *adsorption*, in which the components are selectively adsorbed on the surface of the packing; (2) *partition*, in which the components are selectively partitioned between the eluent and a thin liquid film held stationary on an inert solid support; (3) *ion exchange*, in which ionic constituents of the sample are selectively retarded by exchange with replaceable ions of the packing; and (4) *gel*, in which the column is packed with a permeable gel, causing separations by a sieving action based on molecular size.

ADSORPTION CHROMATOGRAPHY

Adsorbents. As in gas-solid chromatography, many materials have been used, but a few common ones are sufficient for most purposes. The adsorbing power of the material depends on the chemical nature of the surface as well as the extent of the area available. A short list is given in Table 6-1.

TABLE 6-1 Some Common Adsorbents in Order of Decreasing Adsorptive Power

Alumina	Sucrose
Silica gel	Starch
Magnesia	Powdered cellulose
Calcium carbonate	

The adsorptive activity of alumina can be controlled by varying the amount of water it contains. Thus we can prepare a tailored adsorbent by dehydrating at 360° C for 5 hours and then allowing the dehydrated material to pick up a suitable amount of adsorbed water. The *Brockman scale of activity* is based on the amount of water that the alumina contains: I $= 0\%$ H_2O, II $= 3\%$, III $= 6\%$, IV $= 10\%$, V $= 15\%$. The scale values can be obtained empirically by observing the behavior of certain azo dye mixtures under carefully controlled conditions.

example. A column, 1.5 cm diameter × 10 cm long, is filled to a height of 5 cm with the alumina. A 10-ml aliquot of a mixture containing 20 mg azobenzene (A) and 20 mg *p*-methoxyazobenzene (B) in 50 ml benzene-petroleum ether (1:4) is added to the top of the column. The solvent is allowed to flow out at a rate of 20 to 30 drops per minute. Just as the top of the dye solution reaches the top of the alumina, another 20 ml of the solvent is added to develop the chromatogram. If, at the end of this development, dye A has reached the bottom of the column while dye B remains at the top, the alumina used has activity I. If the dye A passes completely through the column while dye B is found at the bottom, then the alumina has activity II. Lower activities (higher Brockman numbers) are determined with other dyes in the series which are less firmly adsorbed.

Solvents. In contrast with the small number of carrier gases used in gas chromatography, many liquids are used for the mobile phase. It is advantageous to introduce the sample in a solvent in which it is highly soluble in order to keep the sample volume at a minimum. However, this is not necessarily the solvent which will give the optimum resolution in a reasonable time. In addition to the relative solubilities of the solutes in the eluting solvent, it is necessary to consider the competition between the solutes and the solvent for adsorption sites on the surface of the stationary phase. A solvent which elutes the solutes too fast will not separate them, whereas a solvent which elutes the components too slowly will give inconveniently long retention times. Long retention times also cause excessive band broadening and unnecessary dilution of the sample. It is fortunate that a long list of solvents is available. If necessary, mixtures of solvents are used, or even a series of mixtures (gradient elution) with an increasing fraction of the more polar eluent. A short list of solvents is given in Table 6-2.

TABLE 6-2   SOME COMMON SOLVENTS IN ORDER OF INCREASING ELUTING POWER FROM ALUMINA

Petroleum ether	Ethyl acetate
Carbon tetrachloride	Acetone
Trichloroethylene	Ethanol
Toluene	Methanol
Benzene	Water
Chloroform	Organic acids and bases
Ether	

The eluting power of a solvent depends on the solid phase and also on the nature of the solutes. An examination of Tables 6-1 and 6-2 indicates that the substances are listed rather closely in order of polarity (see Table 2-2). Essentially non-polar hydrocarbon solutes will be held more tightly on non-polar column materials than polar solutes will be. On the other hand, the surface of alumina is very polar, and the order of retention will be quite the opposite. The effect of substituent groups on adsorbability is very important and can be predicted qualitatively from the list in Table 6-3.

TABLE 6-3   SOME GROUPS OF SOLUTES IN ORDER OF INCREASING ADSORBABILITY ON ALUMINA COLUMNS

Perfluoro carbons	Aldehydes and ketones
Saturated hydrocarbons	Alcohols and thiols
Unsaturated hydrocarbons	Acids and bases
Halides and esters	

Packing and Operating the Column.   Irregularly shaped zones, which are one of the most annoying features of chromatography, are caused by non-uniform packing. Columns to be used for liquid chromatography are usually of large enough diameter so that they can be mechanically vibrated, or tamped with a long plunger during packing. Alternatively, the packing can be poured into the column as a slurry, and the particles allowed to settle before adding more slurry. If columns develop channels in use, they can be rejuvenated by back-flushing; i.e., a reversal of the liquid flow to stir up the particles after which they are allowed to settle more uniformly.

A sintered glass disk or a small plug of glass wool is used at the bottom of the column to support the packing. Similarly, the top of the packing can be protected from disturbances when pouring in sample or eluent by covering it with a piece of filter paper or other innocuous material. Once the column is packed properly, the level of the liquid must never be allowed to go below the top of the packing. If this happens, small air bubbles will be entrapped and cause channeling in further use.

The flow rate of the eluent must be kept constant so that meaningful data can be easily recorded. The flow rate depends on the particle size of the packing, the dimensions of the column, the viscosity of the liquid, and the pressure applied to force the liquid through (or the position of a stopcock at the outlet of the column). Satisfactory results are obtained if the average linear velocity of the eluent is of the order of 1 cm/min.

Detection Methods. Most common stationary phases are white or nearly colorless, making it possible to observe visually the band of colored components. A number of organic compounds fluoresce in ultraviolet light. In a special technique, called development chromatography, the column is eluted only until the first band appears at the end. Then the column packing is extruded carefully and streaked with color-developing reagents to indicate the position of the bands. The separated components can be extracted from the packing material if necessary.

Compared with the simple, inexpensive, nearly universal detectors available for gas chromatography, those available for liquid chromatography are often highly selective, cumbersome, expensive, and useful over only very narrow ranges of concentration. Flow-through micro-cells are available for many instruments such as refractometers, ultraviolet and infrared spectrophotometers, fluorimeters, and liquid scintillation counters (for components containing radio-isotopes). In any event, fractions of the effluent can be collected automatically and examined further by any method, or the components can be collected after evaporation of the solvent.

Adsorption chromatography is highly empirical and non-reproducible because of variations in the nature of the adsorbents. It is always necessary to test the behavior of new batches of materials, both the adsorbents and the solvents, because traces of water and other impurities can change the surface characteristics of the adsorbents.

LIQUID-LIQUID PARTITION CHROMATOGRAPHY

From what has already been said about gas-liquid and liquid-solid chromatography, the characteristics of liquid-liquid chromatography should be evident. Two non-miscible solvents must be used. Most often, a thin film of water supported on silica gel is used as the stationary phase. Up to 50% water can be adsorbed by silica gel before it becomes too moist to handle easily. For some purposes it may be desirable to include a buffer system in the aqueous phase to change and/or control the solubility of the solutes.

Some care must be given to the choice of solvent pairs. Optimally the fraction of a solute which is dissolved by the moving phase should be in the range from 0.05 to 0.5; otherwise the retention time will be too long or too short. The list given in Table 6-2 will be helpful in choosing the best solvent.

Partition chromatography offers great advantages over adsorption chromatography. It is far more reproducible and predictable from solubility data. Even more important, the partition coefficient is constant over a much greater range of concentrations, yielding sharper, more symmetrically shaped bands. It is the method of choice whenever a suitable solvent pair can be found.

Reverse-Phase Chromatography. There are some situations in partition chromatography in which it is advantageous to use the non-polar organic solvent as the stationary phase in order to get a more favorable value for the partition coefficient. Obviously, a non-polar solid support is required. Powdered rubber coated with benzene is a very satisfactory stationary phase with an aqueous mobile phase.

ION EXCHANGE METHODS

Many natural clays are able to function as ion exchangers because they are insoluble polymeric materials with a loose structure and many replaceable metal ions. A continual exchange of ions takes place between these clays and the waters passing through them. The detailed process is modified and complicated by the pH and carbonate content of the water. Clays, of course, have varied and unpredictable properties, and it was only with the introduction of synthetic ion exchangers, that a reproducible, scientific technique became possible.

Modern ion exchange resins were first used in 1935 by Adams and Holmes. These resins consist of a three-dimensional network of polymeric chains cross-linked with short chains containing ionizable functional groups. Thus, there is an insoluble phase with fixed ionic sites of one charge, while the oppositely charged species are free to move about and be replaced by other ions of like charge, provided that electroneutrality is maintained. These resins can be used either in a batch process for a wholesale exchange of ions with those in solution, or packed into a column and used in a chromatographic fashion. They have proven invaluable in the separation of ionic substances with closely similar chemical behavior.

TYPES OF RESINS

A typical resin is prepared by a polymerization of styrene and divinylbenzene:

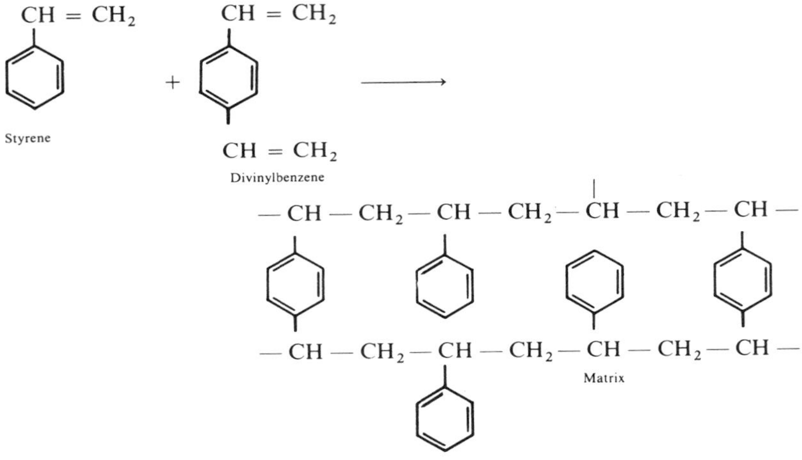

The above structure is repeated in three dimensions, with the number of cross-linkages determined by the ratio of divinylbenzene to styrene. Increasing the cross-linking increases the rigidity, reduces swelling (vide infra), reduces porosity, and reduces the solubility of the polymeric structure. Ordinarily about 10% divinylbenzene is used, but both higher and lower percentages are available in commercial resins. The particle size of the product is determined largely by the extent of mechanical agitation during the reaction, so that resin beads of numerous graded sizes are available.

Cationic Exchangers. Acidic functional groups are easily introduced, for example, by sulfonation in which a sulfonic acid group is attached to nearly every aromatic nucleus. Sulfonic acids are strong acids with essentially completely dissociated protons, although these protons are not free to leave the resin unless replaced by other positive ions. The total number of equivalents of replaceable protons per unit volume of resin determines the *exchange capacity* of the resin. Instead of sulfonic acid groups, carboxylate groups can be added to the aromatic rings. Weak acid groups may result in a high capacity, but the exchange distribution function will depend on the strength of the acid.

Anionic Exchangers. If basic functional groups are introduced, the resin can exchange anions rather than cations. Strong anion exchangers are prepared with a tertiary amine, yielding a strongly basic quaternary ammonium group. Weaker anionic exchangers can be prepared with secondary amines, yielding a weakly basic tertiary amine.

A few common resins are listed in Table 6-4.

TABLE 6-4 SELECTED ION EXCHANGE RESINS

Type	Nature	Capacity	Trade Name
Strong cation	Sulfonated polystyrene	1.9 meq./ml	Dowex 50 Amberlite IR 120
Weak cation	Condensed acrylic acid	4.2	Amberlite IRC 50
Strong anion	Polystyrene with $-CH_2NMe_3Cl$	1.2	Dowex 1 Amberlite IRA 400
Weak anion	Polystyrene with *sec*-amine	2.0	Dowex 3 Amberlite IR 45

Swelling. The high proportion of polar groups within the resin gives it a hygroscopic character. In a sulfonated resin, one can consider that the $-SO_3^-$ and H^+ ions dissolve in the adsorbed water yielding a solution of high concentration. Since the ions cannot diffuse out, there is a tendency for water to diffuse in to equalize the concentration, but the amount of water that can diffuse in is restricted by the space available in the interstices of the resin structure. Even so, large amounts of water, up to a gram per gram of dry resin, are able to penetrate the interior causing distortion of the structure and swelling of the resin bead. The osmotic forces which drive the water from the exterior to the interior of the resin beads cause an enormous internal pressure. Dry beads must never be allowed to swell while tightly packed in a column, and even a change in the nature of the solvent may result in an "explosion" of a tightly packed glass column.

The important properties which determine the behavior of a resin can be summarized:

1. Size of particles—rate of exchange and permeability of the packed column.
2. Degree of cross-linking—rigidity, porosity, swelling.
3. Nature of functional group—kind of ion exchanged.
4. Strength of functional group—distribution coefficient.
5. Number of functional groups—capacity of resin.

Ion Exchange Equilibria. The net result of an ion exchange reaction can be expressed as a replacement of equivalent quantities of like-charged ions:

$$HR + Na^+ = NaR + H^+$$

$$2HR + Ca^{++} = CaR_2 + 2H^+$$

$$RCl + OH^- = ROH + Cl^-$$

where R^+ or R^- represents the resin matrix. The law of mass action applies, and therefore the equilibrium constant (the *selectivity coefficient*) takes the usual form:

$$K = \frac{a_{NaR}\,a_{H^+}}{a_{HR}\,a_{Na^+}} = \frac{(NaR)\,(H^+)}{(HR)\,(Na^+)} \times \frac{f_{NaR}f_{H^+}}{f_{HR}f_{Na^+}} \qquad (6\text{-}1)$$

K is a constant only if the *activities* of the various species are used, otherwise it will vary with relative and total concentrations due to changes in activity coefficients. There is no adequate theory for treating activity coefficients in concentrated solutions of strong electrolytes such as exist within the resin, where concentrations of the order of 2 to 8 M are encountered. The activity coefficient of the resin phase is even more difficult to treat. Consequently, there is little choice but to use a psuedo-equilibrium constant, or concentration ratio. Selectivity coefficients, defined by neglecting activity coefficients, are determined empirically and are reasonably constant for given conditions. Experimental observations have been formulated into a number of useful rules:

1. Selectivity coefficients approach unity as the cross-linking is decreased.
2. The exchange of ions that causes expansion of the resin is less favored than those exchanges that do not; or, the smaller the (hydrated) ion, the greater the affinity for the resin.
3. The greater the charge on the ion, the greater the affinity for the resin.
4. The affinity of high molecular weight organic ions and some anionic complexes of metal ions are unusually high, probably because the electrostatic forces are augmented by short range adsorption (Van der Waal's) forces.

To a first approximation, these rules predict the observed order of affinity for groups of ions:

$$Li^+ < H^+ < Na^+ < NH_4^+ < K^+ < Rb^+ < Cs^+ < Ag^+ < Tl^+$$

$$Be^{++} < Mn^{++} < Mg^{++} < Zn^{++} < Co^{++} < Cu^{++} < Cd^{++} < Ni^{++}$$

$$< Ca^{++} < Sr^{++} < Pb^{++} < Ba^{++}$$

$$Na^+ < Ca^{++} < La^{+++} < Th^{++++}$$

$$OH^-, F^- < CH_3CO_2^- < HCO_2^- < H_2PO_4^- < HCO_3^- < Cl^- < NO_2^-$$
$$< HSO_3^- < CN^- < Br^- < NO_3^- < HSO_4^- < I^-$$

The above orders often show inversions due to changes in pH, relative concentrations, nature of resin, complex formation, ionic strength, etc.

Theories of Column Operation. The *plate theory*, developed by Martin and Synge for partition chromatography, can be applied directly to an ion exchange column with only a change of terminology. We will define a distribution ratio, C, as:

$$C = \frac{\text{quantity of sample in resin of a given plate}}{\text{quantity of sample in interstitial solution of same plate}} \quad (6\text{-}2)$$

Then the volume of eluent required to move the sample through the column, V_e, measured to the peak concentration is

$$V_e = V_c + CV_c \quad (6\text{-}3)$$

where V_c is the interstitial volume of the column.

Likewise, the *rate theory* of Van Deemter originally developed for GLC, is applicable to ion exchange columns with only minor modification. One can expect the same causes and effects of band broadening processes.

Before the sample is introduced, the column is usually converted entirely to the acid form, HR, or to the salt form, NaR, by washing with a solution of hydrochloric acid or sodium chloride. When the sample is introduced, it is first retained at the top of the column by exchange of cations for H^+ or Na^+ from the resin. The cations of the sample can be eluted from the column only by replacement with another ion contained in the eluent. The equilibrium constant, K, defined in Equation 6-1, is to a first approximation independent of the concentration of eluting ion; but the distribution ratio, C, can be changed many-fold by altering the concentration of the eluting ion, because C is defined by the distribution of sample only, and is indirectly affected by the concentration of eluting ion. Thus Equation 6-3 tells us that we can change the elution volume by changing the concentration of the eluting ion. A high concentration of the latter will lead to fast elution with sharper but less well resolved peaks, and vice versa, as shown in Figure 6-1.

Effect of pH of Eluent. The extent of dissociation of weak acids and bases, and the hydrolysis of salts and metal ions is controlled by the pH of the medium. Thus the electrical charge on a species may be increased, decreased, or even reversed by a change in pH. In this manner, we have a delicate but powerful means of influencing the distribution ratio, or of preventing exchange altogether. This behavior is especially important in the separation of amino acids which

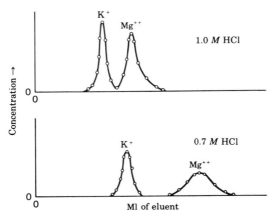

FIGURE 6-1. Elution of potassium and magnesium ions with two different concentrations of hydrochloric acid. (From Kolthoff and Elving, *Treatise on Analytical Chemistry*, Wiley-Interscience, 1961, Part I, Vol. 3, p. 1544.)

can carry a positive, negative, or no net charge depending on the pH of the eluent. Buffered eluents are obviously indicated for separations of this kind, but one must not forget that the ionic constituents of the buffers are also subject to exchange with the resin so that the pH within the column may bear no relation to that which was prepared. The effect of pH on the elution of a typical weak acid is shown in Figure 6-2.

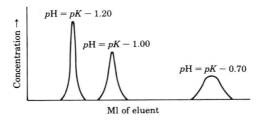

FIGURE 6-2. Effect of pH on the elution of a weak acid anion on an anion exchanger. (From Kolthoff and Elving, *Treatise on Analytical Chemistry*, Wiley-Interscience, 1961, Part I, Vol. 3, p. 1545.)

Effect of Complexing Agents. Ligands which are neutral molecules have no effect on the charge of an ion, but do alter the exchange equilibrium constant. Many metal ions are complexed by anions yielding negatively charged complex ions. Thus, the rare earth metal cations, which are poorly separated by cationic exchangers, can be complexed and separated quite well by anionic exchangers.

Most of the useful complexing agents are themselves weak acids, weak bases or anions or cations thereof. Thus the *p*H and complexing effects are often interdependent. Although there is a sensitive control of the separation, the resulting multiple equilibria are so complicated that theoretical predictions are of little value because of the necessary approximations.

Effect of Column Length. Increasing the length of a column will increase the number of theoretical plates proportionately. Just as in GLC, this will improve the separation of the sample components at the expense of time, materials and greater dilution of the sample.

TECHNIQUE OF ION EXCHANGE CHROMATOGRAPHY

Ion exchange resins can be used either as a batch process or in a column. The former method is analogous to a simple extraction and finds little use except to determine distribution ratios. More commonly the resin is packed in a column and used either in a frontal technique to remove all cations from a sample by replacement with H^+ or Na^+ from the resin, or in an elution technique for multi-component separations.

Selection and Preparation of the Resin. A wide variety of resins are available commercially from which one must select an appropriate mesh size, cross-linking, and quality. Analytical-grade (AG) resins are preferred because they have been more carefully sized and washed to remove foreign organic and inorganic materials. It may be necessary to convert the resin from one form to another; for example, the hydrogen form can be converted to the sodium form by extensive washing in the column with a strong sodium chloride solution until the effluent is neutral. Used resins are "regenerated" in this way.

If it is important to know the weight of resin used, it must be dried or brought to a known moisture content in a hygrostat. In any event, before packing it must be equilibrated with water by prolonged soaking. After the resin has settled, the "fines" which float in the water are poured off.

Packing the Column. Simple columns are constructed from glass tubing with a reservoir at the top for the eluent and a fritted disk or glass wool plug at the bottom to support the resin bed. Usually the bottom of the column is drawn to a narrower diameter and bent in a double-U shape so that the outlet is higher than the top of the resin bed. This prevents air bubbles from leaking into the column. The resin is packed as an aqueous slurry and allowed to settle with occasional tapping. Once packed, the level of liquid should never be allowed to drain lower than the top of the resin bed or air bubbles will be entrapped. The best way to remove air bubbles or channeling is to back-flush the column with an upflow of water. A paper or glass fiber disk placed on top of the bed will minimize disturbance of the resin when adding the sample.

Total Capacity of the Column. The total exchange capacity influences the maximum sample size and is used to check the long term stability of the resin. The capacity of a resin in milli-equivalents per gram of dry resin is normally marked on the bottle by the manufacturer. Experimentally, it is most readily determined by converting it entirely to the hydrogen form (if it is cationic), and then eluting with a sodium chloride solution until it is completely converted to the sodium form. The effluent then must contain hydrochloric acid in an amount equivalent to the capacity of the column—easily determined by titration with sodium hydroxide. Common resins have a capacity of 1 to 5 meq./ml, or roughly 1 to 5 N in acid or base.

Detection Methods. The difficulty of detecting small amounts of sample components in the presence of a large concentration of eluting ion is one of the major disadvantages of ion exchange methods. Continuous recording is not common, although in specific applications, light absorption, refractive index, pH, radioactivity or polarographic measurements have been utilized. The most common practice is to collect numerous small, equal volume fractions and analyze each fraction for the species sought.

SOME APPLICATIONS

Removal of Ions. The household water "softener" is perhaps the most common example of ion exchange. Calcium, magnesium, iron, and all other multiply charged cations are replaced with sodium ion. The softened water then contains sodium salts which are innocuous in plumbing systems and for most home uses. Sodium is chosen because it is harmless in the water and because the resin can be readily regenerated with a strong solution of common salt.

Completely de-ionized water is prepared by passing the raw water through a cation exchanger which replaces all cations with hydrogen ion, and then through an anion exchanger which replaces all anions with hydroxide ion. In effect, the salts are replaced with the ions of water. The two resins can be combined in a single mixed bed so that the water never becomes too acidic or basic as it might if passed through the two resins separately. De-ionized water having a conductivity of less than 10^{-6} mho/cm is prepared more conveniently by ion exchange than by distillation. However, the de-ionization process does not remove non-electrolytes, and thus the water may still be quite impure. Ion exchange offers a convenient and effective method for de-salting solutions of organic or biochemical mixtures.

The removal of one or more interfering ions by replacement with an innocuous ion for a given process or procedure is an obvious application. The determination of total salt content of a solution is simplified by conversion of the cations to hydrogen ion, or the anions to hydroxide ion, followed by a simple acid-base titration.

Concentration of a Trace Constituent. Whenever a trace amount of an ion must be isolated or concentrated from a large volume of aqueous solution, one of the methods of choice is to remove it with an ion exchanger followed by elution into a small volume of eluent. This is a common step in the determination of trace metals in water, copper in milk, or the recovery of precious metals. Perhaps the most spectacular example occurred in the isolation and identification of the first sample of mendelevium. Ten thousand atoms of einsteinium on a gold foil were bombarded with high energy alpha particles. The target was quickly dissolved with aqua regia and the gold extracted with ethyl acetate. The aqueous phase, which contained the einsteinium and any mendelevium produced, was separated with miniature ion exchange columns. At one point the entire world's supply (about 17 atoms) of this newly discovered element was contained in a single resin bead.

Preparation of Reagents. Determinate solutions of strong acids and bases are not easily prepared because of the lack of primary standard reagents. On the other hand, primary standard sodium or potassium chloride is readily available and their solutions are stable indefinitely. Aliquots of these solutions, when passed through a resin in the hydrogen or hydroxide form, will produce equivalent amounts of acid or base. Many other solutions which are difficult to prepare or standardize can be made in a similar fashion.

Separation of Metals. Ion exchange is especially advantageous for the separation of metal ions with very similar properties for which specific methods are not available. For example, the alkali and alkaline earth metals are always difficult to determine in mixtures, but can be readily separated in an ion exchange column. The separation of rare earths is a classic problem formerly accomplished only by numerous and tedious fractional crystallizations. The selectivity coefficients (Equation 6-1) for the rare earth metal ions are nearly identical to each other, but with the addition of chelating agents such as EDTA the selectivity coefficients are altered to varying degrees. Thus the separation becomes much simpler. Ion exchange columns now provide pure rare earth compounds on a commercial scale.

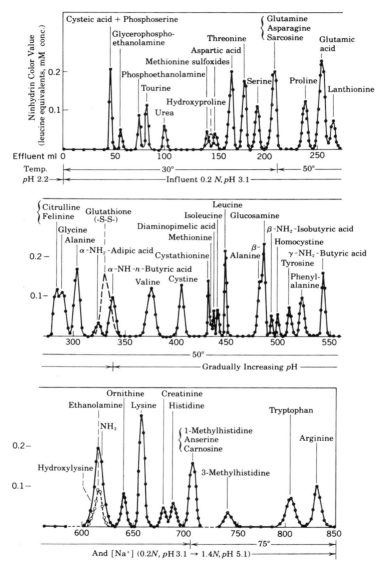

FIGURE 6-3. Separation of amino acids and related compounds on Dowex 50-X4 column 0.9 × 150 cm. [After Moore and Stein, *J. Biol. Chem.*, **211**, 893 (1954).]

Separation of Amino Acids. Perhaps the most impressive example of the versatility and potency of ion exchange methods is the separation of the complex mixtures of amino acids encountered in biochemistry. The amphoteric nature of this group of acids makes it possible to change the sign of the charge or to remove the net charge so that a given acid is amenable to exchange on a cationic or anionic resin, or neither, by controlling the pH of the solution. Thus, at a given pH, a mixture of amino acids can be separated into three groups according to their isoelectric points by passing it through the two types of resins successively. After changing the pH, the groups can be further subdivided as many times as desired.

Alternatively, the original mixture can be resolved in a single pass through an appropriate resin by a graded elution technique in which the pH of the eluent is gradually increased in a stepwise fashion. Moore and Stein were able to separate 50 amino acids by this technique. The conditions for this remarkable separation are given below the diagram in Figure 6-3. Both the pH and temperature were increased during the elution.

GEL CHROMATOGRAPHY

The separation of very high molecular weight substances is most readily accomplished by the use of columns packed with gels. Several varieties of gels have recently become available, all of which separate molecules primarily on the basis of their sizes by a "sieving" or "filtering" process. Hence, the names "gel filtration" used by biochemists, and "gel permeation chromatography" used by polymer chemists describe the same general technique. Adsorption and electrical charge effects may also play a role in these separations.

The gels have a very open, three-dimensional network formed by cross-linking long polymeric chains. Instead of ion exchange sites, most of these gels have polar groups capable of adsorbing water or other polar solvents. A few are able to adsorb non-polar solvents. In either case, the adsorption causes an opening of the structure, or "swelling," leaving interstices within the gel. Depending on the extent of cross-linking, there will be a critical size (exclusion limit) of a molecule that can just penetrate the interior. Larger molecules will pass through the column with no retardation because they cannot enter the gel. Smaller molecules will penetrate the interior to a degree determined by their size. Exclusion limits from about 1000 to several million (molecular weight) are available by selecting the appropriate gel.

Gel chromatography is another variation of the general chromatographic method. Again, the same principles are applicable, although the mechanism of the separation, the handling of the sample and the detection of the components will differ in detail.

TYPES OF GELS

Sephadex. For proteins and most of the large molecules of biochemical interest, Sephadex is the most popular of the gel materials. Sephadex is prepared from polysaccharide dextrans which have been synthesized by the action of a bacterium on sucrose. Each glucose residue contains three hydroxyl groups giving the dextran a polar character. The cross-linking reaction is accomplished with epichlorhydrin, $CH_2 — CHCH_2Cl$. By adjusting the conditions, the amount

$$CH_2 \diagdown \diagup CHCH_2Cl$$
$$O$$

of cross-linking, and thus the size of the pores, can be carefully controlled. Sephadex gels are insoluble in water, and are stable in bases, weak acids, mild reducing and oxidizing agents. Prolonged exposure to 0.1 N hydrochloric acid or strong oxidizing agents will cause breakdown of the gel granules. Temperatures above 120° C should also be avoided. In addition to water in which they are commonly used, Sephadex gels swell in glycol, dimethylsulfoxide, and formamide, but not in glacial acetic acid, methanol, or ethanol. These gels are classified by the amount of "water regain," which is a function of the looseness of the structure or the extent of cross-linking. Several types and their properties are listed in Table 6-5.

TABLE 6-5 TYPES OF SEPHADEX GELS

Type	Water regain, g/g dry Sephadex	Exclusion limit, Mol. Wt.	Fractionation range, Mol. Wt. limits
G-10	1.0	700	up to 700
G-25	2.5	5,000	100–5,000
G-50	5.0	10,000	500–10,000
G-75	7.5	50,000	1,000–50,000
G-100	10.0	100,000	5,000–100,000
G-200	20.0	200,000	5,000–200,000

[Courtesy of Pharmacia, Inc.]

A new gel, Sephadex LH-20, has recently become available. Some of the hydroxyl groups of the dextran gel, described above, are alkylated so that the gel will swell in polar organic solvents, water or mixtures of the two. Methanol, ethanol, *n*-butanol, chloroform, tetrahydrofuran, acetone, ethyl acetate, toluene and combinations of these can be used. The solvent uptake, the amount of swelling, and the fractionation range depend on the particular solvent used. Thus, with this new form of Sephadex, lipids, sterols and other compounds which are relatively insoluble in aqueous solution can be fractionated.

Bio-Gel. A more chemically inert series of gels, called Bio-Gel, is prepared by copolymerization of acrylamide and N,N'-methylene-bis-acrylamide. The polymer is insoluble in water and common organic solvents and is useful in the *p*H range 2 to 11. Strong bases may hydrolyze the amide groups. The inert polyacrylamide matrix minimizes the possibility of adsorption of polar materials. The types which are commercially available are listed in Table 6-6.

TABLE 6-6 TYPES OF BIO-GEL

Type	Water regain, g/g dry gel	Exclusion limit, Mol. Wt.	Fractionation range, Mol. Wt. limits
P-2	1.6	1,600	200–2,600
P-4	2.6	3,600	500–4,000
P-6	3.2	4,600	1,000–5,000
P-10	5.1	10,000	5,000–17,000
P-20	5.4	20,000	10,000–30,000
P-30	6.2	30,000	20,000–50,000
P-60	6.8	60,000	30,000–70,000
P-100	7.5	100,000	40,000–100,000
P-150	9.0	150,000	50,000–150,000
P-200	13.5	200,000	80,000–300,000
P-300	22.0	300,000	100,000–400,000

[Courtesy of Bio. Rad Laboratories]

Styragel. For completely non-aqueous separations, a gel that will swell in an organic solvent is required. Styragel is a rigid cross-linked polystyrene gel which can be prepared in a range of porosities similar to the other gels. It is useful at temperatures up to 150° C with the following solvents: tetrahydrofuran, benzene, trichlorobenzene, perchloroethylene, cresol, dimethylsulfoxide, chloroform, carbon tetrachloride, aromatics, and others, but not with water, acetone or alcohols. Exclusion limits are listed in Table 6-7.

THEORETICAL PRINCIPLES

The Ideal Process. In its simplest form, we shall imagine that the interior of the gel bead consists of conically shaped holes all having identical shapes and sizes. The large molecules to be separated will either be too large to enter the hole at all, or be able to penetrate the interior of the cones to a depth determined by the size of the molecule. If they are reasonably small molecules or simple ions, they will be able to move freely into all parts of the interior of the gel. With this model it is easy to see that the fraction of the interior volume

TABLE 6-7 TYPES OF STYRAGEL

Permeability range	Exclusion limit, Mol. Wt.
40 A	1,600
100	4,000
400	16,000
1,000	40,000
5,000	200,000
10,000	400,000
30,000	1,200,000
100,000	4,000,000
300,000	12,000,000
500,000	20,000,000
1,000,000	40,000,000

[Courtesy of Waters Associates, Inc.]

available to any given molecule varies from 0 to 1 and is a function of the diameter of the molecule relative to the diameter of the pores.

When the gel beads are packed in a column, there will be two kinds of solvent in the column—that within the gel having a volume V_i, and that outside the beads having a volume V_o. Let us assume that the only differentiating feature of the column results from the variation in the fraction of the volume V_i available to different sized molecules. A molecule too large to enter the holes will be swept through the outside volume without ever entering the gel. In this case:

$$V_e = V_o$$

where V_e is the elution volume. Smaller molecules must be swept through V_o plus some additional volume which is a fraction of V_i, or

$$V_e = V_o + K_D V_i \tag{6-4}$$

where K_D is a distribution coefficient which can be defined in several ways. It is the ratio between the "average" concentration of the solute in the interior and the concentration outside the gel. One must remember that in that part of the interior volume available to the solute, its concentration is the same as that outside, but the remaining interior volume has zero concentration. K_D can also be defined as the volume fraction of the interior solvent available to the solute, or in terms of experimentally measurable quantities:

$$K_D = (V_e - V_o)/V_i \tag{6-5}$$

V_i can be obtained from the weight of the dry gel, a, and the water regain value, W_R (Table 6-5):

$$V_i = aW_R \qquad (6\text{-}6)$$

If the sieving action just described were the only mechanism, K_D values should lie between 0 and 1. An interesting consequence of this mechanism is that in gel chromatography the elution volume is usually less than the void volume within the column, whereas in other forms of chromatography the elution volume is always larger than the void volume because of the retention mechanism. In gel chromatography, retention is replaced by exclusion. A simplified illustration of what happens in the column is given in Figure 6-4.

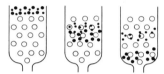

FIGURE 6-4. Separation by exclusion in a gel chromatography column.

Two solutes having K_D values equal to K'_D and K''_D will have elution volumes of $V_o + K'_D V_i$ and $V_o + K''_D V_i$ and will be separated by the difference $(K''_D - K'_D)V_i$. If the eluted bands are no broader than the sample volume, V_s, which was used, then the maximum sample volume for complete separation is:

$$V_s < (K''_D - K'_D)V_i \qquad (6\text{-}7)$$

Non-Ideal Conditions.   The same band broadening processes operate in gel chromatography as in all other forms. For optimum efficiency (minimum HETP) one should use small beads uniformly packed, and slow flow rates as shown in Table 6-8.

So far, we have treated gel separations from a geometric approach; however, the simple theory based on partial exclusion is only an approximation of the true nature of the process. There are, of course, often other mechanisms operating which cause a departure from the simple behavior attributed to sieving alone. The solvent in the primary adsorption layer on the interior surface appears not to be available to the solutes no matter what their size. This presumably explains why many small species have K_D values of about 0.9 rather than the expected 1.0. Other species have K_D values exceeding unity which must result from adsorptive forces retaining the molecules on the interior surfaces. Adsorption is effective with solutes which can react or form complexes with the hydroxyl groups of Sephadex, for example, sodium hydroxide, sodium tetraborate, and aromatic and heterocyclic compounds. K_D values for strongly adsorbed substances can be as high as 20. Still another mechanism appears to be a restricted diffusion within the pores. No doubt the predominant mechanism varies from case to case.

TABLE 6-8 EFFICIENCY OF A SEPHADEX G-200
COLUMN (4 × 42 CM) WITH SERUM ALBUMIN

Particle size, mesh	Flow rate, ml/hr	HETP, cm
100–200	75	0.62
100–200	50	0.48
100–200	25	0.23
200–270	25	0.08

[Courtesy of Pharmacia, Inc.]

TECHNIQUE

Column Preparation.   Gel columns are prepared in the same way as ion exchange columns. The gel beads must first be swelled by equilibration with the solvent—a few hours for dense, highly cross-linked gels, and a day or more for the loosely cross-linked varieties which take up many times as much solvent. Fines can be removed by decantation.

The gel bed is supported in the column on a glass wool plug or nylon net and the previously swollen gel is added in the form of a slurry and allowed to settle. No air bubbles must be entrained within the bed and the level of liquid must never be allowed to go lower than the top of the bed.

Operation.   Samples are introduced as carefully as possible to avoid disturbing the bed itself. Since larger samples are used than in most forms of chromatography, it may be difficult to begin the elution without mixing the sample and the eluent. Sometimes a non-disturbing substance such as sodium chloride is added to the sample to increase its density. Elution is usually carried out under a constant hydrostatic pressure head to achieve a constant flow rate.

Detection.   The common detection methods include: collecting and analyzing fractions and continuous methods with flow-through cells in which ultraviolet absorption, refractive index, or radioactivity is measured.

APPLICATIONS

Desalting. One of the common separation problems in biochemistry is the removal of salts and small molecules from macromolecules. The large difference in distribution coefficients for this separation makes it possible to use simple columns with high flow rates. For example, with Sephadex G-25, solute molecules having molecular weights over 5000 are eluted in a volume V_o. Smaller molecules with molecular weights below 1000 will be eluted following the macromolecules inversely in order of their size. One of the advantages of this method of desalting is that the macromolecules are eluted with essentially no dilution.

Concentrating. Dilute solutions of macromolecules with molecular weights higher than the exclusion limit may be readily concentrated by utilizing the hygroscopic nature of the dry gel. Sephadex G-200 absorbs 20 times its weight of water, although G-25 is preferred because of its more rapid action. Since salts and small molecules are imbibed to the same extent as the water, their concentrations in the supernatant solvent remain essentially unchanged, and the ionic strength and pH of the macromolecular solution remain essentially unaltered.

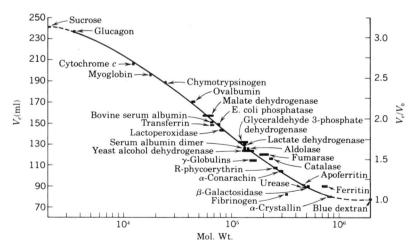

FIGURE 6-5. Relation between elution volume and molecular weight for proteins on a Sephadex G-200 column, 2.5 × 50 cm, at pH 7.5. [After Andrews, *Biochem. J.*, **96**, 595 (1965).]

110   *Fractionation.* The complete separation of mixtures of closely related molecules having small differences in K_D values will require long columns, slow flow rates and much time. However, the distribution of molecular weights in a complex mixture is often sufficient information to characterize the sample or to give a rough idea of its composition. It has been observed, and can be predicted from theory, that the elution volume is related to molecular weight in a simple fashion:

$$V_e = A + B \log \text{Mol. Wt.} \qquad (6\text{-}8)$$

where A and B are constants whose values are determined from a plot of V_e vs. log Mol. Wt. for several known compounds. The equation is valid over a considerable range of molecular weights, provided all compounds are closely related. Values for A and B must be redetermined for each column, each set of operating conditions, and for different classes of compounds. Some representative data are given in Figure 6-5.

Gel chromatography has been used primarily by biochemists to separate proteins, peptides, nucleic acids, polysaccharides, enzymes, hormones and the like, and by polymer chemists to characterize molecular weight distributions in polymeric mixtures.

REFERENCES

A. J. P. Martin and R. L. M. Synge, *Biochem. J.*, **35**, 91 (1941). The classic paper on partition chromatography.

B. J. Mair, "Chromatography: Columnar Liquid-Solid Adsorption Processes," in *Treatise on Analytical Chemistry*, Kolthoff and Elving (Editors), Part 1, Vol. 3, Interscience, New York, 1961, Chapter 34. An extensive discussion.

R. Kunin, *Ion Exchange Resins*, 2nd ed., Wiley, New York, 1958.

E. W. Berg, *Physical and Chemical Methods of Separation*, McGraw-Hill, New York, 1963, Chapter 10.

S. Moore and W. H. Stein, *J. Biol. Chem.*, **192**, 663 (1951); **211**, 893 (1954). Classic papers on the separation of amino acids.

O. Samuelson, *Ion Exchange Separations in Analytical Chemistry*, 2nd ed., Wiley, New York, 1963.

W. Riemann, "Chromatography: Columnar Liquid-Solid Ion Exchange Processes," in *Treatise on Analytical Chemistry*, Kolthoff and Elving (Editors), Part 1, Vol. 3, Interscience, New York, 1961, Chapter 35.

7 PLANE

A drop of liquid
spotted on a piece
of paper or cloth
CHROMATOGRAPHY

spreads in a circular pattern, and if the liquid contains colored substances, concentric rings are easily observed. This simple analytical technique was used by the ancient Romans to test dyes and pigments. About 100 years ago, the German chemists Runge, Schoenbein, and Goppelsroeder introduced improvements to make the technique more nearly reproducible and quantitative. It is only within the last 30 years, however, that paper chromatography has been accepted as a reliable method. A. J. P. Martin, who also was the pioneer in liquid partition and gas chromatography, and his co-workers, Consden and Gordon, published a classical description of paper partition chromatography in which the moisture in the paper served as a stationary phase. Within a few years, this utterly simple scheme of analysis helped to revolutionize research in biochemistry. More recently, and primarily due to the work of Stahl, thin-layer chromatography (TLC) has found widespread use. The "thin layer" of adsorbent is spread on a glass plate and is used much the same as a piece of paper.

In addition to their obvious simplicity, paper chromatography and TLC require only minute amounts of samples. Chromatography on a plane surface, rather than with a column, offers the unique advantage of two dimensional operation. Thus the selective properties of two different solvents can be utilized in developing a single chromatogram.

THEORETICAL PRINCIPLES

Most of the theoretical principles described in column chromatography apply to plane chromatography as well. The concept of a "theoretical plate" may be more difficult to visualize in a piece of paper, but it is clear that the separation is accomplished by successive equilibrations of the sample components between two phases, one of which moves over the other. Likewise the same kinds of non-ideal processes must cause zone spreading on a plane surface as in a column.

The degree of retention in plane chromatography is customarily expressed as the *retardation factor*, R_f:

$$R_f = \frac{\text{distance solute moved}}{\text{distance solvent moved}} \qquad (7\text{-}1)$$

111

The "front" of the solvent is the only point at which the distance it moved can be measured. However, the distance the sample moved is measured to the center of the spot, or to its point of maximum density. We may also define a distribution coefficient, K, in terms of the concentration of solute in the moving phase, C_l, and in the fixed phase, C_s:

$$K = C_s/C_l \tag{7-2}$$

There is a simple relationship between K and the R_f value. The distance an average solute molecule moves is directly proportional to its velocity, which in turn is equal to the velocity of the solvent times the fraction of time the solute spends in the moving phase. The latter can be expressed in terms of the number of molecules in each phase, or as the equilibrium distribution of solute between the two phases:

$$R_f = \frac{\text{number of moles of solute in moving phase}}{\text{total moles of solute in both phases}} = \frac{C_l A_l}{C_l A_l + C_s A_s} \tag{7-3}$$

where A_l and A_s represent the cross-sectional areas of the two phases (perpendicular to the plane of the paper). Dividing numerator and denominator by C_l, and substituting from Equation 7-2, we obtain:

$$R_f = \frac{A_l}{A_l + A_s C_s/C_l} = \frac{A_l}{A_l + K A_s} \tag{7-4}$$

The cross-sectional areas are difficult to determine, so that Equation 7-4 is of little practical use, but it does show that R_f is a modified form of an equilibrium constant, and therefore, R_f values can be expected to depend on the same kinds of parameters as other measures of retention more commonly used in column chromatographic methods. R_f values are also subject to many minor influences such as: variations in the paper, method and direction of development, size and concentration of the sample, and even the distance traveled by the spot. For these reasons, it is more convenient and accurate to use a relative R_f, or R_{std}, value, for which a standard compound is added to the sample (or measured separately under identical conditions). The R_{std} value is simply the ratio of the distances traveled by the two spots during the same time of development.

PAPER CHROMATOGRAPHY

Nature of the Paper. The paper commonly used consists of highly purified cellulose. The polymeric cellulose structure contains several thousand anhydro-glucose units linked through oxygen atoms. Theoretically, there are three hydroxyl groups on each glucose unit, but many of these have been partially oxidized during manufacture to aldehyde, ketone, or carboxyl functional groups. In addition to these variations, the paper will contain traces of many impurities, including inorganic substances held as exchangeable cations on the hydroxyl groups, adsorbed salts or mineral matter left on the paper during processing. Cellulose has a great affinity for water and other polar solvents and holds them tenaciously through the formation of hydrogen bonds. These solvents penetrate the fibers and cause the paper to swell, changing its dimensions. In water, the cellulose is highly polar and becomes electronegative. This effect is decreased in solvents of lower dielectric constants or with increasing salt concentrations. The paper exhibits weak ion exchange properties as well as adsorptive properties. Furthermore, it is a mild reducing agent, and on prolonged contact it will react with many oxidizing agents.

Most of the properties just described vary from paper to paper even within the same lot. Acid-washing, rinsing and drying aid in obtaining reproducible behavior, but, at best, variations in R_f values can be expected. Modified forms of paper are now available in which the paper has been impregnated with alumina, silica gel, ion exchange resins, etc. While these modifications lead to different mechanisms for the separation, the technique is the same.

Apparatus. The apparatus required for paper chromatography consists of a support for the paper, a solvent trough, and an air-tight chamber in which to develop the chromatogram. The closed chamber is necessary to prevent the evaporation of the volatile solvents from the large exposed area of the paper. The size of the chamber may vary from an ordinary test-tube to a large aquarium depending on the size of paper. If a great deal of paper chromatography is to be done, it may be simpler to control the temperature of the entire room, say to 18°C or so. The basic components illustrated in Figure 7-1 are sufficient for

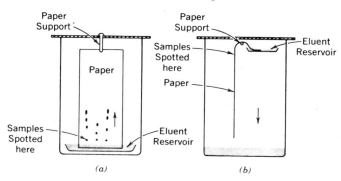

FIGURE 7-1. Basic apparatus for paper chromatography: (*a*) Ascending solvent. (*b*) Descending solvent.

simple paper chromatography, but a number of modifications are available for convenience or for special methods of development to be described below.

The sample is applied prior to dipping into the eluting solvent as a small spot with any device that will transfer a small volume; e.g., a toothpick, loop of platinum wire, capillary tube, micro-pipet, etc. For some methods, the sample may be applied in a narrow line perpendicular to the flow of solvent.

The methods of detection commonly used are: (1) inherent visible colors of the components (whenever possible), (2) reactions with color-producing reagents, (3) ultraviolet absorbance, (4) infrared absorbance, (5) fluorescence, (6) radioactivity, (7) bioautography, or (8) extraction and further chemical or physical tests. Test reagents are easily applied by spraying, immersing, or by exposing to vapors. For example, a ninhydrin reagent sprayed on the paper reacts with amines and amino acids to form a blue or purple color.

Bioautography involves placing the paper in contact with a culture medium for a period of time followed by examination of the relative growth rates of bacteria along the paper strip. Sample compounds may have either a positive or negative effect on the growth rate of the bacteria in the culture medium.

Development. For all types of development, the paper should be equilibrated with solvent vapors before development is begun.

Ascending Development. This is the simplest and most popular type. The paper is suspended vertically with about an inch immersed in the solvent and the sample spot initially located about an inch above the surface of the solvent to prevent diffusion of the sample downwards into the solvent reservoir. The solvent ascends through the paper by capillary action. The rate of ascent is slow and decreases with time because of gravity. However, the slow rate enhances the possibility of achieving partition equilibrium and often results in compact, sharply defined spots.

Descending Development. With a solvent trough at the top of the chamber, the direction of flow is downwards. To prevent rapid siphoning, the paper is folded into a U-shape with a short initial rise from the solvent tank. Although the apparatus is somewhat more elaborate, the method is much faster than the previous one, longer pieces of paper may be used, and large amounts of solvent can be used if necessary for slow-moving spots.

Two-Dimensional Development. In all previously described methods of chromatography, the eluting solvent (or carrier gas) could flow in one direction only—through the column or across the paper. On a plane surface, such as a piece of paper, it is possible to carry out a sequential development in two directions. The sample is applied as a spot close to a corner. This is developed in the normal fashion by ascending or descending procedure until the fastest moving spot approaches the end of the paper. Then the paper is removed, and after evaporating the solvent, it is turned 90° and developed a second time with another solvent having different eluting properties. In this manner, samples which could be only partially separated with either solvent alone, may be completely separated by the combination of solvents as shown in Figure 7-2.

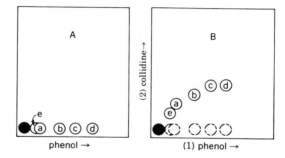

FIGURE 7-2. Two dimensional paper chromatography. Eluents: A, phenol only; B, phenol and collidine, successively. Solutes: (a) Glutamic acid; (b) Serine; (c) Threonine; (d) Alanine; (e) Aspartic acid.

Radial Development. In this method the sample is spotted at the center of a horizontally placed disk of paper with a wick to supply solvent to the center from a supply trough below. The components move outward along radial paths forming circles of increasing diameters. The bands are more or less self sharpening because the solvent moves the trailing edge faster than the leading edge. A covered Petri dish is an adequate container, or the paper can be sandwiched between two glass plates, with a hole in the center of the upper one for the introduction of solvent.

116   For fast development, one can rotate the disk at high speed so that the solvent flows by centrifugal force as well as by capillary action.

Choice of Solvent Systems. The more polar phase, usually water, is preferentially adsorbed by the paper and is held stationary while the less polar phase flows over it. In some cases it may be desirable to remove the water from the paper in a preliminary drying operation and use an alcohol, glycol, formamide, or other polar solvent as a stationary phase. If water is used as a stationary phase, it is not necessary that the mobile solvent be immiscible because the water phase is so tenaciously held by the paper. The aqueous phase may, of course, be buffered if desired. The mobile phase may be a mixture of solvents, e.g., alcohols, acids, ketones, esters, amines, phenols, hydrocarbons, etc., selected so as to achieve maximum separation of the sample components.

In addition to optimum separation, there are other factors to be considered in choosing a solvent system. The more components a solvent system contains, the more difficult it will be to maintain a saturated atmosphere in the chamber. Partial evaporation which changes the composition of the solvent will affect the R_f values. Likewise, temperature change will be more critical in a mixed system. The solvent system must not interfere with the detection procedure (or must be readily and completely vaporizable so that it can be eliminated).

Another very important consideration which is easily overlooked is that minute, non-volatile impurities in the developing solvent can be easily confused with traces in the sample, or may interfere in the detection method.

Ideally, one should choose solvent systems such that the two phases are immiscible, and in which the sample components have a high, but different, solubility in the two phases. This situation will lead to maximum separation with a minimum of spreading in the shortest time.

Reversed-Phase Chromatography. If the paper is coated with a hydrophobic substance, such as rubber latex, mineral oil, or silicone oil, and a polar phase used to elute, a reversal of the normal distributions is obtained. Such systems may be advantageous for the separation of fatty acids and non-polar compounds which may move too fast because of low solubility with a polar stationary phase.

Advantages and Limitations. Paper chromatography is usually used for analyses that would be difficult, time-consuming or expensive by more conventional methods. Though some of the procedures may require several hours, the operator time is indeed very small. It is particularly suitable for samples in the microgram region, and for mixtures of substances that are closely related chemically.

The small sample limitation may well be a disadvantage if detection requires an auxiliary technique. The variability of the paper is a serious problem although this situation is improving. Most of the procedures have been arrived at in an empirical fashion, and could hardly be called quantitative.

Applications. Paper chromatography has been successfully applied to problems in inorganic and organic chemistry as well as in biochemistry. Prospectors have used it to determine metals in ore samples. Isomeric metal complexes can be resolved. Metals with similar chemical properties are easily resolved. Nearly any mixture of organic chemicals can be separated and organic chemists often use it as a quick check for purity or as a pilot method to determine the optimum conditions for a larger scale column chromatographic separation.

The method has made its greatest impact in biochemistry where difficult analytical problems with vanishingly small samples are legion. The literature expands continually: the control of purity of pharmaceuticals and food products, the study of ripening and fermentation, the detection of drugs and dopes in animals and humans, the analysis of cosmetics, the detection of adulterants and contaminants in food and drink, and, of course, the analysis of most of the reaction mixtures studied by biochemists.

THIN-LAYER CHROMATOGRAPHY

The operations performed in thin-layer chromatography are essentially the same as in paper chromatography, and most of the previous discussion applies to this remarkably simple form of chromatography as well. Instead of a piece of paper, a thin layer of finely divided adsorbent supported on a glass plate is used.

Nature of the Thin Layer. The most commonly used adsorbents are silica gel, alumina, diatomaceous earth, and powdered cellulose, but other materials such as Sephadex, ion exchange resins, or inorganics have been used for special purposes. Silica gel is acidic and has a high capacity. It is useful for both adsorption and partition chromatography. Alumina is basic and used primarily for adsorption. Diatomaceous earth is nearly neutral and is used as a support for partition phenomena. Any of these materials can be used in pure form, but it is more convenient to combine them with a binder (adhesive) such as plaster of Paris to make a more cohesive layer.

Preparation of the Layer. The glass plate is usually flat and smooth, or occasionally lightly ground or ridged. The size and shape may be dictated by the apparatus to be used—microscope slides are inexpensive, readily available, and adequate for small scale work. In any event, the glass surface must be scrupulously cleaned with a detergent and/or an organic solvent to remove any grease.

118   The thickness of the layer will determine the capacity of the system. Layers of 0.15 to 2.0 mm thickness are satisfactory. The primary concern is to obtain a layer of uniform thickness. Most thin layers are produced by spreading a film of an aqueous slurry of the adsorbent over the entire surface. The slurry must be neither too thick (viscous) nor too thin, or it will not spread properly. Silica Gel G, which contains 10 to 15% calcined calcium sulfate, mixed with about twice its weight of water, makes a very satisfactory slurry.

In commercial spreading machines a slotted trough travels over the glass and deposits a uniform layer. Alternatively, we can apply tape along opposite edges of the glass and use a glass rod for a trowel, producing a layer the thickness of the tape. For occasional use, a pair of microscope or lantern slides can be dipped back-to-back into a non-aqueous slurry containing 35 g Silica Gel G in 100 ml of chloroform, raised slowly, and allowed to drain and dry.

After spreading, the binder requires about 30 minutes to "set." For adsorption chromatography, the layer is activated by heating at 110° C for several hours. For partition chromatography, no drying is required and the residual water acts as the stationary phase. The edges should be cleaned and the plates stored in a desiccator or an appropriate cabinet. Remember that an activated plate will adsorb water vapor and other vapors from the air, making drastic changes in its chromatographic behavior.

Methods of Development.   The choice of solvent depends on the same factors as already discussed in other forms of liquid chromatography, and the methods of elution are much the same as for paper chromatography. The procedure must, of course, be conducted in a closed chamber to prevent evaporation of the solvent. In order to detect the spots, iodine vapor is used extensively as a "universal" reagent for organic compounds. The iodine spot disappears rapidly but can be made more permanent by spraying with a 0.5% benzidine solution in absolute ethanol. Another common detecting reagent is a spray of sulfuric acid which upon warming chars the sample components, leaving black spots. There are a host of more specific reagents available, and, of course, the spot can be scraped off, eluted and investigated by any available method.

Advantages and Applications.   Compared to paper chromatography, thin-layer is more versatile, faster, and more reproducible. It is often used as a pilot technique for a quick look at the complexity of a mixture or as an aid in establishing the best conditions for large scale column chromatography. Because of its speed and simplicity, it is often used to follow the course of reactions or to monitor more elaborate and complex separation techniques. Thin-layer chromatograms often serve to identify drugs, plant extracts and biochemical preparations, or to detect contaminants or adulterants.

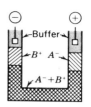

FIGURE 7-3. Basic apparatus for electrophoresis. Resolution of two components under ideal conditions.

ZONE ELECTROPHORESIS

Electrophoresis pertains to the movement of charged colloidal particles or macromolecular ions in an electrical field. Differences in the rates of migration provide a powerful means for the separation and identification of biocolloids such as proteins, polysaccharides and nucleic acids as well as the characterization of their components. Two general classifications are recognized.

In the first, the sample is placed in the bottom of a U-tube with initially sharp boundaries separating the sample from the remaining solution in the tube. A schematic version is shown in Figure 7-3. On the passage of an electric current, the boundary is observed to move in a direction and at a rate determined by the charge and mobility of the charged species. The position of the boundary may be observed by a discontinuity in the refractive index of the solution. The usual electrophoretic pattern (similar to a chromatogram) consists of a plot of the refractive index *gradient* vs. distance along the tube, as shown in Figure 7-4.

The mobility, μ, of the species is one of its characteristic properties and can be determined from the relation:

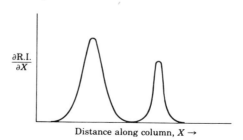

FIGURE 7-4. Electrophoretic pattern for separation in Figure 7-3.

$$\mu = \frac{dAK}{it} \tag{7-5}$$

where d is the distance the boundary travels in time, t; A is the cross-sectional area of the tube, K is the conductivity of the buffer solution, and i is the current flowing. If the sample contains a number of charged components, a corresponding number of boundaries may be formed.

The second method is a combination of electrical migration and paper or column chromatography, and is known as "zone electrophoresis." The additional parameter of electrical migration offers one more way to pull apart complex mixtures. However, electrophoresis on paper (or thin layer) makes possible one of the few forms of truly continuous elution chromatography. A diagram of the apparatus is shown in Figure 7-5. The sample is applied continuously from a wick at the top of the paper and is eluted in a downward direction. With no electrical current flowing, the sample would of course travel in a straight vertical

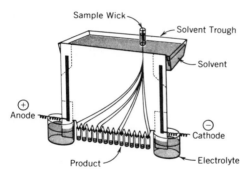

FIGURE 7-5. Continuous electrophoresis on paper. [From Durham, *J. Am. Chem. Soc.*, **73**, 4875 (1951).]

line and emerge unseparated, although each component would be traveling at a different velocity depending on its distribution coefficient. With an electrical current flowing, however, charged particles will travel to the left or to the right depending on their charge with a horizontal velocity depending on their mobility. The resultant direction of travel is the vector sum of the two perpendicular components. Thus each charged component should emerge at a different place at the bottom of the paper while uncharged components will emerge directly below the point of application. Continuous electrophoresis makes possible the preparation of relatively large amounts of purified substances in a short time.

REFERENCES

E. Heftmann, *Chromatography*, 2nd ed., Reinhold, New York, 1966; Chapters 4 and 7.

H. J. Pazdera and W. H. McMullen, "Chromatography: Paper," in *Treatise on Analytical Chemistry*, Kolthoff and Elving (Editors), Part 1, Vol. 3, Interscience, New York, 1961; Chapter 36.

E. W. Berg, *Physical and Chemical Methods of Separation*, McGraw-Hill, New York, 1963; Chapters 6 and 7.

8 ELECTROMAGNETIC RADIATION AND ITS INTERACTION WITH MATTER

Electromagnetic radiation is a form of radiant energy which exhibits both wave and particle properties. The phenomena of refraction, reflection, reinforcement and destructive interference are examples of wave properties. At the other extreme, Einstein's explanation of the photoelectric effect suggests that electromagnetic radiation consists of discrete particles called *photons* which have definite energies and travel through space with the velocity of light. Although waves and particles seem to be incompatible, we must invoke the "particle-wave" duality to explain both electron behavior and the nature of electromagnetic radiation.

NATURE OF ELECTROMAGNETIC RADIATION

Wave Properties. As indicated in Figure 8-1, and as the name implies, an electromagnetic wave has an electric component and a magnetic component. The two components oscillate in planes perpendicular to each other and perpendicular to the direction of propagation of the radiation. Only the electric component is active in ordinary energy transfer interactions with matter. Henceforth, in our discussion of wave behavior we will consider only the electric component. In Figure 8-1, wavelength, λ, is the distance between two corresponding points on the wave. The square of the amplitude, A, of the wave is a measure of the intensity of the wave and is thus proportional to the number of photons which have "wavelength," λ.

Another important property of an electromagnetic wave is its frequency, v, or the number of complete wavelength units which pass a fixed point per unit of time. The units of frequency are cycles per second or $\sec^{-1}$. The wavelength and frequency are related to the velocity of light by the expression:

$$\lambda v = c/n$$

123

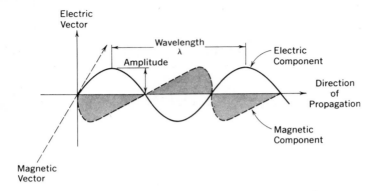

FIGURE 8-1.   An electromagnetic wave.

where c = the velocity of light in a vacuum (2.9976×10^{10} cm/sec) and n is the refractive index (the ratio of the velocity of light in a vacuum to its velocity in the medium in question). The frequency may also be defined as the number of wavelength units in 2.9976×10^{10} cm, a very large number. For many purposes it is more convenient to define frequency as the number of wavelength units in one centimeter. This number is called the wavenumber, $\bar{v}$:

$$\bar{v} = 1/\lambda = vn/c \text{ (units, cm}^{-1})$$

example / problem 8-1:   Green light has a wavelength of approximately 530 millimicrons ($m\mu$) in a vacuum. Calculate the wavelength, λ, and the wavenumber, $\bar{v}$, for green light in water (1 $m\mu = 10^{-7}$ cm).

$$n_{\text{vacuum}} = 1.0000; \qquad n_{\text{water}} = 1.332$$

solution.   The frequency of a given radiation is the same in every medium. Only the velocity and wavelength of the radiation change from medium to medium. Therefore, for green light in a vacuum,

$$v = \frac{c}{n\lambda} = \frac{3.00 \times 10^{10} \text{ cm/sec}}{(1.000)(5.30 \times 10^{-5} \text{ cm})} = 5.66 \times 10^{14} \text{ sec}^{-1}$$

Consequently, in water, $v = 5.66 \times 10^{14}$ sec^{-1}. However, $n = 1.332$. Therefore for green light in water,

$$\lambda_{\text{water}} = \frac{c}{nv} = \frac{3.00 \times 10^{10} \text{ cm/sec}}{(1.332)(5.66 \times 10^{14} \text{ sec}^{-1})} = 3.98 \times 10^{-5} \text{ cm}$$

Since $\bar{v}_{\text{water}} = \dfrac{1}{\lambda_{\text{water}}}$, $\bar{v}_{\text{water}} = 2.51 \times 10^4$ cm^{-1}.

Particle Properties. To describe how electromagnetic radiation interacts with matter, it is useful to think of a light beam as a train of photons. The energy of *each* photon is proportional to the frequency of the radiation and is given by the relationship:

$$E = h\nu = hc/n\lambda \qquad (8\text{-}1)$$

where E = the energy of the photon in ergs, ν = the frequency of the electromagnetic radiation in cycles per second and h = Planck's constant, 6.624×10^{-27} erg-sec. A photon of high frequency (short wavelength) has a higher energy content than one of lower frequency (longer wavelength). The intensity of a light beam is proportional to the number of photons and is independent of the energy of each photon.

The Spectrum. Electromagnetic radiation which is of interest in chemistry varies from the highly energetic gamma rays to the very low energy radiowaves. The entire range of radiation is commonly referred to as the electromagnetic spectrum; the portion of chemical interest is presented in Table 8-1. The various regions of the spectrum are defined by the type of apparatus used to generate or detect the radiation, e.g., the human eye, infrared spectrophotometer, X-ray machine, etc. The limits indicated in Table 8-1 are arbitrary and diffuse—the regions overlap.

INTERACTION OF ELECTROMAGNETIC RADIATION WITH MATTER

Absorption of Radiation. A variety of phenomena may occur when electromagnetic radiation passes through matter. If the photons of the radiation have the appropriate energies, they may be absorbed by the sample and cause electronic transitions, vibrational changes or rotational changes, or combinations of these. The excited atoms and molecules which result from absorption return to the ground state very quickly either by losing energy in the form of heat to the surroundings or by reemitting electromagnetic radiation. In general, the absorption of X-ray, ultraviolet and visible radiation causes electronic transitions within samples, with accompanying vibrational and rotational changes also noted for molecular substances. Infrared absorption promotes molecular vibrational changes with superimposed rotational changes. Infrared photons are *not* energetic enough to cause electronic transitions. Far infrared and microwave radiation can initiate only rotational changes. The absorption of radiofrequency radiation is too weak to be observed except under special conditions when certain nuclei are placed in an intense magnetic field, a phenomenon known as "nuclear magnetic resonance."

Part of the radiation which passes into matter, instead of being absorbed, may undergo scattering, or reflection, or may be re-emitted at the same wave-

TABLE 8-1 The Electromagnetic Spectrum

Quantity												
λ	0.01 A	0.1 A	1 A	10 A	100 A (10 mμ)	1,000 A (100 mμ)	1 μ (1,000 mμ)	10 μ	100 μ (0.01 cm)	1,000 μ (0.1 cm)	1 cm	10 cm
ν (cps)	3×10^{20}		3×10^{18}		3×10^{16}		3×10^{14}		3×10^{12}		3×10^{10}	
$\bar{\nu}$ (cm^{-1})							10,000	1,000	100	10	1	0.1
E (electron volts)				1240	124	12.4	1.24	0.124	0.012	0.001		
E (cal/mole)					2850	285	28.5 (2.85 kcal/mole)	2.85 kcal/mole (2850)	285	28.5	2.85 cal/mole	

Spectral regions (by increasing wavelength):

- Gamma rays — Nuclear Transitions
- X-rays — Inner Shell — Electronic Transitions
- Ultraviolet — Valence Shells — Electronic Transitions
  - Vacuum UV
  - Near UV
- Visible
- Infrared — Molecular Transitions
  - Near IR — Vibrations
  - Fund. IR — Vibrations
  - Far IR — Rotations
- Microwave — Rotations
- Radio — Spin Orientations

length or a different wavelength upon emerging from the sample. Electromagnetic radiation which is neither absorbed nor scattered may, however, undergo changes in orientation or polarization as it passes through a sample. We will return to a discussion of these "other" interactions shortly.

Atomic Absorption of Electromagnetic Radiation. Monatomic substances normally exist in the gaseous state and are able to absorb electromagnetic radiation only through an increase in their electronic energy. Recall that electrons in a given atom occupy discrete energy levels and are thus "quantized." These quantized levels take the form of the various electron-cloud subshells whose energy levels are indicated in Figure 8-2. Thus electronic absorption of electromagnetic radiation can occur only if the attacking photon has an energy which is equal to the *energy difference* between two quantized energy levels, i.e. $\Delta E = hv$ (where ΔE is the energy difference between two quantum levels and v is the frequency of the photon which can cause the transition.)

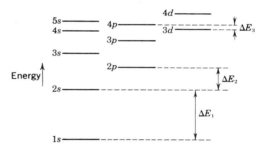

FIGURE 8-2. Energy level diagram for subshells in polyelectron atoms.

In the case of a polyelectron atom, we see that a multiplicity of absorptions are possible. The energy required to cause a $1s \rightarrow 2s$ electron transition (ΔE_1) corresponds to X-ray radiations; $2s \rightarrow 2p$ (ΔE_2) requires far ultraviolet radiation; $3d \rightarrow 4p$ (ΔE_3) requires visible radiation.

Molecular Absorption of Electromagnetic Radiation. The absorption of electromagnetic radiation by molecules is far more complex than absorption by individual atoms. The total energy state of a molecule includes electronic, vibrational and rotational components. All of these energy components are quantized. The energy difference between molecular electronic levels is much greater than that between vibrational states; and the energy difference between vibrational states is significantly greater than that between rotational states.

Thus, for each electronic level of a molecule, there are also superimposed vibrational and rotational states as illustrated in Figure 8-3. A given electronic change may also involve a vibrational change as well as a rotational change

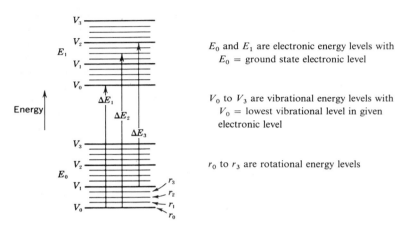

E_0 and E_1 are electronic energy levels with
E_0 = ground state electronic level

V_0 to V_3 are vibrational energy levels with
V_0 = lowest vibrational level in given electronic level

r_0 to r_3 are rotational energy levels

FIGURE 8-3. Schematic representation of molecular electronic, vibrational and rotational energy levels.

resulting in a range of photon energies that can be absorbed. For example, in Figure 8-3 ΔE_1, ΔE_2, and ΔE_3 all represent electronic transitions involving the same electronic levels. Quantum mechanical selection rules indicate that some of these possibilities are not allowed and that some are more probable than others. *Each* absorption thus corresponds to energy transfer by photons of a given frequency or wavelength. Therefore, for an *electronic* transition we observe a broad absorption spectrum as illustrated in Figure 8-4, where $\lambda_{\max}$ corresponds to the most probable ΔE for the transition. This type of spectrum is called a "broad band" spectrum and is typical of most absorptions of ultraviolet and visible radiation. In the solid and liquid states, rotational changes are either zero or spread out into a continuum around each vibrational state. Therefore, only vibrational changes at rather specific energies should occur in condensed states, and these should produce rather narrow absorption bands. These are noted in most absorptions of near and fundamental infrared radiation. As might be expected, infrared spectra of gas molecules exhibit somewhat broader bands due to the greater number of possible superimposed rotational changes. Absorption spectra of gaseous molecules in the microwave region exhibit very sharp lines

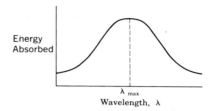

FIGURE 8-4. Typical broad absorption band.

because absorption of this low energy radiation can initiate only rotational changes with no other superpositions. We shall now take a closer look at the nature of molecular electronic transitions and vibrational changes induced by the absorption of electromagnetic radiation.

MOLECULAR ELECTRONIC TRANSITIONS

We have already discussed the quantized nature of the energies of electrons in atomic orbitals of individual atoms. We indicated how the differences between the energies of these quantized states determine the frequencies of electromagnetic radiation which can be absorbed. We also find that molecular electronic energy states determine the nature of electromagnetic radiation which may be absorbed. The two most useful theories which help to explain the transitions noted in electronic absorption spectra are the molecular orbital theory and the ligand field theory.

Molecular Orbital Theory. When two atoms form a chemical bond, electrons from both atoms participate in the bond and occupy a new orbital, a molecular orbital. The bonding electrons are associated with the molecule as a whole and not with any particular nucleus. Two atomic orbitals from the two bonding atoms combine to form one "bonding" molecular orbital of low energy and one "antibonding" molecular orbital of very high energy. Recall that covalent bonds consisting of electron pairs may be σ (sigma) or π (pi) bonds. Sigma bonds are formed when there is "head-on" atomic orbital overlap and pi bonds result when there is "parallel" atomic orbital overlap, e.g., parallel overlap of two atomic p orbitals. Thus, according to molecular orbital theory, each bonding σ orbital must have a corresponding σ^* antibonding orbital; and each π bonding orbital must have a corresponding π^* antibonding orbital. Electron-cloud probability distributions for these four types of molecular orbitals are illustrated in Figure 8-5. Valence electrons which are not participating in chemical bonding in molecules are referred to as non-bonding or "n" electrons. In organic molecules,

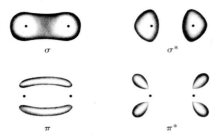

σ

σ^*

π

π^*

FIGURE 8-5. Bonding and antibonding molecular orbitals.

n electrons are located principally in the atomic orbitals of nitrogen, oxygen, sulfur, and the halogens. Electronic transitions for organic molecules involve the absorption of ultraviolet or visible radiation by electrons in n, σ or π orbitals and result in their promotion to some higher energy antibonding orbital (excited state). The order of energy levels of the various molecular orbitals is indicated in Figure 8-6. Ultraviolet and visible radiation absorption promotes the electronic transitions $\sigma \rightarrow \sigma^*$, $n \rightarrow \sigma^*$, $n \rightarrow \pi^*$, and $\pi \rightarrow \pi^*$. The energy level diagram in Figure 8-6 indicates that the ΔE values for transitions are in the order: $n \rightarrow \pi^* < \pi \rightarrow \pi^* < n \rightarrow \sigma^* \ll \sigma \rightarrow \sigma^*$. The energy required for the $\sigma \rightarrow \sigma^*$ transition is very large; consequently, compounds such as saturated hydrocarbons with no n electrons and only σ bonds do not absorb *ordinary* ultraviolet radiation. For example, propane exhibits a $\sigma \rightarrow \sigma^*$ absorption maximum at 135 mμ which is well into the far ultraviolet region and inaccessible for study except under extraordinary conditions. As indicated above, compounds which contain non-bonding electrons display absorptions due to the $n \rightarrow \pi^*$ and $n \rightarrow \sigma^*$ transitions. Compounds which have characteristic $n \rightarrow \sigma^*$ transitions include methyl chloride, H_3CCl ($\lambda_{max} = 173$ mμ), methyl alcohol, H_3COH

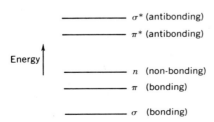

Energy

—————— σ^* (antibonding)

—————— π^* (antibonding)

—————— n (non-bonding)

—————— π (bonding)

—————— σ (bonding)

FIGURE 8-6. Diagram of electronic molecular orbital energies.

(λ_{max} = 183 mμ), and trimethylamine (H$_3$C)$_3$CNH$_2$ (λ_{max} = 227 mμ). The lowest energy transition is represented by $n \rightarrow \pi^*$ and thus requires the longest wavelength for electronic absorption. For example, saturated ketones and aldehydes show a low intensity $n \rightarrow \pi^*$ absorption at about 285 mμ. Molecular electronic transitions may be represented in the following manner.

Some representative molecular electronic transitions are given in Table 8-2. Remember that the electronic transitions we have discussed necessarily include possible superimposed molecular vibrational and rotational changes.

TABLE 8-2 REPRESENTATIVE MOLECULAR ELECTRONIC TRANSITIONS

Compound	Structure	Transition	λ_{max} (mμ)
Ethane	H$_3$C — CH$_3$	$\sigma \rightarrow \sigma^*$	135
Ethylene	H$_2$C = CH$_2$	$\pi \rightarrow \pi^*$	165
Methanol	H$_3$C — ÖH	$n \rightarrow \sigma^*$	183
Acetone	H$_3$C — C — CH$_3$ ‖ O	$\pi \rightarrow \pi^*$ / $n \rightarrow \pi^*$	188 / 279
Toluene	⬡—CH$_3$	$\pi \rightarrow \pi^*$	208
1,2-Butadiene	H$_2$C = C = C(H) — CH$_3$	$\pi \rightarrow \pi^*$	220
Acetophenone	⬡—C — CH$_3$ ‖ O	$\pi \rightarrow \pi^*$	240
n-Butyliodide	H$_3$C — CH$_2$ — CH$_2$ — C(H)(H) — I	$n \rightarrow \sigma^*$	257

132   *Ligand Field Theory.* We have used the molecular orbital theory to explain the electronic absorption of ultraviolet radiation by organic molecules. Since most organic compounds do not absorb any portion of the visible spectrum, they are colorless (exceptions are organic azo dyes, etc.). On the other hand, transition metal complexes exhibit many different colors. Recall that if a substance absorbs a certain color of light, to the eye it appears to be the color of the light which is *not* absorbed, i.e., that which is transmitted. For example, permanganate is purple because it absorbs green light and transmits the red and blue. Cupric ion is blue because it absorbs red and some yellow light, transmitting the blue. What causes different transition metal ions to exhibit different colors; and more fundamentally, what causes transition metal ions to absorb visible radiation? To answer this question, let us examine the structure of the purple hexaquo complex of chromium(III). The complex ion has the octahedral structure indicated below. The chromium(III) ion has the electron configuration:

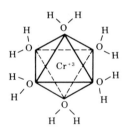

argon core $3d^3$. The electron probability distributions for the five $3d$ orbitals are shown in Figure 8-7. The three $3d$ electrons act as non-bonding electrons. Ligand field theory states that in the process of forming the aquo complex ion, the five "d" orbitals of Cr(III) are split into two sets with different energies. Metal ion electrons located in orbitals along the x, y, and z bonding axes (d_{z^2} and $d_{x^2-y^2}$) will undergo an electrostatic repulsive force from the electron pairs of the water molecules; therefore, the d orbitals located between the bonding axes (d_{xy}, d_{yz}, and d_{xz}) are energetically more stable. So in an octahedral "ligand field" the five d orbitals may be represented on an energy level diagram as shown in Figure 8-8. The two sets of orbitals are referred to as e_g (higher energy) and t_{2g} (lower energy). The magnitude of the energy difference, ΔE, between the two sets depends on the nature of the central metal ion and the nature of the ligands. For a given metal ion, there is large variation of ΔE with variation of ligands. The higher the "ligand field strength," the greater is the energy separation between the e_g and t_{2g} orbitals. The variation in "ligand field strength" is often referred to as the "spectro-chemical series": $I^- < Br^- < -SCN^- < Cl^-$

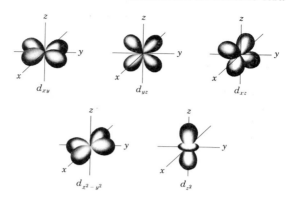

FIGURE 8-7. Electron probability distributions for $3d$ orbitals.

$< NO_3^- < F^- <$ urea $((H_2N)_2CO) \sim OH^- \sim ONO^- < HCOO^- < C_2O_4^{-2} <$ $H_2O < -NCS^- <$ glycine $\sim EDTA^{-4} <$ pyridine $\sim NH_3 <$ en $\sim$ dien $\sim$ trien $<$ dipyridyl $< o$-phenanthroline $< -NO_2^- \ll CN^-$; where $EDTA^{-4} =$ anion of ethylenediaminetetraacetic acid, en $=$ ethylenediamine, dien $=$ diethyl-enetriamine and trien $=$ triethylenetetramine. The absorption of visible light by transition metal complexes involves electron transitions from t_{2g} orbitals to unfilled e_g orbitals. Since ΔE for these transitions is variable, the transmitted color of a given metal ion also varies depending on the nature of the ligand.

Other transition metal complexes may have tetrahedral, tetragonal, or square planar symmetries. In such cases there are different splitting patterns for the five d orbitals of the metal ion. However, the absorption of radiation, for the most part, still involves electron transitions from low energy d orbitals to unfilled higher energy d orbitals. A molecular orbital treatment of transition metal complexes yields essentially the same result for the interpretation of electronic spectra.

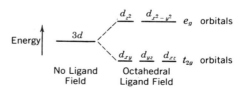

FIGURE 8-8. Octahedral ligand field splitting of $3d$ orbitals.

134   *VIBRATIONAL ENERGY CHANGES*

Atoms in molecules are not static. There are normally a multitude of vibrations associated with the atoms. The vibrational frequencies are dependent on the masses of atoms and the strengths of the bonds connecting them. Some of the molecular vibrations are characteristic of the entire molecule ("fingerprint" vibrations) and others are associated with certain functional groups. There are two major vibration classifications, *stretching* and *bending*. Stretching vibrations are those in which two bonded atoms continuously oscillate, changing the distance between them without altering the bond axis or bond angles. Bending vibrations are characterized by a continuously changing angle between two bonds.

Stretching vibrations are either isolated vibrations (e.g., the carbonyl group

— C = O) or coupled vibrations (e.g., the methylene group $\overset{H}{\underset{}{}}\diagdown C \diagup \overset{H}{}$). Coupled

vibrations are symmetrical or unsymmetrical (asymmetric) as illustrated in Figure 8-9. Stretching vibrations generally require higher energy than bending

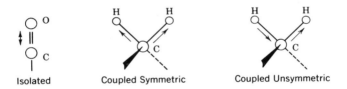

Isolated   Coupled Symmetric   Coupled Unsymmetric

FIGURE 8-9.   Isolated and coupled stretching vibrations.

vibrations and, consequently, the absorption of electromagnetic radiation occurs at shorter wavelength. The vibrational behavior of two atoms connected by a bond is similar to that of a pair of spheres connected by a spring. The stiffness of the spring is described by a force constant, k. If such a simple system is put in motion, the vibrations of the spheres are described by the *law of simple harmonic motion*. Vibrations of atoms in molecules can be described in much the same way. The relationship between the vibrational stretching frequency, bond strength and atomic masses of two atoms is given by:

$$\bar{v} = \frac{1}{2\pi c}\sqrt{\frac{k(M_x + M_y)}{M_x M_y}} \qquad (8\text{-}2)$$

where $\bar{v}$ = the appropriate stretching frequency in cm^{-1} (wavenumbers)

M_x and M_y = the masses of the two atoms in the chemical bond

c = velocity of light

k = force constant of the chemical bond (related to bond strength)

Single, double and triple bonds exhibit force constants of approximately 5.0×10^5, 1.0×10^6, and 1.5×10^6 dynes/cm, respectively.

Bending vibrations may be sub-classified as follows: *wagging*, in which a non-linear three-atom structural unit oscillates back and forth in the equilibrium plane formed by the atoms and their two bonds; *rocking*, where the structural unit oscillates back and forth out of the equilibrium plane; *twisting*, in which the structural unit rotates around the bond which joins it to the rest of the molecule; and *scissoring*, in which two non-bonded atoms move back and forth toward each other. These various bending vibrations are illustrated in Figure 8-10.

Within a polyatomic molecule, each type of vibration has a definite frequency. Thus molecular stretching and bending vibrations are quantized. When electromagnetic radiation of the same frequency as a molecular vibration is directed at the molecule, absorption may occur. In the process of absorption, reinforcement occurs and the *amplitude* of the molecular vibration is increased. When the molecule falls back to the vibrational ground state, the absorbed energy is dissipated as heat.

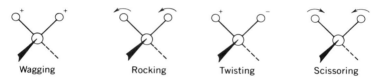

Wagging   Rocking   Twisting   Scissoring

FIGURE 8-10.   Bending vibrations (where + indicates movement *out* of the plane of the page and − denotes movement *back* from the plane of the page).

Modes of Vibration.   Let us consider the number of possible molecular vibrations a polyatomic molecule may have. This information will allow us to make some estimate of the number of absorption bands to expect. In a polyatomic molecule of n atoms, the location of each nucleus in three-dimensional space is specified by three coordinates; therefore, $3n$ coordinates are needed to specify the location of all atoms in a polyatomic molecule, and the molecule is said to have $3n$ degrees of freedom. However, three of these coordinates are related to the translational movement of the molecule as a unit and another three describe the rotation if it is a non-linear molecule. Thus non-linear molecules possess $3n-6$ *normal* vibrational modes which may absorb electromagnetic radiation. Since linear molecules require only two coordinates to describe their rotation, they have $3n-5$ *normal* vibrational modes. We note experimentally that some molecules exhibit more than the *normal* number of vibrational absorptions and some fewer. A larger number of vibrational absorptions may be due to: (1)

"combination tones" (i.e., $\bar{v}_1 + \bar{v}_2$ where $\bar{v}_1$ and $\bar{v}_2$ are normal vibrational frequencies), (2) "overtones" (multiples of given normal frequencies $2\bar{v}$, $3\bar{v}$, etc.), and (3) "difference tones" (i.e., $\bar{v}_1 - \bar{v}_2$). Fewer vibrational frequencies are observed if: (1) a molecule has symmetry such that the absorption of EM radiation results in no change in the electric dipole moment of the molecule and is thus forbidden by quantum mechanical selection rules, (2) some vibrations have identical frequencies as happens for certain highly symmetrical molecules; therefore only one absorption is observed, (3) there is so little difference between some vibrational frequencies that they cannot be resolved by the available instrument, (4) some normal vibrational frequencies are so weak that they are unobservable or overlooked, and (5) some normal vibrational modes are out of the range of the instrument being used.

ROTATIONAL ENERGY CHANGES

Absorption of far infrared and microwave radiation results in a change in rotational energy only. This occurs only if there is a change in dipole moment during the rotation. Thus the molecules must have a permanent dipole moment. Pure rotational transitions are observed only for gases; in liquids and solids the rotational states are no longer well defined and any rotational absorption produces a continuum rather than discrete lines. Rotational changes for the liquid state tend only to broaden out vibrational and electronic absorption bands. The extent of band broadening in liquid and solid states due to the continuum of rotational fine structure is normally insignificant. In this book we are concerned only with absorption by samples in the liquid state, and therefore need not consider rotational fine structure.

EMISSION OF RADIATION

The interaction of electromagnetic radiation with matter is a reversible phenomenon. Species which happen to be in an excited state can emit photons of different energies by returning to lower energy states or to the ground state. Emission spectroscopy utilizes a high-voltage electric arc or high temperature flame to excite the electrons of a species to very high quantized energy states. These electrons subsequently return to lower energy states emitting photons of unique energies and wavelengths. Numerous inorganic systems are studied using this technique. Unfortunately many organic molecules are too fragile to allow this kind of treatment and, at present, emission spectroscopy is comparatively difficult to carry out in organic and biochemical systems.

In some instances a species will absorb high energy radiation exciting some of its electrons to energy levels which are higher than the next level above their ground state. They can then return to the ground state directly or by a series of quantum jumps. If they return directly to the ground state, photons are emitted of the same energy as those that were originally absorbed. If the electrons return to the ground state by a series of steps, photons are emitted with energies corresponding to the changes in energy for the various steps. Clearly, these photons will have lower energies and longer wavelengths than the photons that were originally absorbed. This phenomenon is called *fluorescence*. Many organic and some inorganic compounds fluoresce in the visible region when they are irradiated with ultraviolet light. Fluorescence also is important in the production of low energy, longer wavelength X-rays by the irradiation of samples with shorter wavelength, high energy X-rays.

Raman spectroscopy is another example of a method in which an irradiated sample emits photons of a frequency different from those absorbed. Suppose that a sample absorbs photons of frequency v_1 (ultraviolet or visible) raising the energy of the molecule from its ground state to a higher electronic energy level, requiring an energy of $\Delta E_1 = h v_1$ as shown in Figure 8-11. Each electronic energy level has several superimposed rotational and vibrational states. Now when the molecule returns to the electronic ground state it may not return to the original rotational and/or vibrational level, corresponding to an energy change of ΔE_2 or ΔE_3 and the emission of photons with frequencies v_2 or v_3. The net result is that the molecule absorbed an energy of $\Delta E_1 - \Delta E_2$ causing a change in the vibrational or rotational state (normally observed in the infrared), but the

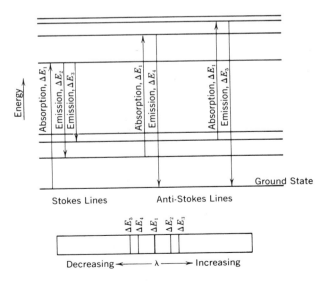

FIGURE 8-11.   Raman effect—Stokes and anti-Stokes lines.

emitted radiant energy is observed in the ultraviolet region. The shifts in frequencies, $v_1 - v_2$, $v_1 - v_3$ give rise to additional lines in the emission spectrum known as *Stokes lines*.

Some molecules, although in the lowest electronic level, may be originally in a higher rotational state. If this is the case, they may eventually return to the lowest rotational state giving rise to *anti-Stokes lines* of higher frequency than the original radiation. The anti-Stokes lines should occur at frequency shifts $v_4 - v_1$ and $v_5 - v_1$ exactly matching the frequency shifts of the Stokes lines but on the opposite side of the incident frequency v_1.

Some energy changes can be observed by Raman spectroscopy but not infrared, and vice versa, so the two techniques are somewhat complementary.

REFRACTION AND REFRACTIVE INDEX

In addition to absorption there are other interaction phenomena which are useful for both identification and structural studies. Refraction is one of these important non-absorptive processes. When radiation passes from one medium to another, it is partially reflected and partially transmitted. The transmitted radiation retains its characteristic frequencies in the new medium; however, both the velocity and direction of propagation may change. Interfacial characteristics for radiation passing from air into glass are illustrated in Figure 8-12. In order to

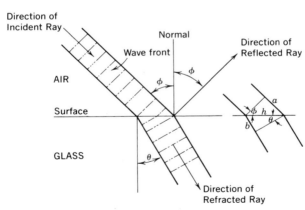

FIGURE 8-12.   Explanation of diffraction when radiation passes from air into glass.

explain this behavior, it is helpful to consider a "wave front" perpendicular to the direction of travel. If the ray strikes the surface of the glass at an angle (ϕ is the angle of incidence), then one side of the wave front reaches the interface and enters the glass before the other. Therefore, while one side of the wave front is traveling in glass, the other side is still traveling in air. We have already defined the ratio of the velocity of light in vacuum to that in another medium as the index of refraction, n, i.e.,

$$n = v_{vac}/v_{medium} \tag{8-3}$$

The index of refraction of air is so close to unity ($n_{air} = 1.00027$), that for ordinary purposes

$$n = v_{air}/v_{medium} \tag{8-4}$$

In Figure 8-12 there are two right triangles with a common hypotenuse, h. Side a is the distance traveled by one side of the wave front in air while the other side of the wave front travels a distance b in glass. Both of these distances must be traveled in the same time in order for the oscillations to remain in phase across the wave front. Therefore,

$$time = \frac{distance}{velocity} = \underset{air}{\frac{a}{c}} = \underset{glass}{\frac{b}{c/n_{glass}}} \tag{8-5}$$

or

$$\frac{h \sin \phi}{c} = \frac{h \sin \theta}{c/n_{glass}} \tag{8-6}$$

or

$$n_{glass} = \frac{\sin \phi}{\sin \theta} \tag{8-7}$$

The above treatment holds as well for the transmission of radiation across the interface between any two media, although two values of n will appear (we have taken $n_{air} = 1$). Thus, for the general case,

$$\frac{n_2}{n_1} = \frac{\sin \phi}{\sin \theta} \tag{8-8}$$

where the subscripts 1 and 2 refer to light going from medium 1 into medium 2. Equation 8-8 is known as *Snell's law*. Once the index of refraction of any medium has been determined with respect to vacuum or air, it can be used as a secondary standard to determine indices of refraction of other media.

The velocity and the index of refraction in any medium other than vacuum are functions of the temperature and the frequency. This last statement is extremely important because it indicates that light of different frequencies is refracted at different angles. In measuring and reporting values of the index of refraction, it is customary to report both the temperature and the frequency used, for example, n_D^{20} means the measurement was made at 20°C with the D line of a sodium lamp ($\lambda_D = 589.3$ mμ). The dependence of the angle of refraction on the frequency is, of course, the explanation of how a prism disperses different wavelengths of radiation.

The determination of the refractive index involves only the determination of two angles. These angles may be measured quite accurately and thus n may be determined with a high degree of precision. Some instruments allow a precision of 10 parts per billion. Very careful control of temperature and wavelength of radiation is extremely important to high precision refractive index measurements. To illustrate the wide applicability of refractive indices, they are used to confirm the identity of substances, analyze mixtures, estimate molecular weights, molecular sizes and shapes, and to calculate properties such as reflectivity and optical dispersion. Some refractive index values of characteristic materials are presented in Table 8-3.

TABLE 8-3 REFRACTIVE INDICES OF SOME CHARACTERISTIC MATERIALS

Substance	n_D^{20}	Substance	n_D^{20}
Methanol	1.3288	n-Hexane	1.3749
Water	1.3328	Cyclohexane	1.4266
Acetone	1.3588	Toluene	1.4929
Ethanol	1.3590	Benzene	1.4979
Acetic acid	1.3698	Pyridine	1.5095
Ethyl acetate	1.3701	Aniline	1.5863

It should be emphasized that the index of refraction is very specific for a pure material. In organic qualitative analysis a conventional approach includes determining elemental composition, solubility, melting point, boiling point, and refractive index.

ROTATION OF PLANE-POLARIZED LIGHT

When we examine the oscillation of a single light wave from an end-on vantage point, the electric vector looks like Figure 8-13. Ordinary light has no specific orientation in three dimensional space and so radiation from a common source might be described as having oscillations in all directions like those shown in Figure 8-14a. Each of the vibrational directions can be resolved into

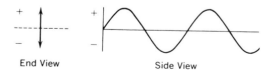

End View   Side View

FIGURE 8-13. Two views of oscillation of electric component of radiation.

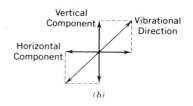

FIGURE 8-14. Vector diagram of (*a*) ordinary light, and (*b*) resolution of random directions into two perpendicular components.

two mutually perpendicular directions as shown in Figure 8-14*b*. The actual vibrational direction is the vector sum of the two components. Now if this ordinary light is collimated and passed through a crystal which allows only one vibrational orientation to be transmitted, the transmitted light is said to be polarized. Many natural crystals produce polarized light, but it is most conveniently obtained with commercially available Polaroid materials.

When plane polarized light is passed through substances which are asymmetric (have no plane of symmetry or center of symmetry), the direction of vibrational oscillation of the incident radiation undergoes rotation either to the right (dextrorotatory, +) or to the left (levorotatory, −). Dextrorotation is shown schematically in Figure 8-15.

What causes polarized light to undergo rotation? We are actually considering the rotation of an oscillating electric field vector as it is propagated through the medium. Even though absorption does not occur, it is not unreasonable to

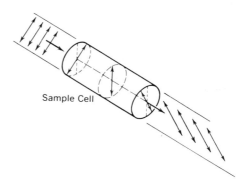

FIGURE 8-15. Dextrorotation of plane polarized light.

assume that there can be some interaction of the oscillating electric field of the radiation with the electric field generated by the electrons of the substance studied. If there is some preferential arrangement of electrons in the material, we might expect the interaction of radiation to be specific and not just random. We might also expect the resultant of the interaction to have specific characteristics, such as preferentially rotating light in one direction more than the other. A model has been proposed to explain preferential rotation in which polarized light is considered to be the vector sum of two oppositely rotating beams of circularly polarized light. In this model as the light is propagated through space, the electric component of each beam traces out a spiral trajectory which is either clockwise or counter-clockwise. If the index of refraction is the same for both beams, they will rotate at the same angular velocity (but in opposite directions) as they travel through the medium. Thus, the vector sum of the rotating electric fields always lies along the same direction as shown in Figure 8-16. However, the behavior is more complex if the medium contains one of the forms of an asymmetric molecule. In this case the indices of refraction for the two circularly polarized beams are not the same. One of the beams interacts with the asymmetric molecule to a greater extent than the other. There is a difference in the angular velocities of the two beams and the resultant vector is no longer in the same plane as the incident radiation; this is illustrated in Figure 8-17. There is continual rotation of the resultant vector until the two beams emerge from the sample and reach a medium where the angular velocities are the same again. At this time, the resultant vector is again plane polarized and

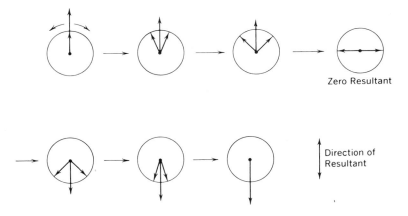

FIGURE 8-16. Combination of circular components to give plane polarization without rotation.

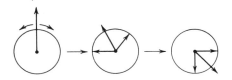

FIGURE 8-17. Result of interaction of two beams of circularly polarized light with asymmetric molecules.

does not rotate. However, the resultant vector produced after the circularly polarized beams emerge from the sample does not have the same orientation as the one which entered the sample; it has undergone rotation. The extent of rotation clearly depends on the type and concentration of molecules present in the sample and the distance which the radiation travels through the sample. We have discussed how the index of refraction and thus the linear velocity of propagation varies with wavelength. The extent of rotation also depends on the wavelength of the polarized light. The sodium D radiation at 589.3 mμ is used for most experimental work. The extent of rotation to some degree also depends on temperature and the nature of the solvent. The *specific rotation* is characteristic for an asymmetric substance and is defined as follows:

$$[\alpha]_{\lambda}^{t_o} = \frac{100\ \alpha}{l \times c}$$

where $[\alpha]_{\lambda}^{t_o}$ = the specific rotation for a substance at temperature t_o, using plane polarized radiation of wavelength λ

α = the experimentally measured number of degrees of rotation undergone by the incident radiation

l = pathlength through the sample in decimeters

c = concentration of the sample in grams/100 ml of solution.

For a pure compound,

$$[\alpha]_{\lambda}^{t_o} = \frac{\alpha}{l \times d}$$

where d = density of the liquid in grams per milliliter. Another commonly used expression in this field is molecular rotation which is defined as follows:

$$[M]_{\lambda}^{t_o} = \frac{[\alpha]_{\lambda}^{t_o} \times M}{100}$$

where M = the molecular weight of the optically active substance. Techniques which are used to measure the angle of rotation are all classified under the general title of polarimetry. Polarimetry is used commonly for kinetic and structural studies involving optically active compounds.

OPTICAL ROTATORY DISPERSION

The variation of the *molecular rotation* of an optically active substance with variation in the wavelength of the plane polarized light used is called *optical rotatory dispersion*. This technique has recently become extremely helpful in the elucidation of the absolute configuration of complicated structures (i.e., steroids) as well as in conformational analysis. Typical dispersion curves are shown in Figure 8-18.

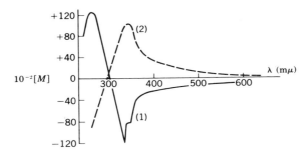

FIGURE 8-18. Optical rotatory dispersion curves for (1) 3β-hydroxy-5α-androstan-16-one in methanol, and (2) 5α-androstan-17-one in dioxane. [From Djerassi, et al., *J. Am. Chem. Soc.*, **78**, 6362 (1956).]

QUESTIONS AND PROBLEMS

8-1. Calculate the following terms. Assume that the index of refraction is 1.000.

(*a*) The wavelength (in microns) of radiation with frequency = 8.58×10^{13} sec^{-1}. *Ans.* 3.50 microns.

(*b*) The wavelength (in cm) of radiation with energy = 7.95×10^{-12} erg/photon. *Ans.* 2.50×10^{-5} cm.

(*c*) The wavenumber of radiation with wavelength = 6.00 microns.

(*d*) The energy per photon (in ergs) of radiation with wavelength = 380 millimicrons (mμ). *Ans.* 5.23×10^{-12} erg/photon.

(*e*) The frequency (in sec^{-1}) of radiation with wavelength = 700 mμ.

(*f*) The wavenumber of radiation with energy = 4.41×10^{-13} erg/photon. *Ans.* 2.22×10^3 cm^{-1}.

8-2. Using the data in Table 8-2, calculate the transition energies (in electron-volts and kcals) for:

(a) acetone $n \rightarrow \pi^*$ and $\pi \rightarrow \pi^*$ transitions.

Ans. $n \rightarrow \pi^*$, 4.44 eV and 102 kcal; $\pi \rightarrow \pi^*$, 6.59 eV and 152 kcal.

(b) toluene $\pi \rightarrow \pi^*$ transition. *Ans.* 5.96 eV and 137 kcal.

(c) acetophenone $\pi \rightarrow \pi^*$ transition. *Ans.* 5.16 eV and 119 kcal.

8-3. The transition metal ion M(III) aquo complex absorbs visible radiation with a maximum at 480 mμ. Predict the wavelength (in mμ) of maximum absorption for the complex MY^{-1} if the colorless Y^{-4} ligand splits the high energy and low energy d-orbitals of M(III) by a factor of 1.750 compared to water. Assume that M(III) forms octahedral complexes and has some vacant or partially filled d-orbitals. *Ans.* 274 mμ.

8-4. Consider two atoms, X and Y, connected by a single bond. All other factors being constant, would the *inherent* frequency of the X — Y stretching vibration increase, decrease, or remain the same if:

(a) the atomic masses of X and Y are each doubled.

(b) the stretching force constant of the X — Y bond decreases.

(c) the frequency of the radiation entering the sample is twice the natural absorption frequency of the X — Y bond.

8-5. Calculate the characteristic vibration frequencies (in cm^{-1}) for the carbon-hydrogen (C — H) and carbon-deuterium (C — D) bonds. (Use Equation 8-2.)

Ans. C — H, 3030 cm^{-1}; C — D, 2220 cm^{-1}.

8-6. Calculate the fundamental vibration frequencies (in cm^{-1}) for the following bonds:

(a) carbon-oxygen double bond. *Ans.* 1570 cm^{-1}.

(b) carbon-carbon double bond. *Ans.* 1680 cm^{-1}.

(c) carbon-carbon triple bond. *Ans.* 2060 cm^{-1}.

(d) carbon-nitrogen triple bond. *Ans.* 1990 cm^{-1}.

REFERENCES

R. Bauman, *Absorption Spectroscopy*, Wiley, New York, 1962. Excellent advanced level treatment of the field.

N. Bauer and K. Fajans, *Techniques of Organic Chemistry*, A. Weissberger, Editor, Vol. I, Part II, 2nd ed., Interscience, New York, 1949; Chapter 20. Excellent discussion of theory of refraction.

R. T. Conley, *Infrared Spectroscopy*, Allyn & Bacon, Boston, Massachusetts, 1966.

W. Heller, *Techniques of Organic Chemistry*, A. Weissberger, Editor, Vol. I, Part II, 2nd ed., Interscience, New York, 1949; Chapter 23. Comprehensive discussion of polarized light and its interaction with matter.

H. A. Strobel, *Chemical Instrumentation*, Addison-Wesley, Reading, Mass., 1960. Very good discussion of optical methods of analysis.

9 QUANTITATIVE ANALYSIS BY ABSORPTION OF ELECTROMAGNETIC RADIATION

In quantitative absorption studies, a beam of radiation is directed at a sample and the intensity of the radiation which is transmitted is measured. The radiation which is absorbed by the sample is determined by comparing the intensity of the transmitted beam when no absorbing species is present to the transmitted intensity when there is absorbing species present. The radiant power (i.e., intensity) of a collimated beam is proportional to the number of photons per second passing through a unit cross section. If the photons which strike the sample possess energy equal to that required to cause a quantized energy change, absorption *may* occur. The fraction of the radiant energy absorbed depends on the probability for the energy change involved. The absorption thus decreases the radiant power of the transmitted radiation. Scattering and reflection also lower the power of the radiation; however, for most systems which are studied, these losses are small compared to absorption. The instrumentation which is used to make absorption measurements will be discussed in Chapter 10.

QUANTITATIVE LAWS

Consider the changes in radiant power which occur as monochromatic radiation passes through the absorption cell in Figure 9-1. We first fill the cell with a "blank" solution, which normally consists of the solvent plus sample constituents *other than the principal absorbing species*. With this "blank" solution in the cell, the radiant power of the transmitted radiation represents the incident radiant power minus that lost by scattering, reflection and any absorption by the other constituents (normally quite small). We denote this radiant power as P_o, because it serves as a "corrected" *incident* radiant power when the "blank" is replaced by the sample itself (this is a relatively good approximation).

Referring to Figure 9-1, let us consider what happens to the radiation as it passes through segment A of the sample. Using the differential notation of

147

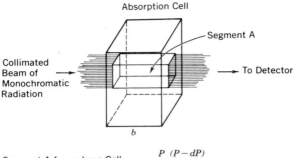

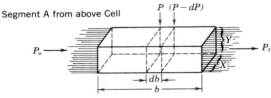

FIGURE 9-1. The absorption process.

calculus, dP represents the decrease in radiant power in an infinitesimally small layer, db, i.e., the amount of radiation absorbed in this layer. We will assume that the absorption of energy requires a physical interaction between a photon and an absorbing species. Therefore, the number of possible "collisions" occurring in this layer is proportional to both the number of absorbing species in the layer and the number of photons passing through. If the number of absorbing species is doubled, the number of collisions is doubled; likewise, doubling the number of photons also doubles the number of collisions. Thus the loss in radiant power, dP, is directly proportional to N (the number of absorbing species) and P (the number of photons per unit cross sectional area per second). For layer db, the number of absorbing species is given by:

$$N = (6.02 \times 10^{20} \text{ species/mmole}) (c \text{ mmole/ml}) (db \times X \times Y \text{ ml})$$

(assume 1 cc = 1 ml)

Since X and Y are constant,

$$N = k'c \, db$$

where, $k' = (6.02 \times 10^{20}) (X \times Y)$ species-cm^2/mmole

The number of collisions is proportional to the product $N \times P$ or

$$dP \propto NP = k'Pc \, db$$

therefore,

$$dP = -kPc \, db \qquad (9\text{-}1)$$

where k is a proportionality constant; the negative sign is introduced because radiant power decreases as db increases. Integration of Equation 9-1 over the entire cell length, b, gives the loss in radiant power due to absorption by the sample. Separating the variables in Equation 9-1 gives:

$$\int_{P_o}^{P_t} \frac{dP}{P} = -k \int_o^b c \, db$$

Solving,

$$\ln \frac{P_t}{P_o} = -kbc$$

and, converting from natural logarithms to base 10 logarithms (designated by "log"), we obtain:

$$2.303 \log \frac{P_t}{P_o} = -kbc$$

or

$$\log \frac{P_t}{P_o} = \frac{-k}{2.303} bc = -\epsilon bc \qquad (9\text{-}2)$$

where ϵ is defined as the molar absorptivity (commonly called the molar extinction coefficient). If the concentration is given in grams/liter, ϵ is replaced by a, the specific absorptivity. The term P_t/P_o is defined as the *transmittance* (symbol, T) which is the fraction of the incident radiant power which is transmitted by the sample. The percent transmittance is defined as $100 \times T$. Therefore, from Equation 9-2,

$$\log T = -\epsilon bc \qquad \text{or} \qquad -\log T = \epsilon bc$$

$-\log T$ is also defined as *absorbance* (symbol, A) or optical density; thus:

$$-\log T = A = \epsilon bc \qquad (9\text{-}3)$$

The value of ϵ is characteristic of the absorbing molecule or ion in a particular solvent and at a particular wavelength. The value of ϵ is independent of concentration and the path length of the radiation. Equation 9-3 has been alternately referred to as the Beer-Lambert law, the Bouger-Beer law, or more simply, *Beer's law*. In the derivation of this law it is assumed that: (1) the incident radiation is

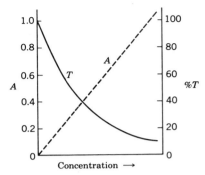

FIGURE 9-2. Absorbance and transmittance *vs.* concentration at a given wavelength and cell pathlength.

monochromatic, (2) the absorbing species act independently of each other in the absorption process, and (3) the absorption occurs in a volume of uniform cross section. Equation 9-3 demonstrates that a determination of absorbance or transmittance will yield the concentration if ϵ and b are known.

Contemporary instruments are calibrated to readout in either percent transmittance, or absorbance, or both. The relationships between absorbance, transmittance and concentration at a given wavelength are illustrated graphically in Figure 9-2. A typical spectrum is plotted in both coordinates in Figure 9-3. Both systems are in common use, and one must realize that absorption peaks appear as deep valleys in a transmittance plot.

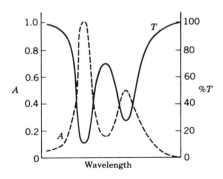

FIGURE 9-3. A typical absorption spectrum plotted in both absorbance and transmittance.

example / problem 9-1: Potassium chromate (K_2CrO_4) in basic solution exhibits an absorption maximum at 372 mμ. A basic solution containing 3.00×10^{-5} M K_2CrO_4 transmits 71.6% of the incident radiation at 372 mμ when it is placed in a 1.000 cm cell.

(a) What is the absorbance of this solution?

solution:

If % T = 71.6; T = 0.716 and from Beer's law, $\log \dfrac{1}{T} = A$

therefore, $A = \log \dfrac{1}{0.716} = \log 1.396 = 0.145$.

(b) What is the molar absorptivity of potassium chromate at 372 mμ?

solution:

$A = \epsilon bc$ or $0.145 = \epsilon(1.000 \text{ cm})(3.00 \times 10^{-5} \text{ mole/liter})$

therefore, $\epsilon = 4.83 \times 10^3$ liter/mole-cm.

(c) What would be the percent transmittance if the cell length were 3.000 cm?

solution:

$\log \dfrac{1}{T} = \epsilon bc$

$\log \dfrac{1}{T} = (4.83 \times 10^3 \text{ liter/mole-cm})(3.000 \text{ cm})(3.00 \times 10^{-5} \text{ mole/liter})$

$\log \dfrac{1}{T} = 0.435$

therefore, $T = 10^{-0.435} = 10^{0.565} \times 10^{-1} = 0.367$

and % T = 36.7%.

example / problem 9-2: Compound X exhibits a molar absorptivity of 2.45×10^3 liter/mole-cm at 450 mμ. What concentration of X in a solution will cause a 25% decrease in radiant power for 450 mμ radiation when the solution is placed in a 1.000 cm absorption cell?

solution. If the solution of X causes a 25% decrease in radiant power, then the percent transmittance of the solution is 75%. From Beer's law:

$\log \dfrac{1}{T} = \epsilon bc$

$\log \dfrac{1}{0.75} = \log 1.33 = (2.45 \times 10^3 \text{ liter/mole-cm})(1.000 \text{ cm})c$

or $0.124 = (2.45 \times 10^3 \text{ liter/mole})c$

and $c = 5.06 \times 10^{-5}$ mole/liter.

Multiple Component Systems. When systems which contain more than one absorbing component are studied, it is assumed that the species act independently of one another and that their absorbances are additive. Figure 9-4 shows the

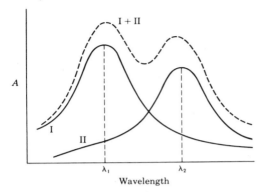

FIGURE 9-4. Overlapping spectra of two components and the spectrum of a mixture of the two components.

absorption spectra of components I and II and their mixture. At the absorbance maximum for component I, λ_1, component II also has an appreciable absorbance; at the absorbance maximum for component II, λ_2, component I also absorbs radiation. The absorption spectrum for a mixture of I and II is simply the sum of the two individual curves. We can set up equations for the total absorbance at each wavelength as follows:

$$A^{\lambda_1} = A_I^{\lambda_1} + A_{II}^{\lambda_1} = \epsilon_I^{\lambda_1}bc_I + \epsilon_{II}^{\lambda_1}bc_{II} \tag{9-4}$$

and

$$A^{\lambda_2} = A_I^{\lambda_2} + A_{II}^{\lambda_2} = \epsilon_I^{\lambda_2}bc_I + \epsilon_{II}^{\lambda_2}bc_{II} \tag{9-5}$$

where A^{λ_1} and A^{λ_2} = observed absorbances of the mixture at wavelengths λ_1 and λ_2, respectively;

$A_I^{\lambda_1}$ and $A_I^{\lambda_2}$ = absorbances of component I in the mixture at λ_1 and λ_2;

$A_{II}^{\lambda_1}$ and $A_{II}^{\lambda_2}$ = absorbances of component II in the mixture at λ_1 and λ_2;

$\epsilon_I^{\lambda_1}$, $\epsilon_I^{\lambda_2}$, $\epsilon_{II}^{\lambda_1}$, and $\epsilon_{II}^{\lambda_2}$ = the molar absorptivities of components I and II at λ_1 and λ_2; and

c_I and c_{II} = the respective concentrations of components I and II in the mixture.

The molar absorptivities are determined by obtaining the absorption spectrum of each component separately in a solution of known concentration. Thus the two unknown concentrations are obtained by solving two simultaneous equations (9-4 and 9-5) obtained by measuring A at two different wavelengths. In general, if there are n components, the total absorbance expression at any wavelength, λ, takes the form:

$$A^\lambda = \sum_n A_n^\lambda = b\sum_n \epsilon_n^\lambda c_n \qquad (9\text{-}6)$$

In principle, n absorbance measurements at n different wavelengths are required to determine the concentration of n components in a mixture. This provides n independent simultaneous equations in n unknowns. If possible, we select wavelengths so that all components do not absorb, thus reducing the number of terms in Equation 9-6. In general, select those wavelengths where the absorptivities vary the most.

DEVIATIONS FROM BEER'S LAW

Many absorbing systems in dilute solution follow Beer's law rather closely. For some systems, however, absorbance varies in a non-linear way with respect to concentration. Such behavior is called a "deviation from Beer's law." In order to treat these systems, a curved calibration plot may be prepared with samples of known concentration. Then the concentration of an "unknown" can be determined from its absorbance in the same cell following the same procedures used for the standard samples. A typical calibration curve is shown in Figure 9-5.

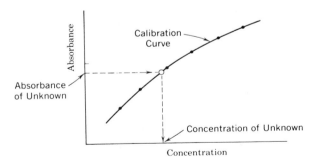

FIGURE 9-5. Non-linear calibration curve of absorbance *vs.* concentration at a given absorption maximum.

It is important to examine the reasons for deviations from Beer's law in order to provide some indication of the quantitative limitations of absorption measurements. True deviations from Beer's law occur only in systems where the concentration of the absorbing species is so high that the index of refraction for the absorbed radiation is changed. Consequently, Beer's law methods are used primarily in solutions with concentrations below 10^{-2} M. The lower limit of about 10^{-7} M is determined primarily by the ability of the instrument to detect small differences in radiant power. Apparent deviations from Beer's law may be due both to limitations of instrumentation and to effects of non-symmetrical chemical equilibrium.

Instrumentation Limitations. Indeterminate instrumental variations which cause apparent deviations include: (1) stray radiations reaching the detector (reflected within the instrument), (2) sensitivity changes in the detector, and (3) power fluctuations of the radiation source and detector amplification system. Double beam operation (to be discussed in Chapter 10) tends to cancel out most of the random causes of deviation.

A more unavoidable instrumental cause of deviation is the necessity of working with a band of wavelengths rather than truly monochromatic radiation. Unless the molar absorptivity is invariant within the wavelength band used, the absorbance measured is an "average" absorbance over the band. Due to the logarithmic nature of absorbance, this is not a true average. The greater the slope of the absorption curve through the wavelength band, the greater the deviation.

Figure 9-6 demonstrates that the shape of the calibration curve often depends on the band width. Two wavelength bands of equal width are designated

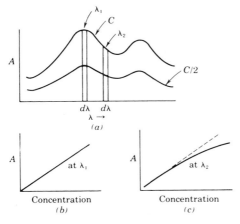

FIGURE 9-6. Effects of finite bandwidth. (*a*) One component at two concentrations. (*b*) Linear calibration curve at λ_1. (*c*) Non-linear calibration curve at λ_2.

λ_1 and λ_2. The best wavelength for quantitative analysis is λ_1, for two reasons. First, at the absorption maximum the change in absorbance with concentration is at a maximum; this yields greater sensitivity and higher accuracy. Second, within this band the molar absorptivity is relatively constant and a linear calibration curve is obtained as in Figure 9-6b. However, if a wavelength is selected on the side of an absorption peak, e.g., λ_2 in Figure 9-6a, the molar absorptivity varies across the band. At this wavelength the system does not follow Beer's law and a curved calibration is obtained, as in Figure 9-6c.

Narrow band widths are obviously desirable for best accuracy, but as the band is decreased, less energy reaches the detector. Consequently, there is always a compromise between accuracy, sensitivity, and detector requirements.

We normally assume that all absorption cells used in a given analysis have the same transparency. To verify this assumption we may fill two cells with solvent; using a single beam instrument we then set $\% \ T = 100$ for one cell and measure the $\% \ T$ of the other cell. The second cell should also read $100\% \ T$ at every wavelength studied. The difference between the two is the *transparency correction* (converted to units of absorbance). This correction is usually negligible above $300 \ m\mu$ wavelength.

Non-Symmetrical Chemical Equilibrium. An absorbing species which is involved in non-symmetrical chemical equilibrium may exhibit "apparent deviations" from Beer's law. A few examples of such systems are presented below.

1. Let us consider an aqueous solution of a weak acid HB which has an absorption maximum at λ_1. The anion of the acid B^- is non-absorbing at λ_1. HB is involved in the equilibrium:

$$HB + H_2O = H_3O^+ + B^-$$

for which the mass action expression is:

$$K_a = \frac{(H_3O^+)(B^-)}{(HB)}$$

The analytical concentration, C_{HB}, includes both forms: $C_{HB} = (HB) + (B^-)$. As long as the ratio $(HB)/C_{HB}$ remains constant, Beer's law is valid when using either (HB) or C_{HB}. But this ratio depends on the pH of the solution:

$$\text{fraction undissociated} = \frac{(HB)}{C_{HB}} = \frac{(HB)}{(HB) + (B^-)}$$

$$= \frac{(HB)}{(HB) + K_a(HB)/(H_3O^+)} = \frac{1}{1 + K_a/(H_3O^+)}$$

If $(H_3O^+) \gg K_a$, the acid exists primarily as HB, and there is no problem. If

$(H_3O^+) \ll K_a$, the acid is highly dissociated with a correspondingly small absorbance. At a constant pH in the intermediate region (buffered solution), the fraction dissociated does not vary with total concentration and absorbance is proportional to C_{HB}. However, in unbuffered solutions the fraction dissociated changes with pH, which in turn is a function of total concentration, C_{HB}. Such a system will show an apparent deviation from Beer's law if C_{HB} is used as the concentration.

example / problem 9-3: An aqueous solution of a weak acid, HB $(K_a = 1.00 \times 10^{-5})$, absorbs ultraviolet radiation with a maximum at 280 mμ, $\epsilon = 975$. B^- does not absorb. Assume that you start with a 2.000×10^{-3} F solution of HB and then perform three successive one to one dilutions. The absorbance of each of these solutions is measured. Would the system show a positive or negative apparent deviation from Beer's law? A 1.000-cm absorption cell is used for all measurements.

solution. First determine the equilibrium concentration of HB in each solution using K_a. For example, for the first solution:

$$\frac{(H_3O^+)(B^-)}{(HB)} = 1.00 \times 10^{-5}$$

$$C_{HB} = 2.000 \times 10^{-3} \ F \quad \text{and} \quad (HB) = C_{HB} - (B^-)$$

Since $(H_3O^+) = (B^-)$,

$$\frac{(H_3O^+)^2}{2.000 \times 10^{-3} - (H_3O^+)} = 1.00 \times 10^{-5}$$

Solving quadratically,

$$(H_3O^+) = 1.37 \times 10^{-4} \text{ or } (HB) = 1.86 \times 10^{-3} \ M$$

From Beer's law, $\quad A = \epsilon b c_{HB} = (9.75 \times 10^2)(1.000)(1.86 \times 10^{-3})$

$$A = 1.813$$

The other solutions are treated in a similar manner with the results summarized in Table 9-1. With increasing analytical concentration of HB, C_{HB}, absorbance shows a positive deviation from Beer's law. However, the absorbance is linear with the "true" equilibrium concentration; thus the deviation is an "apparent deviation." As the concentration is increased, a larger fraction of the acid remains undissociated.

TABLE 9-1 DATA FOR EXAMPLE PROBLEM 9-3

C_{HB}	(HB), M	(HB)/C_{HB}	pH	A	A/C_{HB}
2.000×10^{-3}	1.86×10^{-3}	0.930	3.86	1.813	0.907
1.000×10^{-3}	9.05×10^{-4}	0.905	4.02	0.881	0.881
5.00×10^{-4}	4.34×10^{-4}	0.868	4.18	0.422	0.845
2.50×10^{-4}	2.05×10^{-4}	0.820	4.34	0.200	0.800

2. A similar approach to that used with the weak acids is applied in studying inorganic complexes. For example, in systems such as Cu(II)-ammonia or Co(II)-ethylenediamine there is a series of complexes formed. As an example, in the Co(II)-ethylenediamine system in aqueous solution, possible complexes might be $Co(en)(H_2O)_4^{+2}$, $Co(en)_2(H_2O)_2^{+2}$ and $Co(en)_3^{+2}$, where en represents an ethylenediamine molecule. Each of these complexes exhibits a different absorption maximum, and there is considerable overlap of the absorption spectra of some of the complexes. Therefore, in the absence of a large excess of ligand (en), the total analytical concentration of Co(II) is distributed (according to respective equilibrium constants) among more than one absorbing species. Consequently, the assumption that the total analytical concentration of Co(II) exists as a single complex ion will cause "apparent deviations" from Beer's law. However, if enough excess ligand is present the only complex in the system is the one of highest coordination (i.e., $Co(en)_3^{+2}$). In this case Beer's law could be applied to the spectra of this one complex and no deviation would be noted. This technique of having excess ligand present is commonly used to measure the concentration of inorganic complexes spectrophotometrically. It should also be pointed out that in most complexing media, metal ions are in competition with protons to bond with various ligands. Therefore, it is often necessary to adjust the pH to a rather high value to insure that the metal ion complexation reaction is essentially complete.

3. Aqueous solutions of potassium chromate offer another example of an "apparent deviation" from Beer's law which may be attributed to unsymmetrical chemical equilibria. In this system, CrO_4^{-2}, $HCrO_4^-$ and $Cr_2O_7^{-2}$ all absorb radiation. The relative amounts of the three species depend on the total concentration of Cr(VI) and the pH. This is illustrated by considering the equilibria:

$$2 CrO_4^{-2} + 2 H_3O^+ = 2 HCrO_4^- + 2 H_2O = Cr_2O_7^{-2} + 3 H_2O$$

The overall mass action expression for this system is given by,

$$\frac{(Cr_2O_7^{-2})}{(CrO_4^{-2})^2(H_3O^+)^2} = K_{equilibrium}$$

When aqueous solutions of chromate or dichromate are diluted with water, there are apparent deviations from Beer's law. If the solutions are *strongly* acidic, essentially all of the Cr(VI) is in the form of $Cr_2O_7^{-2}$ and Beer's law is followed. Also, if the system is made *strongly* alkaline, the Cr(VI) is present as CrO_4^{-2} and Beer's law is again followed.

The three example systems discussed above illustrate the importance of understanding the chemical system under study and controlling conditions so that quantitative absorption measurements are meaningful.

PHOTOMETRIC ERROR

At high values of transmittance, the incident and the transmitted radiant powers are nearly the same. Thus there is a relatively large error in the absorbance, which the instrument sees as a difference between the two transmittances. On the other hand, at low values of transmittance, too little radiant power reaches the detector for accurate measurement. It can be shown that there is an intermediate range of transmittance values which give the best precision and accuracy in the measurement of concentration.

The response of spectrophotometer detectors is directly proportional to the radiant power of the transmitted radiation. Let us assume that the relative error in the determination of concentration is due to the uncertainty in the response of the detector. The *relative* error in the concentration, c, is dc/c, where dc represents the absolute error. From Beer's law,

$$c = -\frac{1}{\epsilon b} \log T \qquad (9\text{-}7)$$

For a given species, ϵ and the path length, b, are constant; therefore, all of the uncertainty in the measured concentration is due to the error, dT, in the measured transmittance, T. Differentiating Equation 9-7 above and dividing by c, we obtain:

$$\frac{dc}{c} = -\frac{1}{\epsilon bc} \frac{(\log e)dT}{T} \qquad (9\text{-}8)$$

where $e = 2.718$.

Equation 9-8 may be used to determine the relative percent error in concentration at various transmittance values when the uncertainty in the transmittance measurements (dT) is known.

The value of transmittance at which the relative error in concentration is the smallest is found by minimizing dc/c. This is accomplished by differentiating Equation 9-8 and setting the derivative equal to zero. A simplification is made first:

$$\frac{1}{\epsilon bc} \frac{\log e}{T} = -\frac{\log e}{T \log T} \qquad (9\text{-}9)$$

Differentiating Equation 9-8 and minimizing yields:

$$\frac{d\left[(\log e/T \log T)dT\right]}{dT} = dT(\log T + \log e) = 0 \qquad (9\text{-}10)$$

and

$$\log T + \log e = 0$$

Therefore, $\log T = -0.4343$ and $T_{\text{optimum}} = 0.368$ or $A_{\text{optimum}} = 0.434$.

Figure 9-7 shows a plot of the relative error in concentration *vs.* transmittance for potassium permanganate solutions at 523 mμ where $\epsilon = 2400$. In this figure, it is assumed that the absolute uncertainty in transmittance, dT, is $\pm 1\%$ and that the cell path length is 1 cm. Figure 9-7 indicates that the best accuracy and precision will be obtained if the transmittance of the sample is in the range from 0.2 to 0.65. If possible, the concentration of the absorbing species, or the cell thickness, or both should be adjusted to keep the transmittance within this range.

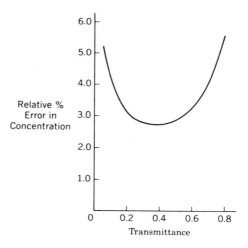

FIGURE 9-7.   Photometric error *vs.* transmittance for potassium permanganate solutions. Uncertainty in transmittance, ± 0.01.

QUESTIONS AND PROBLEMS

9-1.   The nucleic acid adenine exhibits a molar absorptivity of 13,100 at 263 mμ. What is the molar concentration of an adenine solution which exhibits 75.0 percent transmittance when 2.00 ml of the solution is placed in a 1.000 cm absorption cell?

Ans. 9.54×10^{-6} mole/liter.

9-2.   A 1.28×10^{-4} *M* solution of potassium permanganate has a transmittance of 0.500 at 525 mμ in a 1.00 cm cell.

(*a*) What is the absorbance of this solution?   *Ans.* 0.301.

(*b*) If the concentration were doubled, what would be the absorbance and transmittance?   *Ans.* $A = 0.602$; $T = 0.250$.

(*c*) What concentration would have a transmittance of 0.750 in this cell?

Ans. 5.32×10^{-5} *M.*

(*d*) What cell path would give the optimum accuracy for the concentration first quoted? *Ans.* 1.44 cm.

9-3. A 2.00×10^{-4} *M* solution of a certain compound has an absorbance of 1.00 in a 1.00 cm cell at 320 mμ.

(*a*) What is the molar extinction coefficient at this wavelength?

Ans. 5.00×10^3.

(*b*) What fraction of the incident light is transmitted through the cell? *Ans.* 0.100.

(*c*) What fraction would be transmitted through a 4.00×10^{-4} *M* solution of this compound in the same cell? *Ans.* 0.010.

9-4. A 500-mg sample containing a colored component X is dissolved and diluted to 500 ml. The absorbance of an aliquot of this solution, measured at 400 mμ in a 1.00-cm cell, is 0.900. 10.0 mg of pure X is dissolved in 1 liter of the same solvent and the absorbance measured in a 0.100-cm cell at the same wavelength is 0.300. What is the % X in the first sample? *Ans.* 0.300.

9-5. A sulfuric acid solution of cupric sulfate is analyzed for copper by transferring exactly 5.00 ml to a 1.000 cm absorption cell. The measured % transmittance is 75.3% at the wavelength of maximum absorption. A 1.000 ml portion of standard 0.01000 *M* cupric sulfate is added to the cell (original 5.00 ml of unknown still present) and the % transmittance changes to 62.5%. What is the concentration of the cupric ion (in moles/liter) in the original solution? *Ans.* 2.03×10^{-3} *M.*

9-6. Standard solutions of Y were used to construct a calibration curve: 1.00 ppm, $A = 0.26$; 2.00 ppm, $A = 0.44$; 3.00 ppm, $A = 0.54$; 4.00 ppm, $A = 0.61$. If an unknown solution of Y had an absorbance of 0.50 under the same conditions, what is the concentration of Y?

9-7. The molar absorptivity of benzoic acid (Mol. Wt. = 122.1) in methanol at 275 mμ is about 1950. If it is desired to use an absorbance not exceeding 1.25, what is the maximum allowable concentration in g/l that can be used in a 2.00-cm cell?

9-8. A weak acid with a dissociation constant of $K_a = 1.00 \times 10^{-4}$ shows an absorbance of 1.500 when a 0.100 *F* solution is measured at 500 mμ in a 1.00 cm cell. The anion is colorless.

(*a*) What is the absorbance of a 1.00×10^{-3} *F* solution under the same conditions?

(*b*) Plot a Beer's law curve (*A* vs. *F*) for this acid over the range from 0.100 *F* to 1.00×10^{-5} *F*.

(*c*) Plot a Beer's law curve (*A* vs. *F*) for this acid in a buffered solvent (*p*H = 1.50) over the same range.

9-9. Estimate the K_a of a weak acid from the data below. One-gram samples are dissolved in equal quantities of the various buffers and all solutions are measured under the same conditions. The anion of the acid is the only substance which absorbs at the wavelength used.

*p*H:	4	5	6	7	8	9	10	11
A:	0.00	0.00	0.06	0.39	0.95	1.13	1.18	1.18

9-10. (*a*) Estimate the K_a of a weak acid from the data below. All of the various buffered solutions are 1.00 millimolar in sample, and all solutions were measured under the same conditions. The anion of the acid is the only substance which absorbs at the wavelength used. A is the absorbance.

pH:	4	5	6	7	8	9	10	11
A:	0.000	0.000	0.100	0.750	1.000	1.150	1.250	1.250

Ans. $K_a = 1.5 \times 10^{-7}$.

(*b*) What is the transmittance of the sample at pH 4 using the conditions above?

Ans. $A = 0$; $T = 1.00$.

(*c*) What is the value of the molar extinction coefficient for the anion at this wavelength if a 1.00 cell is used?

Ans. 1.25×10^3.

9-11. P and Q, which are colorless, form the colored compound PQ: P + Q = PQ. When 2.00×10^{-3} moles of P are mixed with a large excess of Q and diluted to 1 liter, the solution has an absorbance which is twice as large as when 2.00×10^{-3} moles of P are mixed with 2.00×10^{-3} moles of Q and treated similarly. What is the equilibrium constant for the formation of PQ? *Ans.* 1.00×10^3.

9-12. Absorbances were measured for three solutions containing Y and Z separately and in a mixture, all in the same cell. Calculate the concentrations of Y and Z in the mixture.

	Absorbance	
	475 mμ	670 mμ
0.001 M Y	0.90	0.20
0.01 M Z	0.15	0.65
Mixture	1.65	1.65

Ans. $C_Y = 5.50 \times 10^{-4}$ M; $C_Z = 7.70 \times 10^{-2}$ M.

9-13. Component A has a molar absorptivity coefficient of 3.07×10^3 at wavelength 520 mμ. Component B has a molar absorptivity coefficient of 2.20×10^2 at 520 mμ. Component A exhibits a molar absorptivity coefficient of 2.16×10^3 at 600 mμ. Component B has a molar absorptivity coefficient of 1.47×10^3 at 600 mμ. An unknown solution containing both A and B is analyzed spectrophotometrically in a 1.000-cm cell. At 520 mμ the percent transmittance is 54.4%. The percent transmittance at 600 mμ is 35.0%. What are the molar concentrations of Components A and B in the unknown?

Ans. $C_A = 7.16 \times 10^{-5}$ M; $C_B = 2.06 \times 10^{-4}$ M.

REFERENCES

R. P. Bauman, *Absorption Spectroscopy*, Wiley, New York, 1962. Good general discussion of quantitative methods.

Louis Meites and H. C. Thomas, *Advanced Analytical Chemistry*, McGraw-Hill, New York, 1958; Chapter 8. Good treatment of quantitative laws and limitations.

10 INSTRUMENTATION AND TECHNIQUES FOR SPECTRO-PHOTOMETRY

We have discussed the theoretical principles of absorption of electromagnetic radiation in Chapters 8 and 9. We shall now consider how these principles are applied to the solution of chemical problems. In this chapter it is not our purpose to provide a detailed examination of all the electronic components which are used for absorption measurements. However, we do hope to take the student somewhat beyond the "black-box," "twiddle-the-knobs" level of understanding of some typical instruments and how they function.

The instruments that are used to study the absorption or emission of electromagnetic radiation as a function of wavelength are called "spectrometers" or "spectrophotometers." The optical and electronic principles employed in these instruments are basically the same for all of the regions of the spectrum from the vacuum ultraviolet to the far infrared. There are, however, some important differences in the specific components used in the various regions.

The essential components of a spectrophotometer include: (1) a stable source or radiant energy, (2) a monochromator to resolve the radiation into component wavelengths or "bands" of wavelengths, (3) transparent containers to hold the sample, and (4) a radiation detector with an associated readout system (meter or recorder). Commercial instruments may be very complex, but all spectrophotometers represent variations of the simple diagram in Figure 10-1.

SOURCES OF RADIANT ENERGY

Sources of radiant energy consist of materials which are excited to high energy states by a high voltage electric discharge or by electrical heating. As the materials return to lower energy states or their ground states, they emit photons of characteristic energies corresponding to ΔE, the energy difference between the excited and lower quantum states. Some materials have numerous energy levels which are so close together that the wavelengths of emitted radiation take the form of a continuum of radiation extending over a rather broad region.

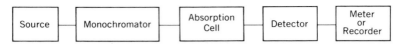

FIGURE 10-1.   Block diagram of absorption apparatus.

An ideal source of radiation for absorption measurements would emit a continuous spectrum of high, uniform intensity over the entire wavelength range of interest. Unfortunately, the intensity of a real source varies with wavelength as shown for a typical source in Figure 10-2. A change in the electrical power which provides energy for the source shifts the intensity-wavelength curve; consequently, a stable power supply is needed for sequential comparative absorption measurements when single-beam instruments are used. Otherwise, the radiant power of the incident radiation (P_o in Beer's law) may vary between the time of standardization of the instrument and the time of the measurement of the radiant power transmitted by the sample (P_t), causing an error in the measured transmittance of the sample. Double-beam instruments are designed so that P_o and P_t are measured and compared simultaneously; in these instruments, high source stability is not so critical. The source must also furnish sufficient radiant power over the entire wavelength range to allow detection by the appropriate device.

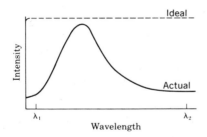

FIGURE 10-2.   Source radiation intensity *vs.* wavelength at a given temperature or energy.

Sources of Ultraviolet Radiation.   The hydrogen lamp and deuterium lamp are the most common sources of ultraviolet radiation. They consist of a pair of electrodes which are enclosed in a glass tube provided with a quartz window and filled with hydrogen or deuterium gas at low pressure. When a stabilized high voltage is applied to the electrodes, an electron discharge occurs which excites other electrons in the gas molecules to high energy states. As the electrons return to their ground state they emit radiation which is continuous in the region roughly between 180 and 350 mμ. Similarly, a xenon discharge lamp is used as a source of ultraviolet radiation. The xenon lamp produces higher intensity radiation, but it is not as stable as the hydrogen lamp. It also emits visible radiation which may appear as stray radiation in ultraviolet applications.

Sources of Visible Radiation. A tungsten filament lamp is the most satisfactory and inexpensive source of visible and near infrared radiation. The filament is heated by a stabilized d-c power supply, or by a storage battery. The tungsten filament emits continuous radiation in the region between 350 and 2500 mμ. The carbon arc provides more intense visible radiation, however it is seldom used.

Sources of Infrared Radiation. The Globar and Nernst glower are the primary sources of infrared radiation. The Globar is a silicon carbide rod heated to approximately 1200° C. It emits continuous radiation in the 1- to 40-μ region. The Globar is an extremely stable source with an intensity profile similar to that shown in Figure 10-2. The Nernst glower is a hollow rod of zirconium and yttrium oxides heated to approximately 1500° C by electric current. It emits radiation in the range between 0.4 and 20 μ. It is not as stable a source as the Globar.

MONOCHROMATORS

As we have indicated, the sources of radiation commonly used emit *continuous* radiation over wide ranges of wavelengths. However, *narrow* band widths have many advantages: (1) narrow band radiation will allow the resolution of absorption bands which are quite close to each other, (2) with narrow band radiation a peak may be measured at its absorption maximum, thus increasing the sensitivity, and (3) the absorption of narrow band radiation will tend to show greater adherence to Beer's law because only that radiation which can be absorbed is measured.

Clearly, we must employ devices which resolve wide band polychromatic radiation from the source into narrow bands or, even better, monochromatic radiation. There are two types of resolution devices in use today, *filters* and *monochromators*. Filters synthesized from special materials allow transmission of only limited wavelength regions while absorbing most of the radiation of other wavelengths. Filters typically transmit radiation with an effective band width of from 20 to 50 mμ. The *effective band width* is defined as the range of wavelength over which the transmittance is at least one-half of its maximum value. This is illustrated in Figure 10-3. Monochromators, on the other hand, typically resolve polychromatic radiation into effective band widths varying from 35 mμ to 0.1 mμ. In years past, filter instruments were common because of the high cost of monochromators. However, at the present time, spectrophotometers which incorporate monochromators can be purchased for as little as $300. These are the only instruments which will be considered here.

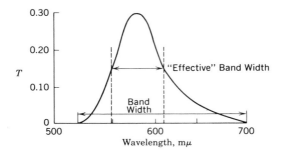

FIGURE 10-3. Effective band width of a band of radiation.

As the name implies, a monochromator resolves polychromatic radiation into its individual wavelengths and isolates these wavelengths into very narrow bands. The components of a monochromator include: (1) an entrance slit which admits polychromatic radiation from the source; (2) a collimating device, either a lens or a mirror; (3) a dispersion device, either a prism or grating, which resolves the radiation into component wavelengths; (4) a focusing lens or mirror; and (5) an exit slit. All of the components in the monochromator must be transparent in the wavelength range to be studied, and the entire assembly is mounted in a light-tight box. A monochromator employing a prism for dispersion is shown schematically in Figure 10-4. The effective band width of radiation emerging from the monochromator depends on several factors, including the dispersing element and the slit widths of both the entrance and exits slits. Narrow slit widths isolate narrow bands; however, the slit width also limits the radiant power which reaches the detector. Therefore, the minimum band width may be determined by the

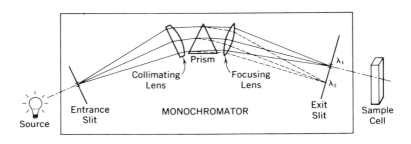

FIGURE 10-4. Prism monochromator.

sensitivity of the detector. Since the effectiveness of the dispersing element is so important, let us consider the two kinds most widely used, namely, prisms and gratings.

Prisms. The prism shown in Figure 10-4 resolves the polychromatic radiation into small bands of wavelengths each emerging from the prism at slightly different angles. To direct a particular wavelength of resolved radiation through the exit slit, the prism is rotated until the desired wavelength (or more correctly, a wavelength band centered about this wavelength) is focused on the exit slit.

How does a prism resolve polychromatic radiation into its component wavelengths? We have already discussed the principles of refraction and defined refractive index in Chapter 8. A prism utilizes the variation of refractive index as a function of wavelength to achieve dispersion. Dispersion is described qualitatively as the *angular separation* of the different wavelengths which make up a beam of radiation; a more quantitative definition will be discussed shortly. When a beam of radiation passes from air into a denser medium, it will be refracted (bent) toward the perpendicular, and will undergo an opposite effect if and when it re-emerges into air. When the two surfaces are parallel, as in a glass plate, the overall effect of the refraction is a small displacement of the beam with no net change in direction or angular deviation. However, the faces of a prism are not parallel and an angular deviation results. These effects are shown in Figure 10-5.

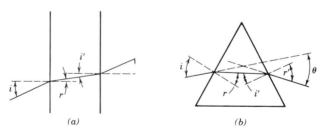

(a)   (b)

FIGURE 10-5. Deviation of monochromatic radiation by (a) a glass plate and (b) a prism.

The angle of incidence to the first surface is represented by i, the angle of refraction at the first surface by r, the angle of incidence to the second surface by i', and the angle of refraction by r'. The angle of deviation which the incident ray has undergone upon passing through the prism is denoted by θ. The angle of refraction and consequently the angle of deviation for any wavelength of radiation is determined by the refractive index of the prism material for that particular wavelength. The variation of refractive index with wavelength is shown for various substances in

Figure 10-6. The refractive index decreases at longer wavelength; therefore, from the laws of refraction, the angle of deviation is larger at shorter wavelength. The fate of a ray of collimated polychromatic radiation is depicted in Figure 10-7.

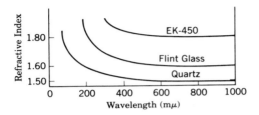

FIGURE 10-6. Refractive index *vs.* λ.

High resolution of polychromatic radiation (e.g., good angular separation of λ_1, λ_2, and λ_3 in Figure 10-7) requires that the *dispersion* be as large as possible. Dispersion is quantitatively defined as $d\theta/d\lambda$, the change in angle of deviation with respect to the change in wavelength. The principle disadvantage of a prism is that the dispersion varies with wavelength. A prism's dispersion is greater for wavelengths close to its own absorption bands. Consequently, since most prism materials absorb low wavelength ultraviolet radiation, dispersion increases with decreasing wavelengths. For example, quartz prisms exhibit high dispersion and thus excellent resolution around 200 mμ; however, dispersion and resolution are poor in the vicinity of 700 mμ. In the infrared region, prisms typically absorb at the longer wavelengths and, correspondingly, dispersion and resolution increase with increasing wavelength.

In terms of resolution, the prism performs best at wavelengths near its own absorption band. However, as the prism absorption band is approached, the total transmitted radiant power decreases. Wider slits may be required in order to have enough radiant power to operate the detector. But wider slits pass broader

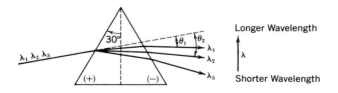

FIGURE 10-7. Dispersion of polychromatic radiation by a 60° quartz prism.

wavelength bands with a significant loss of resolution. Consequently, high
resolution requires the most favorable combination of dispersion characteristics
of the prism material and the slit widths of the monochromator.

Prism Mountings. The common 60° Cornu quartz prism, illustrated in Figure
10-7, is composed of one-half right-handed quartz (+ optical activity) and one-
half left-handed quartz (− optical activity). Cementing the two forms of quartz
together in this manner eliminates birefringence of radiation as it passes through
the prism (i.e., one image is formed rather than two, which would be the case with
normal anisotropic quartz). The Littrow prism is a 30° prism which passes
radiation in both directions by reflection from an aluminized or silvered reflecting
face. The Littrow prism is used in many commercial instruments and is illustrated
in Figure 10-8.

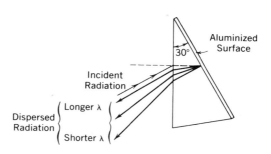

FIGURE 10-8. Littrow prism.

Prism Materials. The prism material used in ultraviolet-visible and infrared
monochromators must be selected wisely for best performance. Both transparency
and dispersion should be considered. Silica (SiO_2) prisms of various types are
used in the ultraviolet region. Quartz (a crystalline form of silica) and fused
silica prisms transmit radiation down to approximately 200 mμ even though a
weak absorption band appears around 245 mμ. High-grade silica transmits down
to 185 mμ. At the higher end, silica is transparent into the near infrared (3.3 μ),
but exhibits very low dispersion in the visible region. Fluorite (CaF_2) is transparent
to 125 mμ and may be used in vacuum ultraviolet monochromators. Ordinary
flint glass (containing lead) shows excellent transmission and dispersion in the
visible and near infrared regions.

Ionic crystalline materials are used in the infrared region. The cut-offs, i.e.,
regions of absorption, for these materials are predictable in terms of the masses
of the atoms since absorption frequencies vary inversely with mass. Light atoms

absorb at lower wavelengths and heavy atoms at higher wavelengths, thus LiF absorbs strongly around 5.6 μ and is used just below this, whereas CaF_2 absorbs strongly at 8.3 μ and is used for the region 5.5 to 8.0 μ. Sodium chloride transmits throughout the visible and infrared regions to approximately 16 μ; however, it shows poor dispersion in the region from 1.0 to 5.0 μ. Potassium bromide cannot be used for the near infrared; however it is quite satisfactory for the region 14.3 to 23.5 μ. The mixed crystalline material, TlBr-TlI (commonly called KRS-5) is transparent from about 1 μ to approximately 35.7 μ; it is insoluble in water although its high reflectivity, tendency for plastic flow, toxicity, and high cost are distinct disadvantages. In the past, KRS-5 has been used in the region just above the KBr region; however, the lower cost CsBr is also used in this region. Cesium bromide is excellent for the region 14.3 to 35.7 μ; unfortunately, it is highly susceptible to attack by water vapor and is quite expensive in comparison to KBr and NaCl. Cesium iodide extends the range of a prism monochromator to approximately 55.5 μ; however, grating monochromators are preferred in this region.

Diffraction Gratings. Reflection diffraction gratings are often used in the monochromators of ultraviolet, visible and infrared instruments. They consist of a highly reflective aluminized surface on which are etched a large number of equally spaced parallel grooves (sometimes called lines). Typical gratings have from 600 to 2000 lines per mm depending on the region of the spectrum for which they are intended.

In order to understand how a diffraction grating can disperse radiation, we must first consider the concepts of constructive reinforcement and destructive interference of radiation. In Figure 10-9, radiant energy "waves" (1) and (2) are "in phase" (i.e., they cross the axis in the same direction at the same time). If (1) and (2) are superimposed, the two waves "reinforce" each other with an amplitude equal to the sum of the two component waves. Light waves (3) and (4) in Figure 10-9 are 180° out of phase and when they are superimposed they cancel each other. The amplitude of the resultant wave is zero—a phenomenon called *destructive interference.*

Polychromatic radiation emitted by a source of radiant energy and collimated by a lens or mirror is coherent, i.e., all radiations of the same wavelength are "in phase." Lines I and II in Figure 10-10 represent the boundaries of a collimated coherent ray which has a "wavefront" that is perpendicular to the direction of travel. Consider the situation when this ray strikes a reflection grating at an angle of incidence, *i*. In order for constructive reinforcement to occur in the reflected radiation, the difference in path lengths along lines I and II must be equal to an integral (i.e., 1, 2, 3, . . . , *n*) number of wavelengths. Application of the laws of diffraction to the many lines of a diffraction (or reflection) grating indicates

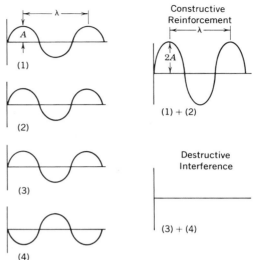

FIGURE 10-9. Constructive reinforcement and destructive interference of monochromatic radiation.

that destructive interference is essentially complete at all angles other than those at which constructive reinforcement occurs. Constructive reinforcement of monochromatic radiation from a reflection grating is illustrated in Figure 10-10. Path II is longer than path I by the distance $CB - AD$. From the geometric construction of the two right triangles ACB and ADB, it is not difficult to see that $CB - AD = d(\sin i - \sin \theta)$. However, θ is considered a negative angle, so the difference between the two paths is $d(\sin i + \sin \theta)$. Therefore, for constructive reinforcement along the reflected path:

$$n = d(\sin i + \sin \theta) \qquad (10\text{-}1)$$

where n is a small integer defined as the order of the radiation. From Equation 10-1, radiation of a particular wavelength striking a reflection grating at an angle of incidence, i, may undergo constructive reinforcement at several angles of θ, depending on the order. The reflection and dispersion of an incident beam of radiation extending from 1200 to 200 mμ is illustrated in Figure 10-11. Equation 10-1 also indicates that overlapping of orders will occur; for instance, along the 600-mμ first-order reflection angle in Figure 10-11, higher-order 300- and 200-mμ radiation will be reinforced. Higher-order wavelengths which overlap a lower order

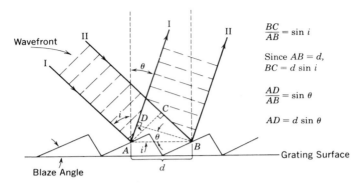

FIGURE 10-10.   Constructive reinforcement of monochromatic radiation by a reflection grating.

may be eliminated by filtering or by appropriate etching of the grating. Higher-order spectra reflected from a grating will decrease the radiant power of the first order. By optimizing the blaze angle of the grating, approximately 75% of the incident radiant power may be concentrated in the first order. The grating is rotated so that successive portions of the first-order radiation fall on the exit slit. Reflection gratings exhibit a *linear* angular dispersion over the entire region of radiation dispersed. For instance, $d\theta/d\lambda$ is constant from 200 to 800 mμ for the gratings commonly used in the visible and ultraviolet regions. The angular

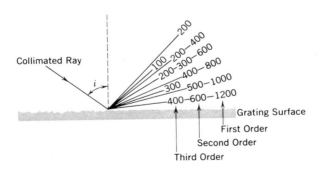

FIGURE 10-11.   Reflection grating and the dispersion of poly-chromatic radiation.

dispersion of a quartz prism changes ninetyfold over the same region. Linear angular dispersion gives gratings a distinct advantage over prisms. With a constant width exit slit, the grating monochromator supplies a constant band width over the entire range of application, whereas the band width of a prism instrument shows tremendous variation.

Wavelength Calibration. The accuracy of the wavelength dial of the instrument may be verified by running the spectrum of a substance which has known absorption maxima and comparing the known values with observed values. The mercury arc produces a sharp line at 546.1 $m\mu$ and the hydrogen discharge tube provides a fairly intense line at 656.3 $m\mu$; either of these may be used to calibrate a spectrophotometer, it is desirable to have the instrument running and use a didymium glass filter. This has nine accurately known, narrow absorption bands in the region 441 to 1067 $m\mu$. A polystyrene film is commonly used to calibrate infrared instruments; polystyrene has a large number of very precisely known absorption bands.

Lenses and Mirrors. Radiation is collimated and focused by lenses and mirrors. Materials used for lenses must, of course, be transparent to the radiation being used. In the infrared region mirrors are used because most materials are not sufficiently transparent to infrared radiation and cause significant energy losses.

Sample Containers. Samples to be studied in the ultraviolet or visible region are usually gases or solutions and are put in cells or cuvettes. Quartz or fused silica cells are used in the ultraviolet region; ordinary glass or more expensive quartz is used in the visible region. Gas cells vary in path length from 0.1 to 100 mm, whereas solution cells have typical path lengths of 1 to 10 cm. Microcells with a beam condenser are available for extremely small samples. The windows of the absorption cells must be kept scrupulously clean; fingerprint smudges and traces of previous samples may cause considerable error in quantitative measurements. Quartz and glass cells may be cleaned by rinsing with water or, if more drastic measures are required, with detergent solutions or hot nitric acid.

Samples for infrared analysis may be gases, liquids, or solids. Infrared gas cells consist of cylindrical glass tubes with NaCl, KBr, or CaF_2 windows. The path lengths vary from a few centimeters to several meters (by multiple reflections in the cell). Liquids are studied either as thin films of the pure compound (commonly referred to as "neat") or as solutions between NaCl, KBr, or CaF_2 salt plates. The plates are separated by 0.005 to 0.1 mm for "neat" liquids and 0.1 to 1 mm for solutions. Infrared cells clearly must *never* come in contact with water. They should be cleaned with organic solvents only. Solids are examined in the infrared as pressed KBr discs or as suspensions in high molecular weight liquids ("mulls"). Potassium bromide discs are prepared by thoroughly mixing approximately 1 mg of the solid sample and 100 mg of dry KBr, and then applying a pressure of 20,000 to 50,000 lb/in.^{2}.

Absorption cells are usually placed after the monochromator in ultraviolet and visible instruments in order to minimize possible decomposition or fluorescence, which might be caused by other high-energy wavelengths of the unresolved radiation. In infrared instruments, the sample is placed before the monochromator so that it will not hinder the focusing of the radiant beam on the detector. Wherever the cell is placed, it should be positioned so that the beam of incident radiation is perfectly normal (perpendicular) to the window or cell face; otherwise, there may be significant losses due to reflection and refraction. In addition, the container should be inserted so that the same cell face is presented to the radiation beam in consecutive measurements. Rectangular cells are preferable to cylindrical cells. However, if the more inexpensive cylindrical cells are used, they should somehow be marked to insure that the same position is used in each measurement.

DETECTION DEVICES

Any detector absorbs the energy of the photons which strike it and converts this energy to a measurable quantity such as the darkening of a photographic plate, an electric current, or thermal changes. Most modern detectors generate an electrical signal which eventually activates some type of meter or recorder. Any detector must generate a signal which is quantitatively related to the radiant power striking it. The "noise" of a detector refers to the "background" signal generated when no radiant power from the sample reaches the detector. This noise may be caused either by random changes within the detector itself or by electrical "pick-up" of other signals in the vicinity of the detector unit. Important requirements for detectors include: (1) high sensitivity with a low noise level in order to allow the detection of low levels of radiant power, (2) short response time, (3) long term stability to insure quantitative response, and (4) an electronic signal which is easily amplified for typical readout apparatus. Performance characteristics of common detectors are summarized in Table 10-1.

Ultraviolet and Visible Radiation Detectors. Ultraviolet and visible photons possess enough energy to cause photoejection of electrons when they strike surfaces which have been treated with specific types of compounds. Their absorption may also cause bound, non-conducting electrons to move into conduction bands in certain semiconductors. Both processes generate an electric current which is directly proportional to the radiant power of the absorbed photons. Devices which employ these systems are called *photoelectric detectors* and are sub-classified as *phototubes* and *photovoltaic cells*.

Phototubes. A phototube consists of: (1) an evacuated glass envelope (with a quartz window for use in the ultraviolet region); (2) a semi-cylindrical cathode

TABLE 10-1 Characteristics of Detectors

Detector	Sensing element	Sensitivity	Response time $1\ \mu sec = 10^{-6}\ sec$ $1\ msec = 10^{-3}\ sec$	Recommended wavelength range of application (microns)	Nature of output
Photographic plate	Silver halide grains in emulsion	High, wavelength dependent	Slow	0.2–1.2	Density of silver metal deposit
Phototube	Alkali metal oxide	High, wavelength dependent	Fast $<1\ \mu sec$	0.2–1	Electric current
Photo-multiplier tube	Alkali metal oxide, metals	*Very* high, wavelength dependent	Fast $<1\ \mu sec$	0.16–0.7	Electric current
Photovoltaic cell	Semiconductor between two metals	Medium, wavelength dependent	Fast	0.4–0.8	Electric current
Photo-conductive cell	Lead sulfide or lead selenide	*Very* high, wavelength dependent	Moderate 100 to 1000 μsec	0.7–3.3	Resistance change
Thermocouple	Junction of two different metals connected to blackened metal leaf	High	50 to 100 msec	0.8–15.0	Electric potential difference at junction of two metals

After Strobel, *Chemical Instrumentation*, Addison-Wesley, Reading, Mass., 1960, p. 198.

which has an inner surface coated with a compound with relatively loosely bound electrons, such as an alkali or alkaline earth oxide; and (3) a central metal wire anode. A potential difference of approximately 90 volts is applied across the electrodes. The phototube and its associated circuitry are shown schematically in Figure 10-12. The radiation enters through the quartz window and strikes the photoemissive surface of the cathode. The photons are absorbed and transfer their energy to the loosely bound electrons of the surface material. The electrons escape from the surface and are collected at the anode causing current to flow in the circuit. If the electron collection is essentially 100% efficient, the phototube current should be proportional to the radiant power of the incident radiation. However, the magnitude of the photocurrent also depends on the voltage applied to the electrodes and the wavelength of the incident radiation. The phototube current at a given radiant power increases with applied voltage until a plateau is reached where it is no longer dependent on the voltage. The voltage at this

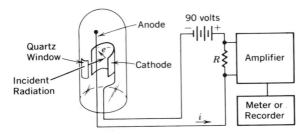

FIGURE 10-12. Schematic of phototube circuit.

point, called the saturation voltage, represents the point at which all the photo-emissive electrons are being collected with 100% efficiency. Consequently, if a phototube is to respond linearly to incident radiant power, it must be operated above the saturation voltage. The variation in phototube sensitivity with wavelength demonstrated in Figure 10-13 clearly points out that narrow band radiation will produce a more linear phototube response than wide band radiation.

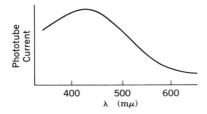

FIGURE 10-13. Phototube current *vs.* wavelength of incident radiation at constant radiation power, *P*.

Phototube currents are quite small (as low as 10^{-11} ampere) and require amplification in order to operate any common type of readout device. This is accomplished by placing a high resistance (*R* in Figure 10-12) in the phototube circuit and applying the electrical potential difference (*iR* drop) across this resistor as the "input" to an amplification circuit. The "output" of the amplifier then is used to drive a meter or recorder.

A small phototube current, known as "dark current," is observed even when there is no incident radiation on the phototube. This is a result of the random thermal emission of electrons from the cathode surface. The magnitude of the dark current increases with increasing cathode surface area and increasing temperature.

Photomultiplier Tubes. In the discussion of phototubes we have indicated the mechanism by which an electron escapes from a photoemissive surface. If the ejected electron is accelerated by an electric field, it acquires more energy; and if it strikes another electron-active surface, it may transfer some of its energy, ejecting several more electrons. These electrons may in turn be accelerated to another surface and produce even more electrons, and so on. This is the principle of the photomultiplier tube; a cross section of this device is shown schematically in Figure 10-14. Each succeeding electron-active plate, or dynode, is at higher

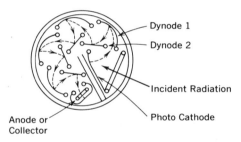

FIGURE 10-14.   Schematic cross section of photomultiplier tube.

electrical potential and thus acts as an amplification stage for the original photon. After nine stages of amplification the original photon has been amplified by a factor of approximately 10^6. In practice, photomultiplier tubes are used only for low radiant power levels; otherwise, they exhibit great instability. The photocurrent may be further amplified by other means.

Near Infrared Detectors.   The photoconductive cell is commonly used for the detection of near infrared radiation (0.8 to 3 μ). The sensing element is a semiconductor (lead sulfide, lead telluride, or germanium with low percent impurity). Upon illumination with radiation of appropriate wavelength, the electrons of the semiconductor, most of which are non-conducting, are raised to conduction bands. The electrical resistance drops, and a large increase in current is noted if a small voltage is applied. The resistance of the system is such that the current may be amplified and finally indicated on a meter or a recorder.

178

Middle and Far Infrared Detectors. When middle and far infrared photons are absorbed, their energies are converted to thermal energy (heat) and a corresponding temperature change is noted. Thus the detectors used in this region are various types of rapid response thermometers such as thermocouples, resistance thermometers (bolometer) and gas thermometers (pneumatic or Golay cell). Thermocouples used in infrared receivers typically consist of a blackened gold leaf-tellurium metal pin junction which develops a voltage that is temperature dependent. The thermocouple is often enclosed in a shielded, evacuated housing to avoid heat loss and unnecessary temperature fluctuations.

AMPLIFICATION AND READOUT OF DETECTOR SIGNALS

The electronic signal generated by any radiation detector must be translated into a form which the experimenter can interpret. The process is typically accomplished with amplifiers, ammeters, potentiometers and potentiometric recorders.

Amplifiers. In order to be measured, most detector signals must be amplified by several orders of magnitude. An *amplifier* takes an "input" signal from the circuit of the sensing component and, through a series of electronic operations, produces an "output" signal which is many times larger than the "input." The amplification factor (ratio of output to input) is called "the gain" of the amplifier. The amplifier input and output signals are normally electrical voltages. If the detector circuit generates an electric current, the input is taken from the voltage drop across a resistor inserted into the circuit (see Figure 10-12 or 10-15). Therefore,

$$E_{\text{input}} = i_{\substack{\text{detector} \\ \text{circuit}}} R_{\substack{\text{detector} \\ \text{circuit}}} \text{ (Ohm's law)}$$

Meter Readout. Let us use a meter as the readout device in an ultraviolet-visible instrument. In Figure 10-15, *A* is an ammeter which measures the electric

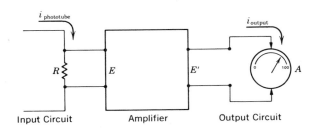

FIGURE 10-15. Schematic of a meter readout system.

current in the output circuit. For convenience we will assume that the meter is calibrated in 100 divisions. Using Ohm's law, the output voltage, $E' = i_{output} R'$, where R' = the resistance of the output circuit (assumed to be constant). Therefore, the following proportionalities should be correct:

Meter reading $\propto i_{ouput} \propto E' \propto E \propto i_{phototube} \propto$ incident radiant power

The validity of the overall proportionality requires linear amplification by the amplifier; that is, $E' = kE$, where k is the gain of the amplifier.

Quantitative Calibration. The circuit illustrated in Figure 10-15 can be easily modified to compensate for the dark current by introducing an additional equal but opposite signal into the input of the amplifier. The compensating signal is adjusted so that the meter reads 0 with no radiant energy striking the phototube (shutter closed). The instrument is then "standardized" by using a "blank" solution (normally the solvent) and adjusting the output signal so that the meter reads 100. This standardizing adjustment can be made by varying the gain of the amplifier, varying the slit width, varying the sensitivity of the meter (electrical shunt), or by partially blocking the light beam with a comb device. Thus the instrument is calibrated so that there are 100 units on the meter from $P_t = 0$ to $P_t = P_o$ and these units are linear with respect to P_t. When an absorbing sample is substituted for the "blank," the detector response will show between 0 and 100 units on the meter. For example, if the detector response for a particular sample produced a meter reading of 80 units (80% transmittance), $P_t = k(80)$ and $P_o = k(100)$, where k is the proportionality constant of the detector. Therefore, for this sample, $\log P_o/P_t = \log 100/80 = A = \epsilon bc$. If ϵ and b are known, the concentration of the absorbing sample may be determined.

Null-Point Determination. A potentiometer (variable voltage source) may also be used as a readout device for radiation measurements. This is an example of a common technique called "null-point determination," illustrated in Figure 10-16.

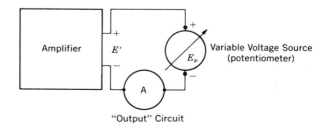

FIGURE 10-16.   Schematic of a null-point circuit.

The input circuit is similar to that shown in Figure 10-15. The variable voltage opposes the output voltage, and the former is adjusted until there is zero current ("null point") in the output circuit as indicated by the ammeter, A. At this point, $E_p = E'$, and thus E_p is proportional to the radiant power of the incident beam. The dial of the potentiometer may be marked in 100 divisions and calibrated with dark current and "blank" solution in the same manner as the direct-reading meter.

A potentiometric recorder also utilizes the null-point design by mechanically adjusting its output voltage to be equal and opposite to the output signal from the detector amplifier. Any difference between the two outputs is used to actuate the balancing mechanism. A recording pen is attached to the balancing mechanism and this pen continuously plots the position (voltage) of the null point. If the amplifier output signal changes, the pen will automatically move to a new null point. The position of the pen is analogous to a meter reading, but it also leaves a permanent trace on a chart paper. The system is adjusted to read 100% transmittance when a "blank" is inserted in the sample radiation beam and 0% transmittance when an opaque object is placed in the radiation beam. Therefore, as the pen moves across the paper, it automatically records the percent transmittance of the samples as it changes with wavelength. The rate of movement of the chart paper (perpendicular to the pen travel) corresponds to the automatic rate of change of wavelength of the radiation from the monochromator. It makes little difference whether the pen travels in one direction and the chart paper moves under it in a perpendicular direction, or the paper is held fixed while the pen moves across the paper and its carriage moves lengthwise along the paper—both systems are used. In this manner, after the instrument is standardized, an absorption spectrum is recorded automatically, as shown in Figure 10-17.

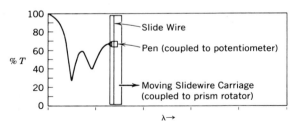

FIGURE 10-17.   Automatic recording spectrophotometer.

SINGLE-BEAM vs. DOUBLE-BEAM OPERATION

Two basic instrument designs are employed in commercial spectrophotometers. One design uses only a single beam, whereas the other provides a double beam. We shall emphasize ultraviolet and visible instruments in the following discussion.

Single-Beam Operation. A beam of radiation from the source enters the monochromator where it is dispersed by a prism or a grating. As the dispersing element is rotated, the various resolved bands of radiation are focused at the exit slit. The radiation then passes through the cell and on to a detector. The instrument is calibrated (0% and 100% T) and used by the methods just described.

The single-beam method requires stable, high quality components in the source, detector, and amplifier for high precision measurements. The instrumental parameters cannot fluctuate between the time of 100% T calibration with the "blank" and the determination of the transmittance of the sample. Direct-reading instruments using meters give immediate readout with an accuracy of $\pm$ 0.2 to 3% in transmittance. The null-point readout design is considerably more accurate ($\pm$ 0.2% in transmittance), but more expensive. Unless high accuracy is required, the meter readout instruments are quite satisfactory. Single-beam instruments are simpler and less expensive than double-beam, but they are not readily adapted to recording because of the necessity of calibration at each wavelength.

Double-Beam Operation. Double-beam instruments employ some type of beam splitter prior to the sample cells. One beam is directed through the "blank" cell (or reference cell) and the other beam through the sample cell. The two beams are then compared either continuously or alternately many times a second. Thus, in the double-beam design, fluctuations in the source intensity, the detector response and amplifier gain are compensated for by observing the difference signal between "blank" and sample. As might be expected, double-beam instruments are more sophisticated electronically and mechanically than the single-beam designs and consequently are more expensive.

In ultraviolet-visible double-beam spectrophotometers, the beam splitting occurs after the monochromator; front surface mirrors and, more commonly, rotating sector mirrors are used. The rotating sector mirror alternately passes and reflects the beam several times a second and thus splits the beam and also chops it. This chopped radiation is used as the input source for a-c amplifiers, which provide amplification stability. An electronic null-readout system is employed in this type of instrument. One of these designs is shown schematically in Figure 10-18. The reference and sample beams alternately reach the detector at intervals which depend on the rotational frequencies of the choppers. The instrument records the ratio of the reference and sample signals. If the radiant powers of both of the beams are the same, the a-c amplifier generates no output signal. If the radiant powers of the two beams are different, the imbalance signal activates a servomotor which drives a potentiometric recorder such that the imbalance signal is "electronically nulled" by the recorder. The electrical bridge of the potentiometric recorder is calibrated in terms of percent transmittance of the sample and thus the position of the bridge balance point is used to determine percent transmittance.

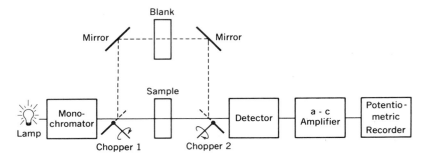

FIGURE 10-18. Double-beam instrument employing a chopper and electronic null readout.

COMMERCIAL INSTRUMENTS

Bausch and Lomb Spectronic 20 Spectrophotometer.   This low-cost instrument (~ \$400) is particularly suitable for student use. It has a range from 340 to 625 mμ, which can be extended to approximately 750 mμ with simple modification. The Spectronic 20 is illustrated schematically in Figure 10-19. Radiation from a tungsten lamp is dispersed by a diffraction grating with 600 lines/mm. The slits allow a constant band width of 20 mμ. The grating is turned by the calibrated wavelength control knob in order to select the desired radiation band. The instrument is standardized separately at each wavelength by (1) adjusting the amplifier control knob so that the meter reads 0% T when no radiation reaches the phototube ("dark current" adjust), and (2) adjusting the light control so that the meter reads 100% T with the "blank" cell in the beam. The sensitivity of the Spectronic 20 phototube is similar to that shown in Figure 10-13. It is clear that

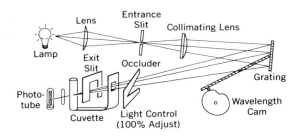

FIGURE 10-19.   Schematic of Bausch and Lomb Spectronic 20.

the calibration of the "blank" to readout 100% T requires more radiant power at 600 mμ than at 400 mμ; the light control adjust performs the desired attenuations. The above calibrations should be made *each time* the wavelength is changed.

Beckman DU Spectrophotometer. This was the first ultraviolet-visible instrument to be produced on a large scale in this country. A schematic optical diagram of this instrument is shown in Figure 10-20. The DU spans the wavelength region

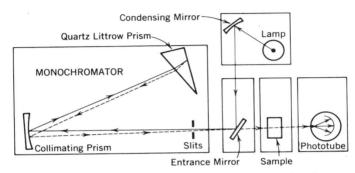

FIGURE 10-20. Schematic of Beckman DU Ultraviolet-Visible Spectrophotometer.

190 mμ to 1000 mμ by employing a hydrogen discharge lamp for the ultraviolet region and a 6-volt tungsten lamp for the visible near-infrared region. The 30° quartz Littrow prism is rotated so that the proper radiation will pass through the exit slit. A calibrated dial which is attached to the prism indicates the wavelengths which are being used. The slit widths are adjusted manually. Two interchangeable phototubes are used; one is most sensitive in the ultraviolet and blue region and the other in the red range.

The DU employs a null balance readout design. The instrument is calibrated in much the same way as the Spectronic 20, except that the "blank" setting (100% T) can be adjusted by changing either the slit widths or the amplifier gain and, of course, one reads a potentiometer dial instead of a meter.

Perkin-Elmer "Infracord" Spectrophotometer. The "Infracord" is a double-beam, low cost, automatic recording infrared spectrophotometer. It operates in the range 2.5 to 15 μ. A schematic diagram of the Infracord is shown in Figure 10-21. The radiation from a heated aluminum oxide source is split in half by a plane mirror and two toroid mirrors. Toroid mirror (1) focuses the sample beam through the sampling area onto an optical comb (100% T adjust optical attenuator); toroid mirror (2) focuses the reference beam onto an optical wedge

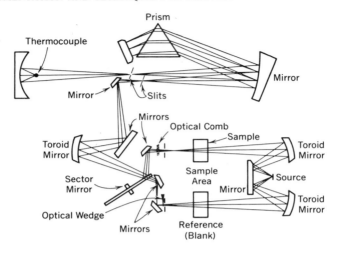

FIGURE 10-21.   Schematic of Perkin-Elmer "Infracord" Spectrophoto-meter.

(reference beam attenuator). The sample cell is placed just in front of the optical comb and the reference ("blank") cell just in front of the optical wedge. After passing through the sample and "blank," the two beams are recombined by a semicircular sector mirror which rotates at 13 revolutions per second. The single beam which emerges from the sector mirror then consists of alternate pulses of sample and reference radiation which eventually undergo dispersion in a double pass through the monochromator. The dispersed radiation is then focused on the exit slit as a band of radiation which finally reaches the thermocouple sensing element. If the two beams are of equal intensity, the thermocouple produces a d-c voltage which is ignored by the a-c amplifier. If the two beams are not equal, the detector produces a pulsating signal which is converted to an alternating voltage and amplified. The amplified signal is used to drive a servomotor which moves an optical wedge into or out of the reference beam to equalize (or null) the beam intensities. The recorder pen is coupled to the wedge and records its position. The position of the wedge is calibrated to correspond to percent transmittance and thus the pen records the percent transmittance of the sample at the wavelength band used. Since the wavelength band is changed by rotating the prism, the prism drive mechanism can also control the movement of chart paper on which the spectrum is to be recorded. The chart paper is precalibrated in units of wavelength (or wavenumbers) along one axis and in % T along the other.

Model 700, introduced in 1968, resembles the Infracord (Figure 10-21) except that it employs a diffraction grating in the monochromator and uses solid state electronics. Its simplified operation (two push buttons), range (2.5 to 15.4 μ), and low price ($3000) make it attractive for student use.

SAMPLE PREPARATION

Solvents. The solvents used in spectrophotometric studies must (1) dissolve the sample and (2) transmit in the wavelength region under study. Common solvents which are used in the ultraviolet and visible regions are listed in Table 10-2 along with their lower transparency limits.

Common solvent absorption bands in the infrared range of 2 to 15 μ (5000 to 666 cm^{-1}) are given in Table 10-3. Carbon tetrachloride, carbon disulfide, and chloroform are the most commonly used.

TABLE 10-2 APPROXIMATE LOWER TRANSPARENCY LIMITS OF SOLVENTS USED IN ULTRAVIOLET-VISIBLE ABSORPTION STUDIES

Solvent (high purity)	Transparency limit (mμ)
Acetone	330
Benzene	285
Carbon tetrachloride	265
Carbon disulfide	375
Chloroform	245
Cyclohexane	215
Dichloromethane	235
Dioxane	225
95% Ethanol	205
Ethyl ether	205
iso-Octane	215
iso-Propyl alcohol	215
Methanol	215
Pyridine	305
Water	200
Xylene	295

Solution Preparation. Components which are to be determined in the ultraviolet and visible regions often exhibit high molar absorptivities at the absorbance maximum. High concentrations of these components will yield a very low percent

TABLE 10-3 INFRARED SOLVENT ABSORPTION BANDS IN RANGE 2 TO 15 μ

| Solvent | Absorption Bands | |
	(μ)	(cm^{-1})
Bromoform	3.2– 3.5	(3120–2860)
	4.2– 4.6	(2380–2170)
	7.4– 7.8	(1350–1280)
	8.2– 9.3	(1220–1080)
	11.3–11.8	(880– 850)
	13.1–15.0	(760– 666)
Carbon disulfide	4.2– 4.8	(2380–2080)
	6.1– 7.1	(1640–1410)
	11.4–11.8	(877– 847)
Carbon tetrachloride	6.2– 6.5	(1610–1540)
	7.8– 8.3	(1280–1200)
	9.9–10.5	(1010– 950)
	11.7–15.0	(855– 666)
Chloroform	3.3– 3.5	(3030–2850)
	4.1– 4.3	(2440–2330)
	6.6– 7.1	(1520–1410)
	10.6–15.0	(943– 666)
Nujol oil (high molecular weight petroleum fraction for mulls)	3.4– 3.8	(2940–2630)
	6.8– 7.4	(1470–1350)
Fluorolube (perfluoro carbon for mulls)	7.7–15.0	(1300– 666)
Tetrachloroethylene	7.2– 7.5	(1390–1330)
	8.5– 9.1	(1180–1100)
	9.9–15.0	(1010– 666)

transmittance. Recall that the percent transmittance of the solution should be in the range 20 to 65%, and that at *low* values of % T, the uncertainty is extremely high. Consequently, the sample may have to be diluted to give an absorbance in the optimum range.

The path length of the infrared solution cell is quite short, and the infrared absorption bands have rather low molar absorptivities. Consequently, fairly concentrated solutions of the absorbing components are required in order to obtain a measurable absorbance. Concentrations of the order of 0.5 to 10 weight percent are common for infrared studies. Quantitative accuracy in the infrared region is rather poor, and is limited primarily by the low energy of infrared radiation coupled with the difficulty of establishing a true 100% T reference line.

REFERENCES

187

R. P. Bauman, *Absorption Spectroscopy*, Wiley, New York, 1962. Very comprehensive discussion of instrumentation.

G. W. Ewing, *Instrumental Methods of Chemical Analysis*, 2nd ed., McGraw-Hill, New York, 1960.

H. A. Strobel, *Chemical Instrumentation*, Addison-Wesley, Reading, Mass., 1960.

H. H. Willard, L. L. Merritt, and J. A. Dean, *Instrumental Methods of Analysis*, 4th ed., D. Van Nostrand, Princeton, N.J., 1965.

11 INTERPRETATION OF ABSORPTION SPECTRA

The determination of molecular structure and the identification of specific structural units are extremely important to the modern chemist. The presence or absence of a particular functional group located at a particular molecular site often determines a specific chemical reactivity of the molecule (e.g., enzyme activity). Many techniques are useful in elucidating molecular structure. In the past, wet chemical methods were used extensively. Recently, however, the instrumental methods of X-ray crystallography, absorption spectrophotometry, nuclear magnetic resonance, and mass spectrometry have provided the means for major advances in structure determination and identification. In this chapter, we consider how molecular electronic and vibrational absorption spectra are applied to these problems.

ELECTRONIC SPECTRA

Recall that electronic transitions in organic molecules involve the promotion of electrons in ground-state bonding or non-bonding molecular orbitals to excited state, antibonding molecular orbitals. The electronic energies of the molecular ground states and excited states are determined by molecular structure; thus the photon energies required for $n \rightarrow \pi^*$, $\pi \rightarrow \pi^*$, and $n \rightarrow \sigma^*$ transitions vary from molecule to molecule, depending on differences in structure. Consequently, the specific absorption bands corresponding to these transitions also vary. It follows that careful examination of the locations, distribution patterns, and intensities of absorption bands may be quite useful in the identification of functional groups and classification of compounds (e.g., alcohols, aldehydes, aromatics, etc.). Unfortunately, because of broad overlapping absorption bands, the interpretation of electronic spectra is somewhat less certain than that for vibrational spectra. Nevertheless, a great deal of research has been directed at correlating structural changes with shifts in the absorption bands of the electronic spectra.

Common terms which are used in discussions of electronic spectra include *chromophore, auxochrome, bathochromic effect*, and *hypochromic effect*. The first two terms apply to the wavelength region near and above 200 mμ, and were introduced before the relatively recent interest in far-ultraviolet studies ($<$ 200 mμ). For our purposes, the definitions are useful because we will discuss electronic

189

transitions only in the wavelength region near and above 200 mμ, which is the lower wavelength limit of common commercial ultraviolet-visible spectrophotometers. *Chromophores* are defined as functional groups which absorb near ultraviolet or visible radiation when they are bonded to a non-absorbing, saturated residue which possesses no unshared, non-bonding valence electrons (e.g., a hydrocarbon chain). Most chromophores have unsaturated bonds. *Auxochromes* are functional groups such as —OH, —NH$_2$, and —Cl which have non-bonding valence electrons and do not absorb radiation at wavelengths > 200 mμ. They do, however, exhibit intense absorption in the far ultraviolet ($n \rightarrow \sigma^*$ transitions). When an auxochrome is attached to a chromophore, the chromophore absorption band typically shifts to longer wavelength (*bathochromic effect*) and increases in intensity (i.e., the molar absorptivity, ϵ_{max}, at the wavelength of maximum absorbance, λ_{max}, increases). The *hypochromic effect* is a shift of the absorption band to shorter wavelength; this effect is often noted when positive charge is introduced into the molecule and when changing from non-polar to polar solvents.

Chromophores. Wavelengths of maximum absorption for some common chromophores are presented in Table 11-1. In this table, the high intensity absorption bands represent higher probability $\pi \rightarrow \pi^*$ transitions, and the low intensity bands are due to the lower probability $n \rightarrow \pi^*$ transitions. The location of a chromophore absorption band will be essentially the same for all of its compounds in which the R constituents are saturated groups which cannot conjugate with the chromophore.

Carbonyl Chromophore. The ultraviolet carbonyl $n \rightarrow \pi^*$ absorption band in the region 270 to 290 mμ is easily recognized and is quite useful in the identification of aldehydes and ketones. 2,4-Dinitrophenylhydrazone derivatives of non-conjugated carbonyl compounds may be prepared which exhibit intense absorption maxima around 350 mμ (the band extends into the visible region).

Solvent Effects. Polar solvents interact electrostatically with polar chromophores (e.g., carbonyl) and tend to stabilize both the non-bonding electronic ground states and the π^* excited states. The result is that the $n \rightarrow \pi^*$ absorptions (which usually occur at longer wavelength than the $\pi \rightarrow \pi^*$ absorptions) shift to higher energy (shorter wavelength) and the $\pi \rightarrow \pi^*$ absorptions move to lower energy (longer wavelength). Consequently, the $\pi \rightarrow \pi^*$ and $n \rightarrow \pi^*$ absorptions of polar chromophores move closer to each other with increasing polarity of the solvent. The solvent shift of the $n \rightarrow \pi^*$ absorption is indicated clearly in the ultraviolet spectrum of N-nitroso-dimethylamine shown in Figure 11-1. Solvent changes do not affect the electronic spectra of non-polar chromophores such as the alkenes and alkynes.

TABLE 11-1 Characteristic Absorption Bands for Common Chromophores

Chromophore	Compound Types	Example	Solvent	Absorption Band	
				λ_{max} (mμ)	ϵ_{max}
Alkene	$RCH = CH - R$	Ethylene	Vapor	$\begin{cases} 165 \\ 193 \end{cases}$	15,000 10,000
Alkyne	$RC \equiv CR$	2-Octyne	Heptane	$\begin{cases} 195 \\ 223 \end{cases}$	2,100 160
Carbonyl (ketone)	$\begin{matrix} R \\ \diagdown \\ R \diagup \end{matrix} C = O$	Acetone	Hexane	$\begin{cases} 189 \\ 279 \end{cases}$	900 15
Carbonyl (aldehyde)	$R - C \begin{matrix} \diagup O \\ \diagdown H \end{matrix}$	Acetaldehyde	$\begin{cases} Vapor \\ Hexane \end{cases}$	180 290	10,000 17
Carboxyl	$R - C \begin{matrix} \diagup O \\ \diagdown OH \end{matrix}$	Acetic acid	95% Ethanol	208	32
Amido	$R - C \begin{matrix} \diagup O \\ \diagdown NH_2 \end{matrix}$	Acetamide	Water	220	63
Nitro	$R - NO_2$	Nitromethane	Methanol	201	5,000
Nitrate	$R - ONO_2$	n-Butyl nitrate	95% Ethanol	270	17
Nitroso	$R - N = O$	Nitroso butane	Ethyl ether	300 665	100 20
Azo	$R - N = N - R$	Azomethane	95% Ethanol	338	4

Multiple Chromophores in Non-Conjugated Systems. Components that have more than one chromophore separated by *more than one* single bond exhibit the characteristic absorption bands of *each* of the chromophores present.

Conjugation Effects, Alkenes and Alkynes. When two chromophoric groups are separated by one single bond, conjugation occurs and the absorption spectra indicate dramatic changes in the absorption bands which were characteristic of the isolated chromophores. In conjugated systems, the π electron distribution is delocalized over a minimum of four atoms which causes a decrease in the $\pi \rightarrow \pi^*$ transition energy. The absorption intensity also increases due to a higher probability for the transition. Consequently, whereas the $\pi \rightarrow \pi^*$ transition occurs near 165 mμ for ethylene, in the conjugated 1,3-butadiene, the transition is near

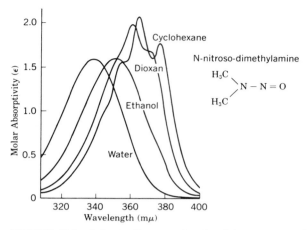

FIGURE 11-1. Solvent effects on the ultraviolet spectrum of *N*-nitroso-dimethylamine. (From Jaffe and Orchin, *Theory and Applications of Ultraviolet Spectroscopy*, Wiley, 1962, p. 188.)

217 mμ and the intensity increases considerably (ϵ_{max} = 20,900) in comparison to the isolated alkene (ϵ_{max} = 15,000). As the length of the conjugated alkene system increases, the absorption band moves to even longer wavelengths and is more intense. For example, 1,3,5-hexatriene has a strong $\pi \rightarrow \pi^*$ absorption near 258 mμ (ϵ_{max} = 35,000). Figure 11-2 demonstrates the bathochromic effect of extended conjugation on absorption spectra.

The carotenoid compounds occur naturally in plant tissues and contain very large numbers of conjugated alkene bonds. Commonly these compounds are isolated by chromatographic methods and then qualitatively and quantitatively determined by spectrophotometric methods. β-Carotene (with a structure similar to vitamin A_1) is a carotenoid with eleven conjugated double bonds. Its very intense $\pi \rightarrow \pi^*$ maximum absorption band is shifted completely into the visible region (λ_{max} = 451 mμ, ϵ_{max} = 13,800). The structure and spectrum for trans-β-carotene are shown in Figure 11-3.

The absorption bands of conjugated alkynes also are shifted to longer wavelength; however, the absorption intensity is significantly lower than for the conjugated alkenes. For example, vinylacetylene ($CH_2 = CH - C \equiv CH$) exhibits an absorption band near 1,3-butadiene (λ_{max} = 219 mμ); however, its ϵ_{max} is 6400 compared to 20,900 for 1,3-butadiene. In extended polyalkyne systems, the weak absorption bands move to even longer wavelength and new intense bands appear around 200 mμ (ϵ_{max} ~400,000).

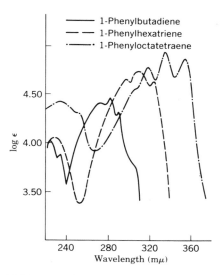

FIGURE 11-2. Spectra of 1-phenylpolyenes. [After Walborsky and Pendleton, *J. Am. Chem. Soc.*, **82**, 1405 (1960).]

Carbonyl Conjugation. α,β-Unsaturated ketones are good examples of a carbonyl conjugated with an alkene group. These compounds exhibit both $\pi \rightarrow \pi^*$ and $n \rightarrow \pi^*$ transitions. The locations of these absorption bands are quite sensitive to solvent effects and the extent and nature of substitution on the α and β carbons. Woodward has provided empirical relationships between substitution and the positions of absorption bands (λ_{max}) for these compounds; these are summarized for the $\pi \rightarrow \pi^*$ transition in Table 11-2 which applies to the structure:

$$\underset{\beta}{\overset{\beta}{\diagdown}} C = \underset{\beta}{\overset{\alpha}{C}} - C \overset{O}{\underset{R}{\diagup}}$$

Aromatic Systems. Benzene exhibits stong ultraviolet absorption at 184 and 202 mμ ($\pi \rightarrow \pi^*$ transitions for three ethylenic groups in cyclic conjugation). The benzene spectrum also shows a characteristic series of low intensity, fine structure bands between 230 and 270 mμ, ($\lambda_{max} = 255$ mμ, $\epsilon_{max} = 230$ for benzene

TABLE 11-2   Absorption Bands for α, β-Unsaturated Ketones in 95% Ethanol

Substitution	λ_{max}, mμ
No substitution	215
Monosubstitution, α or β (no —C=C— in substitution group)	225
Disubstitution, α, β or β, β (no —C=C— in substitution group)	235
Disubstitution, α, β or β, β (one —C=C— in substitution group)	240
Trisubstitution (no —C=C— in substitution group)	247
Trisubstitution (one —C = C— in substitution group)	252

in cyclohexane) as shown in Figure 11-4. The resolution of the benzene fine structure bands is very dependent on solvent effects and ring substitution. Polar solvents tend to blend the bands together into a broad hump, whereas non-polar solvents permit excellent resolution. Benzene fine structure also is diminished significantly upon ring substitution.

Aromatic Auxochrome Substitution.   The effects of auxochromic groups are evident in substituted benzene compounds. It appears that the availability of free, non-bonding electrons determines the extent of interaction of an auxochrome

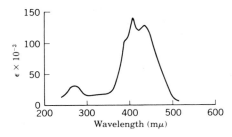

FIGURE 11-3.   Absorption spectrum of *trans*-β-carotene. [After Zechmeister and Polgar, *J. Am. Chem. Soc.*, **65**, 1522 (1943).]

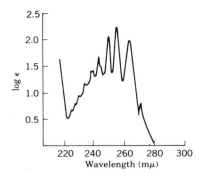

FIGURE 11-4. Ultraviolet absorption spectrum of benzene vapor. (From Friedel and Orchin, *Ultraviolet Violet Spectra of Aromatic Compounds*, Wiley, 1951.)

with a chromophore; this is indicated in the spectral data presented in Table 11-3 for phenol, phenolate anion, aniline and the anilinium cation. The phenolate oxygen has a large number of free valence electrons which may interact with the benzene ring; it exhibits a pronounced auxochromic effect (i.e., significant bathochromic shift and increase in absorption intensity) on both absorption bands. The —NH_2 group of aniline also acts as an auxochrome. However, the anilinium cation has no free valence electrons, the nitrogen carries a positive charge and the molecule exhibits essentially the same absorption properties as

TABLE 11-3 EFFECTS OF AUXOCHROMIC SUBSTITUTION ON THE ABSORPTION SPECTRUM OF THE BENZENE RING

Compound	Solvent	Principal Absorption Band		Characteristic Fine Structure Band	
		λ_{max} (mμ)	ϵ_{max}	λ_{max} (mμ)	ϵ_{max}
Benzene	Vapor	198	8000	255	230
Phenol	Water	210.5	6200	270	1450
Phenolate anion	Aqueous alkali	235	9400	287	2600
Aniline	Water	230	8600	280	1430
Anilinium cation	Aqueous acid	203	7500	254	160

unsubstituted benzene. The auxochromic effect apparently is caused by the interaction of non-bonding, free valence electrons with the delocalized π electron cloud to stabilize the π^* excited state of the molecule.

Aromatic Chromophore Substitution. When chromophores are substituted into the benzene nucleus, there is a mutual electrostatic interaction through conjugation; consequently, the absorption spectrum for the resulting compound is somewhat different from that for isolated benzene and substituent chromophores. Examples of these differences are given in Table 11-4.

TABLE 11-4 COMPARISON OF SPECTRA FOR BENZENE, ISOLATED CHROMOPHORES AND CORRESPONDING BENZENE SUBSTITUTED COMPOUNDS

Compound (Chromophore)	Substituted Chromophore $\pi \to \pi^*$ Band		Substituted Chromophore $n \to \pi^*$ Band		Benzene Fine Structure Band	
	λ_{max} (mμ)	ϵ_{max}	λ_{max} (mμ)	ϵ_{max}	λ_{max} (mμ)	ϵ_{max}
R, R C = O	180	10,000	290	17	—	—
Benzene	—	—	—	—	255	215
(benzaldehyde structure)	244	15,000	328	20	280	1,500
R — NO$_2$	201	5,000	271	19	—	—
Benzene	—	—	—	—	255	215
(nitrobenzene structure)	252	10,000	330	125	280	1,000

Extended Aromatics. The linearly extended aromatic compounds display fine structure similar to benzene. As might be expected with greater π electron delocalization, the absorption bands are shifted to longer wavelengths and are more intense. This shift, in addition to fine structure, is shown quite clearly in the spectra of naphthalene, anthracene and naphthacene in Figure 11-5. Non-linear extended aromatic compounds also absorb in the ultraviolet region and yield spectra which are extremely difficult to interpret.

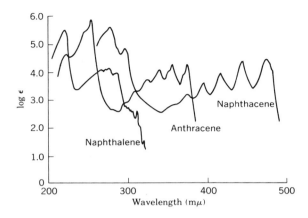

FIGURE 11-5. Ultraviolet spectra of some linear polynuclear aromatic compounds. (From Friedel and Orchin, *Ultraviolet Spectra of Aromatic Compounds*, Wiley, 1951.)

Nucleic Acids. Because of their function as building blocks of the living cell, nucleic acids are extremely important. There are two types of nucleic acids, deoxyribonucleic acid (DNA) and ribonucleic acid (RNA). Both types consist of two long chains of alternating sugar and phosphate residues. The chains are linked at the sugar units by nitrogenous bases which are either substituted purines or substituted pyrimidines. Purine and pyrimidine are heteroaromatic compounds with the structures:

The substituted purines and pyrimidines are the units which absorb ultraviolet radiation in the nucleic acids and their many derivatives. The sugar and phosphate residues are transparent above 200 mμ.

DNA and RNA contain the two substituted purines, adenine and guanine, and the substituted pyrimidine, cytosine. RNA also contains the pyrimidine, uracil, whereas DNA contains thymine. The absorption bands of these various bases in water are listed in Table 11-5.

TABLE 11-5   ABSORPTION DATA FOR NITROGENOUS
BASES OF NUCLEIC ACIDS

	pH	λ_{max} (mμ)	ϵ_{max}
Adenine	2	263	13,100
	12	269	12,300
Guanine	2	248	11,400
		275	7,350
	11	246	6,350
		273	8,000
Cytosine	2	210	9,700
		274	10,200
Uracil	2	259	8,200
	12	284	6,500
Thymine	2	207	9,500
		264	7,900
	12	291	5,440

Steric Effects in Conjugated Systems. Extended conjugation of π orbitals requires coplanarity of the atoms involved within the π cloud delocalization. If large bulky groups are located in positions which hinder a coplanar arrangement (steric hindrance), the absorption band shifts to shorter wavelengths and is lower in intensity. Consequently, the electronic spectra of *cis* and *trans* geometrical isomers of conjugated compounds should be different. The *cis* isomer typically offers steric hindrance to coplanarity and thus hinders conjugation; as a result, the absorption band for the *cis* isomer is less intense and located at shorter wavelengths than the *trans* absorption band. This isomeric absorption band difference is demonstrated vividly in a comparison of the ultraviolet absorption spectra of *cis-* and *trans*-azobenzene shown in Figure 11-6.

VIBRATIONAL SPECTRA

In infrared studies, vibrational absorption bands commonly are identified either in units of wavelength, λ (in microns) or wavenumber, $\bar{v}$ (sometimes loosely referred to as "frequency in cm^{-1}"). Good arguments are advanced by the proponents of both of these expressions and so, since both systems are well established and widely used, both wavelengths and wavenumbers will be quoted in infrared spectra interpretation. The equation for converting wavenumbers to wavelength *in microns* is:

$$\lambda_{microns} = \frac{10^4}{\bar{v}} \text{ cm}$$

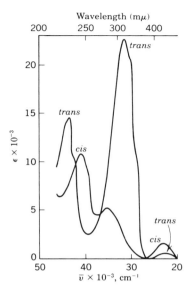

Wavelength (mμ)

FIGURE 11-6. Ultraviolet absorption spectra of *cis*- and *trans*-azobenzene in 95% ethanol. (From Jaffe and Orchin, *Theory and Applications of Ultraviolet Spectroscopy*, Wiley, 1962, p. 430.)

The theories which explain molecular vibrational changes were introduced in Chapter 8. Now let us see how vibrational absorption spectra may be of assistance in determining molecular structure. Recall that for a diatomic molecule, the approximate vibrational stretching frequency may be calculated using Hooke's law (Equation 8-2). Even though this law was derived using a harmonic oscillator model of rigid balls connected by a stretched spring, it provides excellent agreement between the calculated and observed stretching frequencies for diatomic molecules. Unfortunately, most molecules consist of more than two atoms; and, in polyatomic molecules, the vibrational stretching frequencies depend on the geometric structure of the entire molecule. Nevertheless, there are many stretching frequencies for specific molecular segments which are close to those predicted by Hooke's law for the isolated segment. For example, application of Hooke's law to predict the stretching frequency for an isolated $C—H$ bond gives 3.30 μ (3040 cm^{-1}), and compounds which contain methylene and methyl groups actually exhibit $C—H$ stretching absorptions in the region 3.38 to 3.51 μ (2960 to 2850 cm^{-1}).

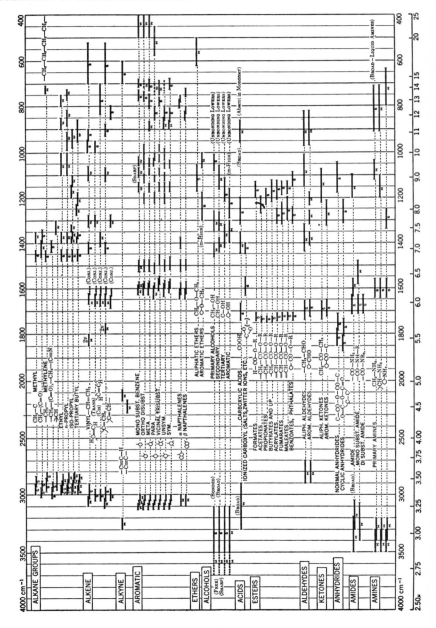

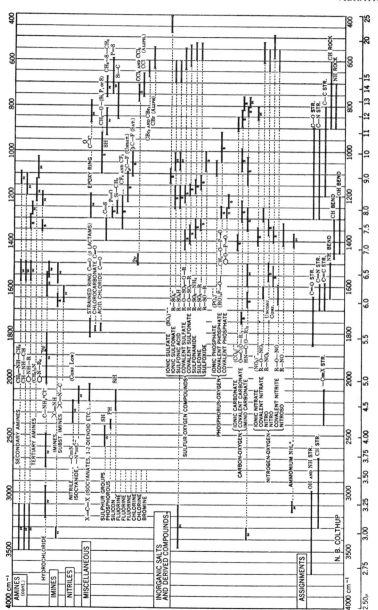

FIGURE 11-7. Colthup chart of characteristic group infrared absorptions. [From Colthup, *J. Opt. Soc. Am.*, **40**, 397 (1950).]

Thus, if force constants are known, we may estimate the general spectral region in which a given functional group should absorb. The specific location of absorption bands varies depending on the extent of electrostatic and steric hindrance in the molecule. Both of these factors affect the bond strengths and vibrational force constants. The estimated positions of absorptions are easily verified by judiciously selecting pure known compounds, taking their spectra and then examining the positions of the recorded absorption bands.

Simple application of Hooke's law indicates that the stretching vibrations associated with bonds such as C—H, O—H, and N—H should be of high frequency and absorb radiation around 2.7 to 3.3 μ (3700 to 2970 cm^{-1}). As indicated above, these absorptions would be expected to show variation with electrostatic and steric changes in the molecule. However, characteristic group stretching vibrations are recognized easily in the spectral region 2.5 to 7.0 μ (4000 to 1430 cm^{-1}). For example, the carbonyl group exhibits an intense, characteristic stretching absorption around 5.8 μ (1724 cm^{-1}). Other characteristic stretching absorption bands in this region are indicated in the Colthup chart in Figure 11-7.

The C—C, C—O, and C—N stretching frequencies are distributed in the region 7.0 to 11.0 μ (1430 to 909 cm^{-1}); unfortunately, most of the molecular bending vibrations also appear in this region. Consequently, the absorption spectra from 1430 to 909 cm^{-1} are often extremely complex and the assignment of specific absorption bands to particular stretching or bending vibrations is difficult and uncertain. However, the locations and relative intensities of the vibrational absorptions in this region are unique to the molecule as a whole. For this reason, the 7.0 to 11.0 μ (1430 to 909 cm^{-1}) range is commonly referred to as "the fingerprint region." Structurally similar molecules often will exhibit essentially the same absorption spectra between 2.5 to 7.0 μ (4000 to 1430 cm^{-1}) and 11.0 to 15.0 μ (909 to 666 cm^{-1}), but differences will be evident in "the fingerprint region."

The various characteristic group infrared absorptions from 2.5 to 15.0 μ (4000 to 666 cm^{-1}) are shown in Colthup's chart in Figure 11-7. These characteristic absorptions are presented in more detailed form in Table 11-6.

Characteristic Absorption Bands of Substituted Benzene Compounds. The number, relative positions, and relative intensities of *weak benzenoid* combination and overtone bands which appear in the 5 to 6 μ (2000 to 1667 cm^{-1}) and 11 to 14 μ (900 to 700 cm^{-1}) regions depend on the type of benzene substitution. If there are no interfering carbonyl stretching bands present, this region may be examined using concentrated solutions. The various substitutions and their corresponding absorption patterns are indicated in Figure 11-8.

Absorption Band Analysis. The material presented in Figure 11-7 and Table 11-6 suggests that infrared absorption analysis is a powerful diagnostic tool for the identification of molecular structure. For example, absorption band analysis may allow us to determine rapidly if an unknown or a new compound contains aromatic, acid, ketone, or aldehyde groups.

TABLE 11-6 CHARACTERISTIC INFRARED ABSORPTION BANDS*
(Absorption Intensity Symbols: s = strong, m = medium, w = weak, v = variable, b = broad, and sh = sharp)

Spectral Region	Vibrational Classification	Group and Environment	Absorption Band Range		Absorption Band Intensity
μ (cm^{-1})			$\lambda(\mu)$	(cm^{-1})	
2.7–3.0 (3704–3333)	O—H stretching	*Alcohols and Phenols* (a) Free O—H	2.74–2.79	(3650–3590)	(v, sh)
		(b) *Inter*molecularly hydrogen bonded OH (changes on dilution) (1) single bridge compounds	2.82–2.90	(3550–3450)	(v, sh)
		(2) polymeric association	2.94–3.13	(3400–3200)	(s, b)
		(c) *Intra*molecularly hydrogen bonded OH-single bridge compounds	2.80–2.90	(3570–3450)	(v, sh)
	N—H stretching	*Amines* (a) Primary, free (2 bands)	~2.86 and 2.94	(~3500) (~3400)	(m) (m)
		(b) Secondary, free (1 band)	2.86–3.02	(3500–3310)	(m)
		Imines (= N—H)(1 band)	2.94–3.03	(3400–3300)	(m)
		Amides (a) Primary, free (2 bands)	~2.86 and 2.94	(~3500) (~3400)	(m) (m)
		(b) Secondary, free (1 band)	~2.92	(~3430)	(m)
		(c) Primary, bonded (2 bands)	~2.99 and 3.15	(~3350) (~3180)	(m) (m)

(Continued)

*Taken from Dyer, *Applications of Absorption Spectroscopy of Organic Compounds*, Prentice-Hall, 1965, pp. 33–38.

Spectral Region μ (cm^{-1})	Vibrational Classification	Group and Environment	Absorption Band Range $\lambda(\mu)$	(cm^{-1})	Absorption Band Intensity
3.0–3.5 (3333–2857)	N—H stretching	Amides (a) Secondary, bonded (1 band)	3.0–3.2	(3320–3140)	(m)
	C—H stretching	Alkyne	~3.03	(~3300)	(s)
		Alkene (a) Monosubstituted (vinyl)(2 bands)	3.23–3.25 and 3.29–3.32	(3095–3075) (3040–3010)	(m) (m)
		(b) Disubstituted, gem	3.23–3.25	(3095–3075)	(m)
		$-CH_2 = C\begin{smallmatrix}R\\ \\ R\end{smallmatrix}$			
		(c) Disubstituted, cis and trans	3.29–3.32	(3040–3010)	(m)
		Aromatic	~3.30	(~3030)	(v)
		Alkane ($-CH_3, -CH_2-$)	3.38–3.51	(2962–2853)	(m–s)
3.0–3.5 (3333–2857)	N—H stretching	Amines (a) Amine salts	3.2–3.3	(3130–3030)	(m)
	O—H stretching	Alcohols and Phenols (a) Intramolecular hydrogen bonded chelate compounds	3.1–4.0	(3200–2500)	(w, b)
3.5–4.0 (2857–2500)	C—H stretching	Aldehydes (characteristic) (2 bands)	3.45–3.55 and 3.60–3.70	(2900–2820) (2775–2700)	(w) (w)
	Hydroxyl stretching	Carboxylic Acids bonded, multiple bands	3.70–4.00	(2700–2500)	(w)
	S—H stretching	Sulfur Compounds	3.85–3.92	(2600–2550)	(w)
4.0–4.5 (2500–2222)	C≡C stretching	Alkyne—disubstituted	4.42–4.57	(2260–2190)	(v, w)
	C≡N stretching	Isocyanates	4.40–4.46	(2275–2240)	(m)
		Alkyl Nitriles	4.42–4.46	(2260–2240)	(m)

(Continued)

TABLE 11-6 *(Continued)*

Spectral Region	Vibrational Classification	Group and Environment	Absorption Band Range		Absorption Band Intensity
μ (cm^{-1})			$\lambda(\mu)$	(cm^{-1})	
		Aryl Nitriles	4.46–4.50	(2240–2220)	(m)
		α,β-Unsaturated Alkyl Nitriles	4.47–4.51	(2235–2215)	(m)
4.5–5.0 (2222–2000)	$C \equiv N$ stretching	*Isocyanides*	4.50–4.83	(2220–2070)	(m)
4.5–5.0 (2222–2000)	$-N=C=N-$ stretching	*Diimides*	4.64–4.70	(2155–2130)	(s)
	$-N_3$ stretching	*Azides*	4.63–4.72 and 7.46–8.48	(2160–2120) (1340–1180)	(s) (w)
5.0–5.5 (2000–1818)	$C = O$ stretching	*Anhydrides*			
		(a) Saturated 5-membered ring	5.35–5.49 and 5.56–5.71	(1870–1820) (1800–1750)	(s) (s)
		(b) α,β-Unsaturated 5-membered ring	5.41–5.56 and 5.47–5.62	(1850–1800) (1830–1780)	(s) (s)
		(c) Saturated, acyclic	5.41–5.56 and 5.59–5.75	(1850–1800) (1790–1740)	(s) (s)
		(d) α,β-Unsaturated and aryl, acyclic	5.47–5.62 and 5.65–5.81	(1830–1780) (1770–1720)	(s) (s)
5.5–6.0 (1818–1667)	$C = O$ stretching	*Acyl Halides*			
		(a) Acyl bromides	~ 5.53	(~ 1810)	(s)
		(b) Acyl chlorides	~ 5.57	(~ 1795)	(s)
		(c) Acyl fluorides	~ 5.41	(~ 1850)	(s)
		(d) α,β-Unsaturated and aryl	5.61–5.72 and 5.72–5.82	(1780–1750) (1750–1720)	(s) (m)
	$C = O$ stretching	*Esters*			
		(a) Saturated, cyclic			
		(1) β-lactones	~ 5.5	(~ 1820)	(s)
		(2) γ-lactones	5.62–5.68	(1780–1760)	(s)
		(3) δ-lactones (and larger rings)	5.71–5.76	(1750–1735)	(s)
		(b) Saturated, acyclic	5.71–5.76	(1750–1735)	(s)
		(c) Unsaturated			
		(1) Vinyl ester type	5.56–5.65	(1800–1770)	(s)
		(2) α,β unsaturated and aryl	5.78–5.82	(1730–1717)	(s)
		(d) Carbonates	5.62–5.75	(1780–1740)	(s)

(Continued)

TABLE 11-6 *(Continued)*

Spectral Region μ (cm^{-1})	Vibrational Classification	Group and Environment	Absorption Band Range $\lambda(\mu)$	(cm^{-1})	Absorption Band Intensity
	$C = O$ stretching	*Aldehydes*			
		(a) Saturated, aliphatic	5.75–5.81	(1740–1720)	(s)
		(b) Aryl	5.83–5.90	(1715–1695)	(s)
		(c) α,β Unsaturated, aliphatic	5.87–5.95	(1705–1680)	(s)
		Note: every aldehyde has characteristic C—H stretching vibrations (2 bands) at	3.45–3.55	(2900–2820)	(w)
			and 3.60–3.70	(2775–2700)	(w)
	$C = O$ stretching	*Ketones*			
5.5–6.0		(a) Saturated, acyclic	5.80–5.87	(1725–1705)	(s)
(1818–1667)		(b) Saturated, cyclic			
		(1) 6-membered ring (or higher)	5.80–5.87	(1725–1705)	(s)
		(2) 5-membered ring	5.71–5.75	(1750–1740)	(s)
		(c) α,β-Unsaturated, acyclic	5.94–6.01	(1685–1665)	(s)
		(d) α,β-Unsaturated, cyclic			
		(1) 6-membered ring	5.94–6.01	(1685–1665)	(s)
		(2) 5-membered ring	5.80–5.85	(1724–1708)	(s)
		(e) Aryl	5.88–5.95	(1700–1680)	(s)
		(f) Diaryl	5.99–6.02	(1670–1660)	(s)
	$C = O$ stretching	*Carboxylic Acids*			
		(a) Saturated, aliphatic	5.80–5.88	(1725–1700)	(s)
		(b) α,β-Unsaturated, aliphatic	5.83–5.92	(1715–1690)	(s)
		(c) Aryl	5.88–5.95	(1700–1680)	(s)
	$C = O$ stretching	*Amides*			
		(a) Primary, dilute solution	~5.92	(~1690)	(s)
		(b) Secondary, dilute solution	5.88–5.99	(1700–1670)	(s)
	$C = N$ stretching	*Imines, Oximes*			
		(a) Alkyl compounds	5.92–6.10	(1690–1640)	(s)
6.0–6.5	$C = O$ stretching	*Ketones*			
(1667–1538)		β-Diketone	6.10–6.50	(1640–1540)	(s)

(Continued)

TABLE 11-6 *(Continued)*

Spectral Region	Vibrational Classification	Group and Environment	Absorption Band Range		Absorption Band Intensity
μ (cm^{-1})			$\lambda(\mu)$	(cm^{-1})	
	$C = O$ stretching	*Esters*			
		(a) β-Ketoesters (enolic)	~6.06	(~1650)	(s)
		(b) Carboxylate *anion* stretching	6.21–6.45 and 7.15–7.69	(1610–1550) (1400–1300)	(s) (s)
	$C = O$ stretching	*Amides*			
		(a) Primary, solid and concentrated solution	~6.06	(~1650)	(s)
		(b) Secondary, solid and concentrated solution	5.95–6.14	(1680–1630)	(s)
		(c) Tertiary, solid and all solution	5.99–6.14	(1670–1630)	(s)
	$C = C$ stretching	*Alkenes*			
		(a) Nonconjugated	5.95–6.17	(1680–1620)	(v)
		(b) Monosubstituted (Vinyl)	~6.08	(~1645)	(m)
		(c) Disubstituted, *cis*	~6.03	(~1658)	(m)
		(d) Disubstituted, *trans*	~5.97	(~1675)	(m)
		(e) Disubstituted, gem	~6.05	(~1653)	(m)
		(f) Trisubstituted	~5.99	(~1669)	(m)
		(g) Tetrasubstituted	~5.99	(~1669)	(w)
6.0–6.5 (1667–1538)	$N—H$ bending	*Amines*			
		(a) Primary	6.06–6.29	(1650–1590)	(s–m)
		(b) Secondary	6.06–6.45	(1650–1550)	(w)
		(c) Amine salts	6.25–6.35 and ~6.67	(1600–1575) (~1500)	(s) (s)
	$N—H$ bending	*Amides*			
		(a) Primary, dilute solutions	6.17–6.29	(1620–1590)	(s)
	$C\!\dot{\frown}\!C$ stretching	*Aromatics*			
		(4 characteristic bands due to skeletal carbon stretching vibrations)	~6.25 ~6.33 ~6.67 ~6.90	(~1600) (~1580) (~1500) (~1450)	(v) (v) (m) (m)
	$—N=N—$ stretching	*Azo Compounds*	6.14–6.35	(1630–1575)	(v)
	$C—NO_2$ stretching	*Nitro Compounds*			
		(a) Aliphatic	6.37–6.45 and 7.25–7.30	(1570–1550) (1380–1370)	(s) (s)
		(b) Aromatic	6.37–6.67 and 7.30–7.70	(1570–1500) (1370–1300)	(s) (s)

(Continued)

TABLE 11-6 *(Continued)*

Spectral Region μ (cm^{-1})	Vibrational Classification	Group and Environment	Absorption Band Range $\lambda(\mu)$	(cm^{-1})	Absorption Band Intensity
	$O-NO_2$ stretching	*Nitrates*	6.06–6.25 and 7.70–8.00	(1650–1600) (1300–1250)	(s) (s)
	$C-NO$ stretching	*Nitroso Compounds*	6.25–6.67	(1600–1500)	(s)
	$O-NO$ stretching	*Nitrites*	5.95–6.06 and 6.15–6.21	(1680–1650) (1625–1610)	(s) (s)
6.5–7.5 (1538–1333)	$N-H$ bending	*Amides* (*a*) Secondary amides (dilute solution)	6.45–6.62	(1550–1510)	(s)
	$C-H$	*Alkanes* (*a*) —CH$_2$— (scissoring) (*b*) C—CH$_3$ (*c*) Gem dimethyl (isopropyl) (*d*) Tertiary-butyl (*e*) C—H	6.74–6.92 6.80–7.00 and 7.25–7.30 7.22–7.25 and 7.30–7.33 7.17–7.22 and ~7.33 7.46	(1485–1445) (1470–1430) (1380–1510) (1385–1380) (1370–1365) (1395–1385) (~1365) (~1340)	(m) (m) (s) (s) (s) (m) (s) (w)
7.5–9.5 (1333–1053)	$O-H$ bending and $C-O$ stretching	*Alcohols and Phenols* Two bands—shorter wavelength due to O—H bending and longer wavelength band caused by characteristic C—OH stretching vibration (a) Primary alcohols (b) Secondary alcohols (c) Tertiary alcohols (d) Phenols	7.4–7.9 and 9.30–9.90 7.4–7.9 and 8.93–9.05 7.1–7.6 and 8.55–9.09 7.1–7.6 and 8.13–8.77	(1350–1260) (1075–1010) (1350–1260) (1120–1105) (1410–1310) (1170–1100) (1410–1310) (1230–1140)	(s) (s) (s) (s) (s) (s) (s) (s)
	$C-O-C$ stretching	*Ethers* (*a*) Unsaturated, Aryl (*b*) Aliphatic	7.87–8.13 8.70–9.43	(1270–1230) (1150–1060)	(s) (s)

(Continued)

TABLE 11-6 *(Continued)*

Spectral Region	Vibrational Classification	Group and Environment	Absorption Band Range		Absorption Band Intensity
μ (cm^{-1})			$\lambda(\mu)$	(cm^{-1})	
	C—O stretching and OH$^-$ bending	*Carboxylic Acids* (a) C—OH stretching (usually characteristic doublet near 8.00 μ, 1250 cm^{-1} (b) OH bending	7.58–8.28 6.95–7.17	(1320–1210) (1440–1395)	(s) (w)
11.0–15.0 (909–666)	*Aromatic* out of plane bending	*Aromatics* *Substitution Type* (a) 5 adjacent hydrogens (monosubstituted)	~13.3 (not always present) and ~14.3 (always present)	(~750) (~700)	(v, s) (v, s)
		(b) 4 adjacent hydrogens (disubstituted)	~13.3	(~750)	(v, s)
		(c) 3 adjacent hydrogens (trisubstituted)	~12.8	(~780)	(v, m)
	C—H bending	*Alkenes* (a) Disubstituted, *cis*	~14.5	(~690)	(s)
	C—Cl stretching	*Chloro Compounds*	12.5–16.6	(800–600)	(s)
	—(CH$_2$)$_n$— bending	Any compound where $n \geqslant 4$	~13.8	(~722)	(s)

Component and structural information obtained solely from the analysis of an absorption spectrum seldom provides enough data to make an absolute identification of an unknown compound. However, identification from spectra is becoming more feasible with the recent advances in computer applications to chemical problems. In general, to make an identification, infrared absorption data are combined with information provided by other methods, for example, data gathered by elemental analysis (to determine empirical formula), nuclear magnetic resonance, ultraviolet absorption and mass spectrometry. In some cases, the data may be consistent with more than one possible structure for the unknown material. If there are only a small number of possibilities, spectra of the appropriate

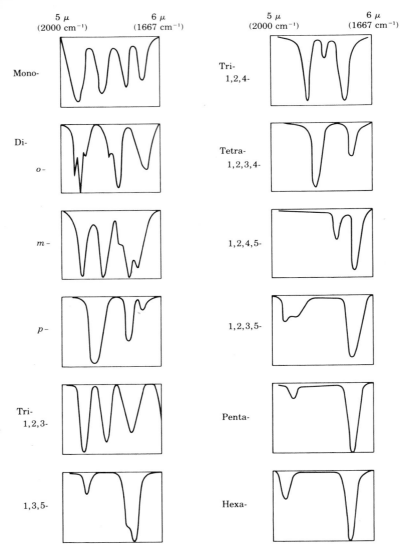

FIGURE 11-8. Spectral patterns for substituted benzenes in the 5 to 6 μ (2000 − 1667 cm^{-1}) region. (From Dyer, *Applications of Absorption Spectroscopy of Organic Compounds*, Prentice-Hall, 1965, p. 52.)

pure compounds may be obtained and compared to the unknown. If possible, this type of comparison should be made even if the data lead to only one possible structure.

Let us examine the infrared spectra of some representative compounds and correlate absorption bands with molecular structure. We will begin with a simple hydrocarbon, *n*-hexane, and then modify the molecule in several ways. Most of the data quoted are also listed in Table 11-6.

The infrared spectrum of *n-hexane* (Figure 11-9) exhibits vibrational absorption bands which are characteristic of aliphatic hydrocarbons, i.e., asymmetric and

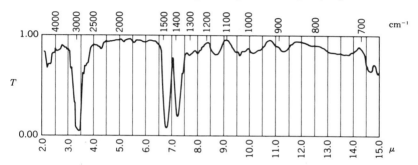

FIGURE 11-9.   Infrared spectrum of *n*-hexane. (Courtesy of Sadtler Research Laboratories.)

symmetric C—H stretching (averaged at ~ 3.45 μ, 2899 cm^{-1}), —CH$_2$— scissoring (~ 6.80 μ, 1471 cm^{-1}) and C—CH$_3$ bending (~ 7.24 μ, 1381 cm^{-1}). The weak band near 13.8 μ (725 cm^{-1}) is caused by bending vibrations of the —(CH$_2$)$_4$— unit.

The *2-methylpentane* molecule represents a branched chain isomer of *n*-hexane. Let us consider how branching affects the absorption spectra (Figure 11-10). The

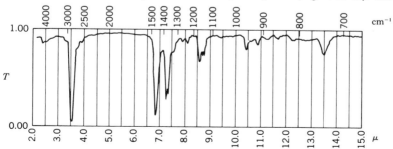

FIGURE 11-10.   Infrared spectrum of 2-methylpentane. (Courtesy of Sadtler Research Laboratories.)

C—H stretching and —CH_2— scissoring vibrations are not changed significantly compared to the straight chain analogue. However, the C—CH_3 bending vibrations indicate a strong "doublet" at 7.26 μ (1377 cm^{-1}) and ~7.3 μ (1361 cm^{-1}). This doublet and a band at ~8.58 μ (1166 cm^{-1}) are characteristic of the isopropyl group.

If the saturated hydrocarbon is rearranged into the form of an unstrained ring, the C—H stretching vibration is essentially unchanged and the —CH_2— scissoring vibration is displaced slightly to longer wavelength. For example, the spectrum of *cyclohexane* (Figure 11-11) exhibits C—H stretching vibrations at ~3.49 μ (2865 cm^{-1}) and —CH_2— scissoring at ~6.89 μ (1451 cm^{-1}) compared to the respective 3.45 μ (2899 cm^{-1}) and 6.80 μ (1471 cm^{-1}) values for *n*-hexane. When the ring compound is sterically strained, the C—H stretching vibrations move to shorter wavelength (higher frequency). For example, for bromocyclopropane the symmetric and asymmetric C—H stretching vibrations appear at ~3.25 μ (3077 cm^{-1}) and ~3.35 μ (2985 cm^{-1}), respectively.

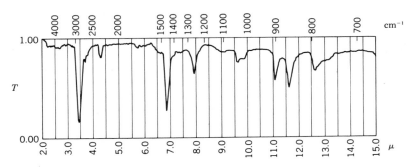

FIGURE 11-11. Infrared spectrum of cyclohexane. (Courtesy of Sadtler Research Laboratories.)

When two hydrogens are removed from *n*-hexane to give *hexene-1*, the spectral effect is shown in Figure 11-12. Two classes of C—H stretching vibrations are apparent in this spectrum. The absorption band at ~3.26 μ (3067 cm^{-1}) is characteristic of alkene carbons and, in particular, the vinyl group. Alkene C—H bonds which are not terminal normally absorb in the 3.30 to 3.32 μ (3030 to 3012 cm^{-1}) region. The C = C alkene stretching vibration is noted at ~6.11 μ (1637 cm^{-1}). Out of plane bending vibrations for alkene C—H groups occur at ~10.08 μ (992 cm^{-1}) and 11.08 μ (903 cm^{-1}). The typical aliphatic C—H stretching and bending vibrations are noted for the remaining groups of the molecule.

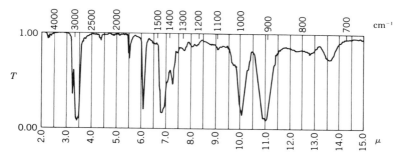

FIGURE 11-12. Infrared spectrum of hexene-1. (Courtesy of Sadtler Research Laboratories.)

The spectrum for *benzene* is shown in Figure 11-13. Aromatic C—H stretching vibrations appear at ~3.30 μ (3030 cm^{-1}). Ring skeletal vibrations (—C=C— vibrations) are indicated in the 6.2 to 6.8 μ (1613 to 1471 cm^{-1}) region with a strong maximum at ~6.75 μ (1481 cm^{-1}). C—H out of plane bending occurs in the broad absorption region above 13 μ (769 cm^{-1}).

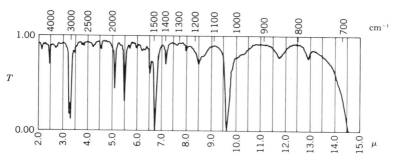

FIGURE 11-13. Infrared spectrum of benzene. (Courtesy of Sadtler Research Laboratores.)

When an aliphatic hydrocarbon hydrogen atom is replaced by a —OH group, the spectrum changes to include absorptions due to the new O—H and C—O vibrations in addition to the carbon-hydrogen vibrations already mentioned. The spectrum of *n-hexanol* (Figure 11-14) shows an intense O—H stretching band at ~2.98 μ (3356 cm^{-1}). The broadness of this band is due to hydrogen bonding among the alcohol molecules. The broad band distributed around the 9.42 μ (1062 cm^{-1}) peak is characteristic of the C—O stretching vibration of primary alcohols. The C—H stretching and bending vibrations are essentially identical to those of the unsubstituted alkane.

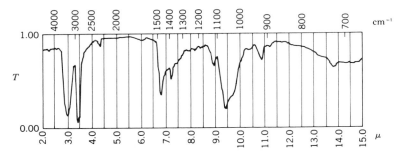

FIGURE 11-14. Infrared spectrum of *n*-hexanol. (Courtesy of Sadtler Research Laboratories.)

The effect of hydroxy substitution in benzene is illustrated in the spectrum of *phenol* (Figure 11-15). The O — H stretching vibration appears over a very broad band with a maximum at $\sim 3.00\,\mu$ (3333 cm^{-1}) and a "shoulder" at $\sim 3.30\,\mu$ (3030 cm^{-1}) (caused by aromatic C — H stretch). The bands at 6.27 μ (1595 cm^{-1}), 6.68 μ (1497 cm^{-1}) and 6.81 μ (1468 cm^{-1}) represent the common benzene skeletal vibrations. The band at $\sim 7.36\,\mu$ (1359 cm^{-1}) is due to O — H bending, and the intense broad band with a maximum at $\sim 8.21\,\mu$ (1218 cm^{-1}) is characteristic of the C — OH stretching vibration of phenol and its derivatives. The aromatic C — H out of plane bending vibrations at $\sim 13.33\,\mu$ (750 cm^{-1}) and 14.60 μ (685 cm^{-1}) indicate that the benzene ring is monosubstituted.

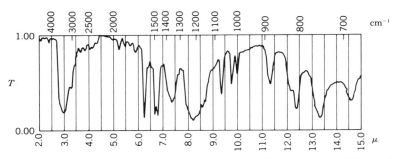

FIGURE 11-15. Infrared spectrum of phenol. (Courtesy of Sadtler Research Laboratories.)

If a terminal hydrogen on *n*-hexane is replaced by an amine group, C — N and N — H stretching and N — H bending vibrations appear. The spectrum of the resulting compound, *n-hexylamine* is given in Figure 11-16. An N — H stretching

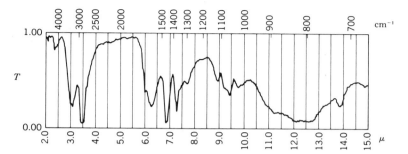

FIGURE 11-16. Infrared spectrum of *n*-hexylamine. (Courtesy of Sadtler Research Laboratories.)

vibration doublet appears at ∼3.00 and 3.08 μ (3333 and 3247 cm^{-1}). The location of this doublet is somewhat variable because hydrogen bonding tends to shift it to longer wavelength (lower wavenumber). N — H bending vibrations are indicated in both the broad band with the maximum at ∼6.28 μ (1592 cm^{-1}) and the very broad band from 11 to 14 μ (909 to 714 cm^{-1}). The familiar aliphatic group vibrations also are present.

The replacement of a methylene group of *n*-hexane with an oxygen atom yields an ether, for example, *n-butyl-methyl ether*. The absorption spectrum for this compound (Figure 11-17) exhibits a strong C — O — C absorption band around 8.88 μ (1126 cm^{-1}) in addition to the other C — H vibrational bands.

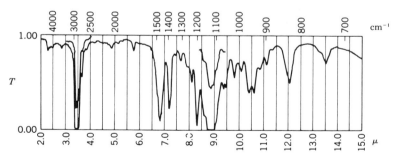

FIGURE 11-17. Infrared spectrum of *n*-butyl-methyl ether. (Courtesy of Sadtler Research Laboratories.)

The *carbonyl stretching absorption* band is an excellent barometer for molecular structure determination. The band intensity is very large and its wavelength maximum can be very precisely determined. The exact location of the carbonyl absorption band varies with (1) the physical state of the molecule, (2) electrostatic interactions with neighboring constituents, (3) conjugation, (4) hydrogen bonding and (5) ring strain. The position of the band is essentially the same for aliphatic aldehydes, 5.75 to 5.82 μ, (1740 to 1720 cm^{-1}) and ketones, 5.80 to 5.87 μ, (1725 to 1705 cm^{-1}); however, it appears at considerably different locations for conjugated unsaturated systems, carboxylic acids, esters, anhydrides and acyl halides. The locations of these various C = O stretching vibrations should be studied carefully.

Hexanal represents the aldehyde oxidation product of 1-hexanol. Its spectrum (Figure 11-18) shows a strong carbonyl stretching vibration at $\sim$5.79 μ (1727 cm^{-1}). In addition to the familiar methyl and methylene C — H stretching vibrations at $\sim$3.42 and 3.52 μ (2924 and 2841 cm^{-1}), a sharp aldehyde C — H stretching vibration appears at $\sim$3.69 μ (2710 cm^{-1}). This vibration is characteristic of the aldehyde functional groups and may be used to decide if the compound studied is an aldehyde or ketone; the C = O absorption band is not diagnostic for this purpose. The absorption peaks at $\sim$6.83 and 7.08 μ (1464 and 1412 cm^{-1}) represent methylene bending vibrations and the one at $\sim$7.18 μ (1393 cm^{-1}) indicates the typical C — CH$_3$ bending vibration.

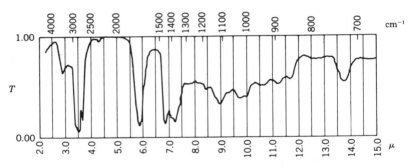

FIGURE 11-18.   Infrared spectrum of hexanal. (Courtesy of Sadtler Research Laboratories.)

The characteristic carbonyl stretching vibration is shifted to *longer* wavelength in conjugated systems. This is indicated in the spectrum of *acetophenone* (Figure 11-19) in which the C = O absorption band appears at $\sim$5.91 μ (1692 cm^{-1}).

The position of the C = O stretching vibration of esters also depends on conjugation and ring size. For example, compare *n-butyl acetate* (Figure 11-20) and *ethyl benzoate* (Figure 11-21). The C = O stretching vibration occurs at $\sim$5.75 μ (1739 cm^{-1}) in the aliphatic ester, whereas in the aromatic ester it appears at $\sim$5.80 μ (1724 cm^{-1}). In the *n*-butyl acetate spectrum, we also note a broad C — O stretching band centered at $\sim$8.05 μ (1242 cm^{-1}), characteristic for the

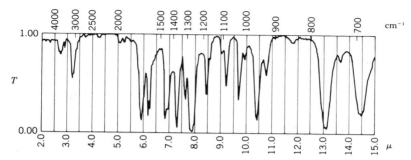

FIGURE 11-19.   Infrared spectrum of acetophonone. (Courtesy of Sadtler Research Laboratories.)

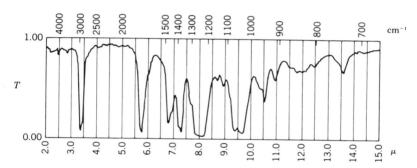

FIGURE 11-20.   Infrared spectrum of *n*-butyl acetate. (Courtesy of Sadtler Research Laboratories.)

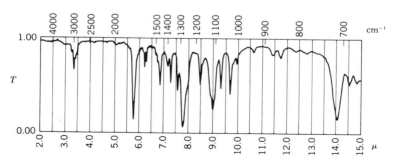

FIGURE 11-21.   Infrared spectrum of ethyl benzoate. (Courtesy of Sadtler Research Laboratories.)

acetate group. Formates, propionates and *n*-butyrates exhibit similar broad bands centered around 8.41 μ (1189 cm^{-1}). Esters of α, β-unsaturated and aromatic acids have two strong bands around 7.63 to 8.00 μ (1310 to 1250 cm^{-1}) and 8.33 to 9.09 μ (1200 to 1100 cm^{-1}). These are evident as the 7.83 μ (1277 cm^{-1}) and 9.02 μ (1109 cm^{-1}) peaks in the ethyl benzoate spectrum.

Carboxylic acids commonly exist as dimers in the solid and liquid states. The two monomer units are held together by fairly strong hydrogen bonding between the two carboxyl groups. As a consequence, there are essentially no free O — H stretching vibrations in these molecules even in dilute solution, and the carboxylic acid O — H stretching absorption often consists of a continuous series of bands distributed over a very broad region (usually between 3.0 and 4.0 μ, 3330 and 2500 cm^{-1}). These absorption bands are illustrated in the spectrum of *n-hexanoic acid* (Figure 11-22). Even though the O — H stretching band is quite broad, the

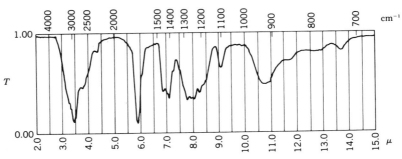

FIGURE 11-22. Infrared spectrum of *n*-hexanoic acid. (Courtesy of Sadtler Research Laboratories.)

characteristic aliphatic C — H stretching vibration is evident at 3.43 μ (2915 cm^{-1}). The carbonyl stretching band appears at $\sim$5.89 μ (1698 cm^{-1}); it is more intense than the corresponding ester band. The doublet with maxima at $\sim$6.85 and 7.10 μ (1460 and 1408 cm^{-1}) is caused by —CH$_2$— scissoring and O—H bending. The broad absorption band between 7.5 and 8.4 μ (1330 and 1190 cm^{-1}) represents C — OH stretching vibrations (usually a doublet near 8.00 μ, 1250 cm^{-1}).

The spectrum of *benzoic acid* (Figure 11-23) also exhibits the very broad acid O — H stretching region between 3.1 and 4 μ (3230 and 2500 cm^{-1}) and a superimposed aromatic C — H stretching vibration at $\sim$3.32 μ (3012 cm^{-1}). The intense band at $\sim$5.96 μ (1678 cm^{-1}) is characteristic of the conjugated carbonyl group, and the group of benzene skeletal vibration bands at $\sim$6.23 μ (1605 cm^{-1}), 6.30 μ (1587 cm^{-1}) and 6.87 μ (1456 cm^{-1}) indicate aromaticity. The strong

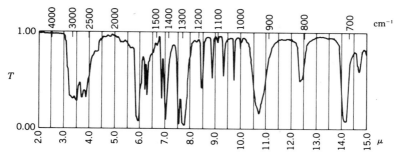

FIGURE 11-23. Infrared spectrum of benzoic acid. (Courtesy of Sadtler Research Laboratories.)

band at $\sim 7.02\ \mu$ (1425 cm^{-1}) is caused by O — H bending vibrations, and C — O stretching vibrations are evidenced in the maxima at ~ 7.55 and 7.78 μ (1325 and 1285 cm^{-1}). The strong band around 14.17 μ (706 cm^{-1}) is characteristic of a monosubstituted aromatic compound.

Let us next try to analyze the spectra of pure unknown compounds and predict their structure. This procedure is much like a puzzle in which we fit together various bits of information or clues and attempt to identify the whole molecule.

example/problem 11-1: Chemical analysis of an unknown, compound X, gives the molecular formula $C_5H_8O_2$. The infrared spectrum of a neat sample of X is shown in Figure 11-24. Identify compound X.

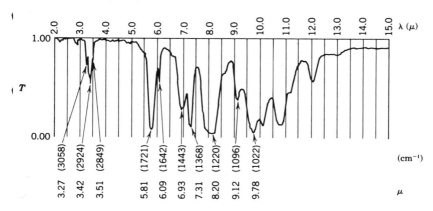

FIGURE 11-24. Infrared spectrum of compound X. (Courtesy of Sadtler Research Laboratories.)

spectrum analysis. The weak peak at ~3.27 μ (3058 cm^{-1}) could represent an alkene C—H stretching vibration; the weak absorption at ~6.0 μ (1642 cm^{-1}) suggests a —C═C— bond and adds support to the possible presence of a C═C—H linkage in the molecule. The band at ~6.93 μ (1443 cm^{-1}) might represent a C—H bending vibration and the strong band at ~7.31 μ (1368 cm^{-1}) is in the region for the C—CH$_3$ bending vibrations. The broad band in the region 7.9 to 8.3 μ (1266 to 1205 cm^{-1}) with a maximum at ~8.20 μ (1220 cm^{-1}) is characteristic of the C—O stretching vibration of unconjugated carboxylic acids and acetate esters. However, the acids are ruled out because no broad carboxyl—OH stretching band is present between 3 and 4 μ (3333 and 2500 cm^{-1}). Thus, so far, we have established that two functional groups are present in

the unknown molecule, $CH_3C\overset{\displaystyle O}{\underset{\displaystyle O-}{\diagdown\diagup}}$ and C═C. From the molecular formula, one more

carbon is required. The following structures seem feasible:

(I) $CH_3C\overset{\displaystyle O}{\diagup}$
$\diagdown$ OCH═CHCH$_3$

and

(II) $CH_3C\overset{\displaystyle O}{\diagup}$
$\diagdown$ OCH$_2$CH═CH$_2$

The high intensity of the C—CH$_3$ bending vibration at 7.31 μ (1368 cm^{-1}) would tend to favor structure (I). However, a comparison with pure compounds indicates that compound X is structure (II), allylacetate.

example/problem 11-2: Compound Y has the molecular formula C_7H_6O. Use the infrared spectrum of this compound (Figure 11-25) to make an identification.

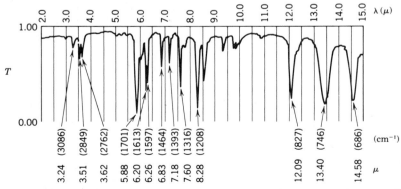

FIGURE 11-25. Infrared spectrum of compound Y. (Courtesy of Sadtler Research Laboratories.)

spectrum analysis. We should immediately note that the formula of the compound suggests an aromatic structure. The strong peak located at ~ 3.24 μ (3086 cm^{-1}) indicates an unsaturated C — H stretching vibration. The sharp 3.62 μ (2762 cm^{-1}) peak is in the region which is characteristic for the aldehyde C — H stretching vibration. A broad carbonyl absorption band is confirmed between 5.90 and 6.02 μ (1695 and 1661 cm^{-1}). The quartet of bands at 6.20, 6.26, 6.67 and 6.83 μ (1613, 1597, 1499 and 1464 cm^{-1}) suggests an aromatic ring. An aromatic benzene ring and a substituted aldehyde group sum up to the molecular formula of compound Y. The compound is confirmed as benzaldehyde by comparison with a known sample.

QUESTIONS AND PROBLEMS

11-1.   The absorption band maximum of 2-pentanone occurs at shorter wavelength in 95% ethanol solvent than in *n*-hexane solvent. Why?

11-2.   Use molecular orbital theory to explain the following experimental data. Ethylene exhibits an absorption maximum at 193 mμ with a molar absorptivity of 10,000 whereas 1,3,5-hexatriene has an absorption maximum at 258 mμ with a molar absorptivity of 35,000.

11-3.   What infrared band or bands (give *all* the useful absorptions, if more than one) would you expect if you thought an unknown compound might be one of the following: (*a*) an ester, (*b*) an acetylenic alcohol, (*c*) an aromatic ether, (*d*) a primary amide, and (*e*) an olefinic ketone (non-conjugated). Give the *type of vibration* (e.g., "C — C stretch") and the *approximate region* (to the nearest 0.3 μ or 100 cm^{-1}).

11-4.   Compound A, C_5H_8O, has the following infrared bands (among others): 3.31, 3.45, 5.90, and 6.20 μ (3020, 2900, 1690, and 1620 cm^{-1}); in the ultraviolet it absorbs at 227 mμ ($\epsilon = 10^4$). Propose a structure and say whether it is the only possible one. The compound is *not* an aldehyde.

11-5.   The IR spectrum of an unknown compound has strong absorption bands at 3.42 μ (2924 cm^{-1}), 3.52 μ (2841 cm^{-1}), 3.69 μ (2710 cm^{-1}), 5.81 μ (1721 cm^{-1}), 6.83 μ (1464 cm^{-1}), and 7.18 μ (1393 cm^{-1}). Elemental analysis of the unknown indicates that it has the following composition *by weight*: 66.6% C; 22.2% O: and 11.2% H. Determine the molecular formula for this compound. Show all reasoning and calculations.

Molecular formulas and infrared absorption spectra are provided for a series of unknown compounds in the following problems. All of the peaks which are "tagged" in each spectrum are not required necessarily for spectral identification. Predict a possible structure (or structures) for each unknown. State whether the structure is the only possible one, and if not, in what regard it is uncertain. Indicate the logic you apply in reaching your decision.

11-6.　Compound 11-6. Molecular formula $C_5H_{12}O$.

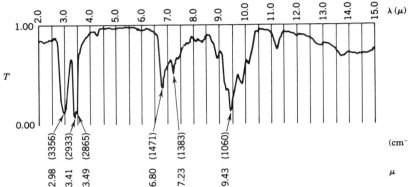

FIGURE 11-26.　Infrared spectrum of compound 11-6. (Courtesy of Sadtler Research Laboratories.)

11-7.　Compound 11-7. Molecular formula C_8H_{10}.

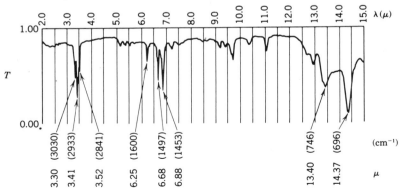

FIGURE 11-27.　Infrared spectrum of compound 11-7. (Courtesy of Sadtler Research Laboratories.)

11-8. Compound 11-8. Molecular formula $C_5H_{10}O_2$.

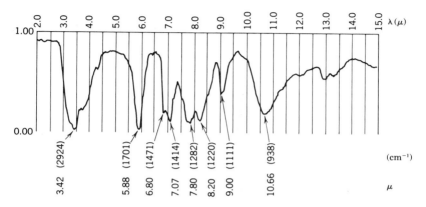

FIGURE 11-28. Infrared spectrum of compound 11-8. (Courtesy of Sadtler Research Laboratories.)

11-9. Compound 11-9. Molecular formula $C_6H_{12}O_2$.

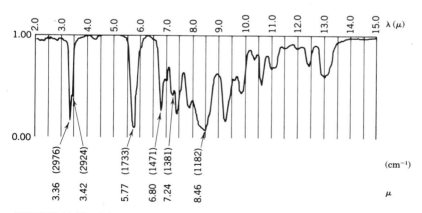

FIGURE 11-29. Infrared spectrum of compound 11-9. (Courtesy of Sadtler Research Laboratories.)

11-10. Compound 11-10. Molecular formula $C_7H_7O_2N$.

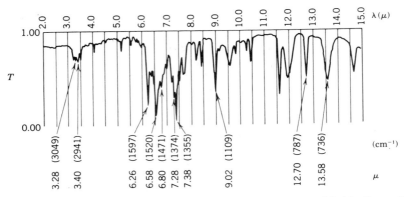

FIGURE 11-30. Infrared spectrum of compound 11-10. (Courtesy of Sadtler Research Laboratories.)

11-11. Compound 11-11. Molecular formula $C_6H_{12}O$.

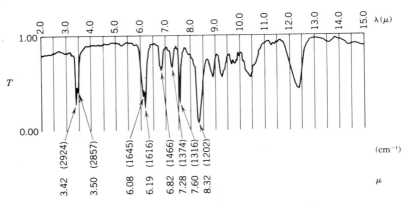

FIGURE 11-31. Infrared spectrum of compound 11-11. (Courtesy of Sadtler Research Laboratories.)

11-12. Compound 11-12. Molecular formula $C_6H_{12}O$.

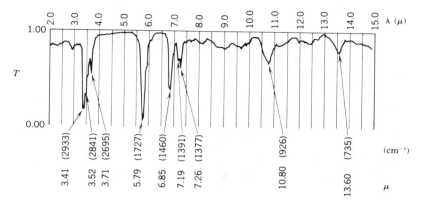

FIGURE 11-32. Infrared spectrum of compound 11-12. (Courtesy of Sadtler Research Laboratories.)

11-13. Compound 11-13. Molecular formula $C_9H_{10}O$.

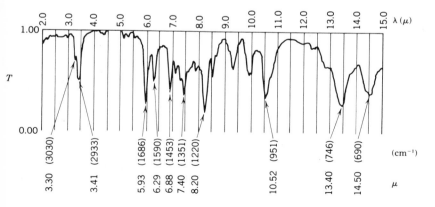

FIGURE 11-33. Infrared spectrum of compound 11-13. (Courtesy of Sadtler Research Laboratories.)

REFERENCES

R. P. Bauman, *Absorption Spectroscopy*, Wiley, New York, 1962. Good general discussion of applications.

J. R. Dyer, *Applications of Absorption Spectroscopy of Organic Compounds*, Prentice-Hall, Englewood Cliffs, N. J., 1965. Very lucid short paperback which includes discussions of ultraviolet and infrared spectrophotometry.

H. H. Jaffe and Milton Orchin, *Theory and Applications of Ultraviolet Spectroscopy*, Wiley, New York, 1962. Excellent advanced treatment.

R. A. Morton *Comprehensive Biochemistry*, M. Florkin and E. H. Stotz, Editors, Vol. 3, Elsevier, Amsterdam and New York, 1962; Chapter 4. Good discussion of ultraviolet and visible spectrophotometry of compounds of biochemical interest.

The Sadtler Standard Spectra, Sadtler Research Laboratories, Philadelphia, Pa., 1965. Comprehensive collection of known compounds. Index available.

R. M. Silverstein and G. C. Bassler, *Spectrometric Identification of Organic Compounds*, 2nd ed., Wiley, New York, 1967; Chapters 3 and 5. Thorough presentation of applications of ultraviolet and infrared absorption spectrophotometry in organic chemistry.

12 NUCLEAR MAGNETIC RESONANCE SPECTROSCOPY

In 1946 two physicists, Purcell at Harvard University and Bloch at Stanford University, independently announced a far-reaching discovery about the behavior of the atomic nucleus. Most nuclei (including the proton) and the electron possess inherent magnetic fields, albeit the effects of the nuclear fields are too small to be observed in the ambient magnetic field of the earth. However, in an intense magnetic field, the nuclei can assume specific orientations with corresponding potential energy levels. Bloch and Purcell invented techniques to detect the minute amount of energy absorbed or emitted as the nuclei jump from one energy level to another. Thus was born nuclear magnetic resonance, or n.m.r., a new spectroscopic tool. There are few methods which have developed so fast from a highly theoretical study to practical applications as varied as the determination of the detailed structure of complex biochemical compounds to the prospecting for minerals.

MAGNETIC PROPERTIES OF THE NUCLEUS

The magnetic properties of certain nuclei are conveniently explained if we assume that the nuclear charge is spinning around an axis. Such a nucleus possesses angular momentum represented by a spin quantum number, I, which is assigned half-integral values $0, \frac{1}{2}, 1, \frac{3}{2}, \ldots, \frac{9}{2}$ depending on the particular nucleus. Some representative nuclei and their spin quantum numbers are listed in Table 12-1.

Nuclei which have either an *odd* number of protons *or* an *odd* number of neutrons, but not both odd, exhibit half-integral spin quantum numbers; for example, H^1, B^{11}, F^{19}, and P^{31}. Figure 12-1 portrays one of these nuclei as a spinning sphere. The circulating charge generates a magnetic field, much like an electric current in a coil of wire. There is an associated nuclear magnetic moment, μ, along the axis of spin.

For nuclei in which the numbers of neutrons and protons are *both odd*, the charge is distributed non-symmetrically. For example, H^2 and N^{14} have an integral spin number, $I = 1$.

Nuclei in which the number of protons and the number of neutrons are *both even* have no angular momentum ($I = 0$) and exhibit no magnetic properties.

TABLE 12-1   NUCLEAR SPIN QUANTUM NUMBERS

Number of Protons	Number of Neutrons	Spin Number, I	Examples
even	even	0	C^{12}, O^{16}, Si^{28}, S^{32}
odd	even	$\frac{1}{2}$	H^1, N^{15}, F^{19}, P^{31}
even	odd	$\frac{1}{2}$	C^{13}
odd	odd	1	H^2, N^{14}
odd	even	$\frac{3}{2}$	B^{11}, Br^{79}
even	odd	$\frac{5}{2}$	I^{127}

Thus C^{12}, O^{16}, S^{32}, etc., are magnetically inert and are not detected in n.m.r. experiments.

Magnetic nuclei ($I > 0$) interact with an external magnetic field by assuming discrete orientations with corresponding energy levels. The number of quantized energy levels available depends on I, and is given by the series:

$$I, I - 1, I - 2, \ldots, -I$$

For a given nucleus, there are $2I + 1$ possible levels or orientations. For the proton in particular, with $I = \frac{1}{2}$, there are only two available orientations, described as aligned with the applied field (lower energy) or against the applied

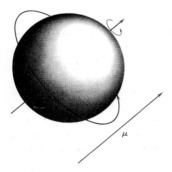

FIGURE 12-1. Spinning charge in nucleus generates a magnetic field with a magnetic moment, μ, directed along the axis of spin.

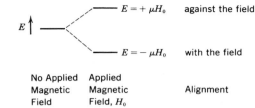

FIGURE 12-2. Proton spin states under the influence of an applied magnetic field.

field (higher energy). Figure 12-2 shows this separation into two levels, each with an energy of $+\mu H_0$ or $-\mu H_0$, where H_0 is the intensity of the applied magnetic field. The difference in energy, ΔE, is equal to $2\mu H_0$. This is a special case of the general relationship:

$$\Delta E = \mu H_0 / I \qquad (12\text{-}1)$$

NUCLEAR RESONANCE

Equation 12-1 embodies a wealth of information. ΔE is determined in part by the value of the magnetic moment, μ, a characteristic property of each kind of nucleus. Typical values of μ are included in Table 12-2. ΔE is also directly proportional to the intensity of the applied magnetic field. In n.m.r. experiments, a field of about 14,000 gauss is common. For protons in this field, we find from Equation 12-1 and data in Table 12-2 that ΔE is 5.7×10^{-3} cal/mole, a very small energy indeed. At room temperature, the thermal energy is considerably larger, and is sufficient to maintain nearly equal populations in the two levels. In fact, at 25° C the Boltzmann distribution tells us that for every million protons,

	μ erg gauss^{-1} $\times 10^{23}$	γ gauss^{-1} sec^{-1} $\times 10^{-4}$	ν, at 14092 gauss Mc
Nucleus			
H^1	1.410	2.674	60.0
B^{11}	1.357	2.573	19.25
C^{13}	0.354	0.6721	15.1
F^{19}	1.326	2.515	56.4
P^{31}	0.5708	1.082	24.3

TABLE 12-2   NMR DATA FOR COMMONLY STUDIED NUCLEI

there is an excess of only three protons in the lower level. What kind of radiant energy corresponds to this small energy difference?

$$\Delta E = h\nu = 2\mu H_0 \qquad (I = \tfrac{1}{2}) \qquad (12\text{-}2)$$

from which $\nu = 60 \times 10^6$ cycles per second (cps) or 60 megacycles (Mc). This is in the radio-frequency range with $\lambda = 5$ m.

Now suppose that we are able to supply energy of just this frequency. A radio-frequency transmitter is an appropriate energy source. A proton in the lower level may absorb this energy and jump to the upper level. This absorption process is called "magnetic resonance," or we may say that the nucleus "resonates" at the proper "resonance frequency." Equations 12-1 and 12-2 are easily combined

$$2\pi\nu = \frac{2\pi\mu H_0}{hI} = \gamma H_0 \qquad (12\text{-}3)$$

where 2π is introduced to convert linear frequency to angular units of frequency and a new parameter, γ, is introduced. Obviously, $\gamma = 2\pi\mu/hI$ and is a characteristic property of the nucleus, called *the gyromagnetic ratio*. Another definition of γ is easily derived from Equation 12-3:

$$\text{Gyromagnetic ratio} = \gamma = \frac{2\pi\nu}{H_0} \qquad (12\text{-}4)$$

Equation 12-4 is a fundamental equation for n.m.r. It defines the "resonance .condition"—a function of the *ratio* of frequency to field. With a fixed field, H_0 (for example, 14,092 gauss), we may vary the frequency until we locate the resonance condition. Each type of nucleus will resonate at a different frequency as required by its gyromagnetic ratio. Typical resonance data are given in Table 12-2 and Figure 12-3.

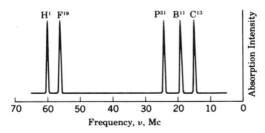

FIGURE 12-3. The n.m.r. spectrum of H^1, F^{19}, P^{31}, B^{11}, and C^{13} at $H_0 = 14,092$ gauss. (*Note*: n.m.r. spectra are customarily plotted with frequency increasing to the left.)

Some instruments are built to maintain a fixed frequency and vary the magnetic field. This is an entirely analogous procedure, and gives us the same information. In this type of experiment it is common to convert values in gauss to values in cycles per second, using Equation 12-4. For the proton, 1 gauss is equivalent to 4260 cps.

Let us summarize the information we have given thus far. A nucleus ($I > 0$) in an intense magnetic field may find itself in one of $2I + 1$ equally spaced energy levels. The energy differences between levels are small, so that although the nucleus would prefer to be in the lowest energy level, thermal motions nearly equalize the populations. The small excess number of nuclei in the lower level can be promoted to higher levels by absorption of radiant energy, in this case in the radio-frequency region. If we can detect this absorption, we obtain a spectrum, for example, Figure 12-3. We must now ask, "What processes allow the nuclei to return to the lower level?" Unless the nuclei can fall back to lower levels, absorption of energy will cease as soon as the populations come to equilibrium. This question brings us to the study of nuclear relaxation—or, "How does an excited nucleus 'relax' to a lower energy condition?"

NUCLEAR RELAXATION

A sophisticated discussion of the theory of radiation is beyond our scope, but it can be shown that the emission of radiation may occur either spontaneously or by a process stimulated by an electromagnetic field. At radio frequencies, the probability of spontaneous emission is negligible. However, the probability of the stimulated process of emission is exactly the same as the probability of absorption of energy from the field. If the populations in the lower and upper levels are equal, absorption by nuclei in the lower state, exactly balances induced emission by nuclei in the upper state. Thus, in the n.m.r. experiment, the absorption signal may dwindle to zero as soon as the populations are equalized, unless there are other mechanisms to maintain an excess population in the lower level. We know of two kinds of mechanisms, called spin-spin relaxation (or transverse relaxation) and spin-lattice relaxation (or longitudinal relaxation).

Spin-Lattice Relaxation. The excited nucleus can transfer energy to other nuclei in the surrounding molecular framework (lattice). Such energy is conserved within the system, but appears as extra translational or rotational energy distributed around the lattice. The same sort of process establishes the Boltzmann distribution in the first place and serves to maintain a constant slight excess of population in the lower level. Spin-lattice relaxation is characterized by a relaxation time, T_1, which is a measure of the half-life required for the system in the excited state to return to an equilibrium state.

Spin-Spin Relaxation. In this process, a nucleus in the upper level can transfer its energy to a neighboring nucleus by an exchange of spin. Because of this mutual interchange, there is no net effect on the population distribution; however, it does limit the average time a given nucleus spends in a given spin state. There is an associated spin-spin relaxation time, T_2, which affects the natural line width of an n.m.r. absorption peak.

Natural Width of an Absorption Line. Heisenberg's uncertainty principle tells us that the width of a spectral line is inversely proportional to the average time a system spends in the excited state. Thus narrow lines are associated with long relaxation times and broad lines with short relaxation times. Both T_1 and T_2 enter into the relaxation efficiency. Solids and viscous liquids have relatively rigid lattices, so spin-spin relaxation is efficient, T_2 is small and the lines are relatively broad. In non-viscous liquids and dilute solutions, relaxation times are long and the lines are relatively sharp. Apparently, an examination of line widths in the spectrum can tell us much about the nature of the lattice, but we will not consider this aspect of n.m.r. here. Additional relaxation mechanisms operate in the case of nuclei with $I > \frac{1}{2}$. Therefore, their lines tend to be broader than those associated with nuclei where $I = \frac{1}{2}$. We must also point out that magnetic field inhomogeneity contributes more to line width than T_1 or T_2 in most high resolution work.

NMR INSTRUMENTATION AND TECHNIQUE

An n.m.r. spectrometer contains a massive and intricate collection of electronics of which we can consider only the basic elements. We must remember that we are dealing with intense magnetic fields requiring enormous, precisely controlled power supplies, and precisely controlled frequencies. Unfortunately, most of the kilowatts required by the instrument are dissipated as heat and the few microwatts of signal we obtain from the sample must be amplified by another intricate electronic system. The cost ($20,000 to $100,000) and complexity of operation of the instrument represent a barrier to its widespread use, but even so it is rapidly becoming nearly as available as an infrared spectrometer.

The basic elements of a typical n.m.r. spectrometer, shown in Figure 12-4, include:

1. A magnet with a strong, stable, homogeneous field. The field must be constant over the area of the sample and over the period of time of the experiment to better than 1 part in 10^8.

2. A sweep generator which supplies a variable d-c current to a secondary magnet so that the total applied magnetic field can be varied (swept) over a limited range.

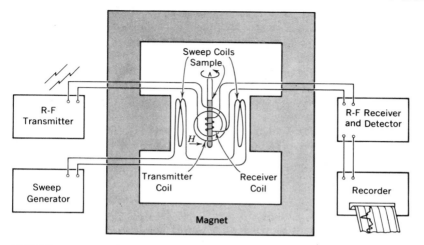

FIGURE 12-4. Schematic diagram of an n.m.r. spectrometer. (Courtesy of Varian Associates.)

3. A radio-frequency oscillator (transmitter) connected to a coil which transmits energy to the sample in a direction perpendicular to the magnetic field.

4. A radio-frequency receiver connected to a coil encircling the sample. The two coils are perpendicular to each other and to the magnetic field.

5. A readout system consisting of an amplifier, recorder, and possibly additional components for increased sensitivity, accuracy, or convenience.

6. A sample container, usually a glass tube spun by an air-driven turbine to average the magnetic field over the sample dimensions.

We hasten to point out that this simple description does not adequately or accurately represent an actual commercial spectrometer. The requirements for high resolution are so severe that it is not practical to construct an instrument for wide range use, thus each instrument is normally used to examine only one kind of nucleus, the proton for example. Some high resolution instruments are provided with interchangeable oscillators, so that several nuclei can be studied, but not simultaneously. For the study of solids, where the lines are inherently broad, high resolution is of little value, therefore some instruments are built for low resolution but greater flexibility.

Sample Handling.   A dilute solution (~ 2 to 10%) is normally used. If we are to study protons in the sample, the ideal solvent should contain no additional protons. Carbon tetrachloride meets this requirement, but deuterated chloroform,

234   CDCl$_3$, or deuterated benzene are often preferred. Deuterated solvents may give a small additional peak for a residual proton impurity. Deuterium oxide (deuterated water) is available for samples soluble only in aqueous solutions.

A 5-mm OD glass tube serves as a sample container. It is held by a propeller arrangement so that it can be spun by a jet of compressed air.

Integration of Peak Areas.   The n.m.r. signal is directly proportional to the number of nuclei which are responsible for the resonance. In effect, the spectrometer "counts protons" (or the relevant nucleus causing the absorption peak). As an aid in measuring peak areas, most recorders are equipped with automatic integrators which give peak areas directly. The integrator trace is often superimposed on the spectrum, and the height of a step on the integration trace measures the area in arbitrary units.

Nuclear magnetic resonance signals may be very weak and lost in the "noise" (random signals introduced by the instrument or its surroundings). By summing repetitive scans, the random fluctuations are averaged to zero, revealing the desired signal. A device known as a "computer of average transients, or CAT," performs this function, and is available as an accessory for this and other applications.

By far the most work has been done with spectrometers built specifically to examine the n.m.r. behavior of protons. In the remainder of this chapter we will consider primarily proton magnetic resonance.

THE CHEMICAL SHIFT

The behavior of an isolated nucleus is really of no concern to a chemist. An actual sample contains an enormous number of charged species (nuclei and electrons). In a magnetic field each is subject to its influence. Electrons in covalent bonds normally have paired spins and have no net magnetic field. But an applied magnetic field induces additional modes of circulation for these paired electrons which generate a small local magnetic field proportional to but opposing the applied field. This phenomenon is called "diamagnetic shielding" because it shields the nucleus to some degree from the effects of the applied field, as shown in Figure 12-5. The nucleus thus finds itself in an effective field which is somewhat smaller than the applied field H_0.

$$H_{eff} = H_0 - \sigma H_0 \tag{12-5}$$

where σ is the shielding parameter. The value of σ depends on the electron density around the proton, and this in turn is a function of the structure of the compound.

Methanol, for example, has two kinds of protons, CH$_3$ and OH. The oxygen atom is more electronegative than the carbon atom, and therefore the electron density around the methyl protons is higher than that around the hydroxyl proton. Stated another way, the shielding parameter is greater for methyl protons,

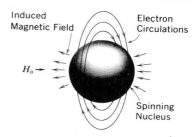

Induced
Magnetic Field

Electron
Circulations

$H_0 \rightarrow$

Spinning
Nucleus

FIGURE 12-5. Induced electronic circulations generate local magnetic field opposing H_0. (Diamagnetic shielding.)

$\sigma_{CH_3} > \sigma_{OH}$. *At a given H_0*, H_{eff} for CH_3 protons must be lower than H_{eff} for the OH proton. Thus the resonance equation (12-4) must be modified by changing H_0 to H_{eff} *at the nucleus*. To bring each kind of proton into resonance *at a fixed frequency*, we must change H_0 as shown in Figure 12-6a. As a result, the n.m.r. spectrum of methanol has two peaks as in Figure 12-6b.

We can repeat the same argument in terms of frequency. *At a fixed applied field*, H_0, the hydroxyl proton finds itself in a greater effective field than do the methyl

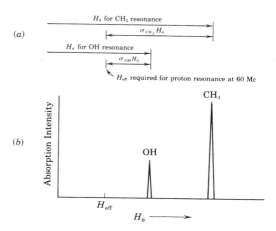

(a)

H_0 for CH_3 resonance

$\sigma_{CH_3} H_0$

H_0 for OH resonance

$\sigma_{OH} H_0$

H_{eff} required for proton resonance at 60 Mc

(b)

Absorption Intensity

CH$_3$

OH

H_{eff}

$H_0 \longrightarrow$

FIGURE 12-6. (a) Different values of H_0 are required to bring CH_3 and OH protons into resonance at 60 Mc. (b) The n.m.r. spectrum of methanol, CH_3OH.

236

protons. Therefore, by Equation 12-4 a higher frequency is required to bring the OH proton into resonance. The variation of the resonance line with chemical structure is called *the chemical shift*, defined as the change in position of a resonance peak from that of an arbitrary reference line.

The most common reference compound used is tetramethyl silane, $(CH_3)_4Si$, hereafter abbreviated TMS. This compound has a symmetrical structure; each proton is identical to all others and is found in an identical electronic environment which provides very high shielding. As a result, TMS exhibits a single sharp resonance line at a high applied field, well beyond the protons in most other organic compounds. In addition TMS is chemically inert, relatively volatile (b.p. = 27° C), and soluble in most organic solvents. TMS is not soluble in aqueous solutions; for these media sodium 2,2-dimethyl-2-silapentane-5-sulfonate (DSS)

$$(CH_3)_3SiCH_2CH_2CH_2SO_3Na$$

may be used as a reference. The protons in the methyl groups of DSS give a strong sharp line. The methylene protons of DSS give a series of small peaks which can be ignored.

Several cautions are in order before we consider how chemical shift is related to chemical structure. First, the absolute magnitude of the shift is extremely small. For example, in a field of 14,092 gauss, methyl protons resonate at 60,000,054 cycles and methylene protons resonate at 60,000,075 cycles, a difference of only 21 cycles out of 6×10^7. Even so, accurate measurement of the *difference* is commonplace. Second, the magnitude of the shift is directly proportional to H_0. Therefore, the absolute value is of little use. We avoid this dilemma by using a reference compound, and employing a relative value, δ, for the chemical shift.

$$\delta = \frac{H_0(\text{reference}) - H_0(\text{sample})}{H_0} \times 10^6 \text{ ppm} \qquad (12\text{-}6)$$

H_0 for the reference is usually higher than H_0 for the sample, so subtraction in the direction indicated gives a positive δ. In terms of frequency units, δ takes the form:

$$\delta = \frac{v(\text{sample}) - v(\text{reference})}{v(\text{reference})} \times 10^6 \text{ ppm} \qquad (12\text{-}7)$$

For the common 60-Mc, 14,092-gauss spectrometer, and with TMS as a reference, a convenient equation is

$$\delta = \frac{\Delta v}{60 \times 10^6} \times 10^6 \quad \text{or} \quad \Delta v/60 \text{ ppm} \qquad (12\text{-}8)$$

Note that δ as defined in Equation 12-6 or 12-7 is independent of the value of H_0, although the simplified Equation 12-8 is restricted to $H_0 = 14{,}092$ gauss and a specific reference, TMS. δ is dimensionless, but is given in parts per million (ppm). Typical values range from 0 to 10. Another common expression for chemical shift is called tau, τ:

$$\tau = 10 - \delta \qquad (12\text{-}9)$$

To recapitulate, let us mark the various ways of expressing the chemical shift and associated terminology on a single chart. Figure 12-7 provides an orientation to the various directional terms; e.g., deshielding or "negative" shielding results in lines found at a low field or "down field." The resonance lines for several simple compounds are included in the figure.

Next, we shall attempt to explain why lines are shifted as they are. Our approach is necessarily qualitative and empirical—it is much easier to explain the behavior after we have observed it than to predict it in advance. We shall consider two effects resulting from (a) local diamagnetic currents and (b) magnetic anisotropy.

Local Diamagnetic Effects. The extent of shielding resulting from local magnetic fields is related to the electron density in the immediate vicinity of the proton, as we have demonstrated above. Thus the order of magnitude of δ is predictable from our general knowledge of electronegativity. For example, we could predict at least the order of the chemical shifts in the following sequences:

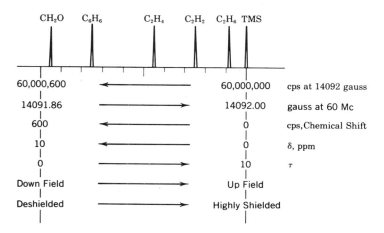

FIGURE 12-7. Chemical shift values for typical protons, with typical terms used to describe the shift.

CH_3-H	CH_3-I	CH_3-Br	CH_3-Cl	CH_3-F
δ: 0.2	2.2	2.7	3.0	4.3

CH_3-CH_3 $CH_3-N\diagup$ CH_3-O- CH_3-F

δ: 0.9   2.2   2.5   4.3

Acidic protons have a very low electron density, and experience low diamagnetic shielding. Their resonance lines are found far downfield. For example, the proton in RCOOH resonates at $\delta = 10.8$ ppm.

Magnetic Anisotropy. Additional shielding and *de*shielding effects arise from electronic circulations induced within molecules. Consider this series of compounds:

CH_3-CH_3 $CH_2=CH_2$ $CH\equiv CH$

δ: 0.9   5.8   2.9

The order of δ values would be predicted erroneously from a consideration of local diamagnetic effects alone. We have similar troubles with the abnormally large shift of an aldehydic proton, $-C\diagup_{\diagdown O}^{H}$, $\delta \sim 10$, and the aromatic protons of benzene, $\delta \sim 7.3$. All these examples contain double or triple bonds, and we must consider the behavior of the π electrons in the unsaturated bonds.

Let us consider first the linear molecule of acetylene, where the electron distribution in the triple bond is symmetric about the axis. If the axis is parallel with the magnetic field, an electronic circulation perpendicular to the axis will be induced. Figure 12-8 shows the orientation of this circulation and the resultant induced

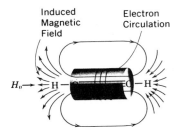

FIGURE 12-8. Anisotropic shielding in the acetylene molecule.

magnetic field which opposes the applied field. The lines of force of the induced field extend beyond the ends of the molecule. Thus the protons of acetylene find themselves in a lower effective field. This shielding effect of the triple bond over-shadows the deshielding effect of electron withdrawal by the carbon atom such as operates in the saturated ethane molecule. We have ignored other non-parallel orientations of the actylene molecule, because in a triple bond the electronic circulations are restricted to a plane normal to the bond axis. All other possible orientations will either have no effect or cancel out.

In the double bond, the restrictions on electronic circulations are different. Consider an ethylene molecule oriented as in Figure 12-9. The π-electron clouds sit to the left and right of the bond axis in a plane normal to the paper. Again,

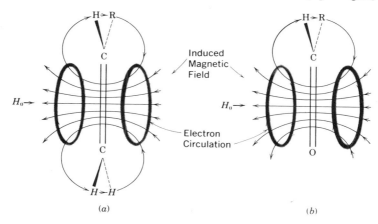

FIGURE 12-9. Anisotropic shielding in (a) olefins and (b) aldehydes.

induced circulations within the planes generate a magnetic field which opposes the applied field, but here the lines of force are perpendicular rather than parallel to the bond axis. The protons of ethylene find themselves in an effective field which is *enhanced* by the induced field. This corresponds to a greater deshielding than we expected from diamagnetic effects alone, and a larger chemical shift. Both effects combine forces in the case of an aldehydic proton, which accounts for its abnormally large chemical shift.

Aromatic rings likewise have π electron clouds situated to the right and left of the ring pictured in Figure 12-10. The explanation of the so-called "ring current" is analogous to that given for ordinary double bonds. As in the first two cases, other orientations of the ring with respect to the field are ineffective and can be ignored.

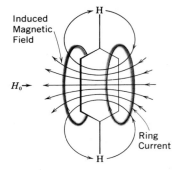

FIGURE 12-10. Anisotropic shielding of aromatic protons caused by ring current effect.

These effects are summarized in Figure 12-11, in which are depicted zones (cones) of (positive) shielding and (negative) deshielding. Obviously the effects vary continuously from point to point with a maximum effect along the cone axes and a maximum opposite effect in regions equidistant from the cones.

The anisotropic effects of the σ electrons in a $C - C$ single bond are much smaller than those we have been discussing and will not be considered here.

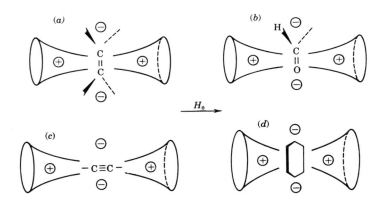

FIGURE 12-11.   Cones of positive shielding for (*a*) double bond, (*b*) aldehydes, (*c*) acetylenes, and (*d*) aromatic rings. Negative space represents deshielding.

Correlation of Chemical Shift with Structure.   In a complex molecule, a number of effects combine to establish the value of the chemical shift of each type of proton. The exact value may also depend on the concentration of the species and the nature of the solvent. The last two effects are normally small, unless the proton is subject to exchange with other protons in the system or hydrogen bonding occurs, as for example with alcohols or amines.

Although in most cases a detailed calculation of δ is not possible, there is already a wealth of data available for known compounds. These data are conveniently summarized in Table 12-3. Silverstein and Bassler suggest that chemical shifts in common organic compounds fall roughly into the eight regions given in Figure 12-12.

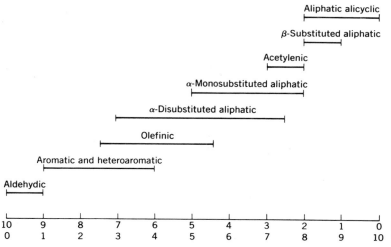

FIGURE 12-12.   General regions of chemical shifts. (From Silverstein and Bassler, *Spectrometric Identification of Organic Compounds*, 2nd ed., Wiley, 1967, p. 118.)

SPIN-SPIN SPLITTING

We have seen that n.m.r. lines are shifted to higher or lower field by the electronic environment of the proton. So far we have neglected the effects of other protons within the molecule. Recall that each proton is considered to be a spinning magnet which in an applied field is oriented with or against the field. We might expect that the resonance position of a proton would be affected by the spin of nearby protons. With high resolution instruments we can observe this effect as a "splitting" of the lines, or a "coupling" of the protons. Coupling occurs through bonds (not space) by means of a slight unpairing of the bonding electrons.

TABLE 12-3 APPROXIMATE CHEMICAL SHIFT OF PROTONS

Methyl Protons		Methylene Protons		Methine Protons	
Proton	δ, ppm	Proton	δ, ppm	Proton	δ, ppm
CH_3-C	0.9	$-C-CH_2-C$	1.3	$C-CH-C$	1.5
$CH_3-C-C=C$	1.1	$-C-CH_2-C-C=C$	1.7		
CH_3-C-O	1.4	$-C-CH_2-C-O$	1.9	$-C-CH-C-O$	2.0
$CH_3-C=C$	1.6	$-C-CH_2-C=C$	2.3		
CH_3-Ar	2.3	$-C-CH_2-Ar$	2.7	$-CH-Ar$	3.0
CH_3-CO-R	2.2	$-C-CH_2-CO-R$	2.4	$-C-CH-CO-R$	2.7
$CH_3-CO-Ar$	2.6				
$CH_3-CO-O-R$	2.0				
$CH_3-CO-O-Ar$	2.4				
$CH_3-CO-N-R$	2.0				
CH_3-O-R	3.3	$-C-CH_2-O-R$	3.4	$-C-CH-O-R$	3.7
		$-C-CH_2-O-H$	3.6	$-C-CH-O-H$	3.9
CH_3-OAr	3.8	$-C-CH_2-OAr$	4.3		
$CH_3-O-CO-R$	3.7	$-C-CH_2-O-CO-R$	4.1	$-C-CH-O-CO-R$	4.8
CH_3-N	2.3	$-C-CH_2-N$	2.5	$-C-CH-N$	2.8
CH_3-C-NO_2	1.6	$-C-CH_2-NO_2$	4.4	$-C-CH-NO_2$	4.7
$CH_3-C=C-CO$	2.0	$-C-CH_2-C-NO_2$	2.1		
$-C=C(CH_3)-CO$	1.8	$-C-CH_2-C=C-CO$	2.4		
		$-C=C(CH_2)-CO$	2.4		
CH_3-C-Cl	1.4	$-CH_2-C-Cl$	1.8	$-CH-C-Cl$	2.0
CH_3-C-Br	1.8	$-CH_2-C-Br$	1.8	$-CH-C-Br$	1.9
CH_3-Cl	3.0	$-CH_2-Cl$	3.4	$-CH-Cl$	4.0
CH_3-Br	2.7	$-CH_2-Br$	3.4	$-CH-Br$	4.1

Proton	δ, ppm	Proton	δ, ppm
$-C=CH_2$	5.3		
$-C=CH-$	5.1		
$-C=CH-$(cyclic)	5.3		
$R-C\equiv C-H$	3.1		
$Ar-H$	$9.0 \sim 7.0$		
$-C=CH-CO$	5.9		
$-CH=C-CO$	6.8		
$R-CHO$	9.9		
$Ar-CHO$	9.9	$CHCl_3$	7.25
$H-CO-O-$	8.0	H_2O	$\simeq 5.0$
$H-CO-N$	8.0		

Let us consider two protons, A and B, on neighboring carbon atoms. The effective field at A is either decreased or enhanced by the local field generated by B, depending on whether B is oriented with or against the applied field. The

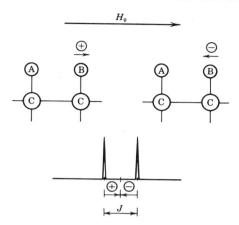

FIGURE 12-13. The effect of the alignment of proton B on the resonance of proton A. Alignment with the field ⊕ shifts the line for A downfield. Alignment against the field ⊖ shifts the line for A upfield.

resonance line for A is shifted to the left by one orientation of B and to the right by the other. In any sample, there are an enormous number of A and B protons, and the distribution between the two orientations is essentially equal. Both the downshift and the upshift will be observed. Figure 12-13 shows the result as a doublet. In a similar fashion, proton B is split into a doublet by A. We would expect intuitively that the separation of lines within the doublets should be the same for both. The spacing between the lines is called the *coupling constant, J,* and is given in cycles per second. We shall return to the use of coupling constants later, but first let us examine the splitting patterns of an actual molecule.

The high resolution n.m.r. spectrum of ethyl bromide is given in Figure 12-14, where the methyl protons are labeled (*a*) and the methylene protons (*b*). Each of the two (*b*) protons is randomly oriented with or against the field, represented by the following possible combinations, all equally probable

$$b_1 \quad \longrightarrow \quad \overbrace{\longrightarrow \quad \longleftarrow}^{\text{equivalent}} \quad \longleftarrow \qquad \underrightarrow{H_0}$$
$$b_2 \quad \longrightarrow \quad \longleftarrow \quad \longrightarrow \quad \longleftarrow$$

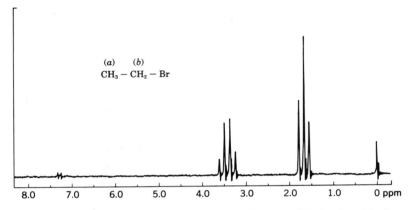

FIGURE 12-14. n.m.r. spectrum of ethyl bromide. (Courtesy of Varian Associates.)

where b_1 and b_2 represent the two (b) protons. The two combinations in the center are indistinguishable and represent no net effect. In a sample, the (a) protons experience three different effective fields due to the splitting effect, and the resonance appears as a triplet with sub-areas in the ratio $1:2:1$. In an analogous fashion, we can sort out the various combinations of orientations of the three (a) protons:

$$
\begin{array}{cccccc}
a_1 & \longrightarrow & \longrightarrow & \longleftarrow & \longleftarrow \\
a_2 & \longrightarrow & \longrightarrow & \longleftarrow & \longleftarrow \\
a_3 & \longrightarrow & \longleftarrow & \longrightarrow & \longleftarrow \\
& & & & & \underline{H_0}_{\longrightarrow}
\end{array}
$$

$$
\begin{array}{ccc}
a_1 & \longrightarrow & \longleftarrow \\
a_2 & \longleftarrow & \longrightarrow \\
a_3 & \longrightarrow & \longleftarrow
\end{array}
$$

$$
\begin{array}{ccc}
a_1 & \longleftarrow & \longrightarrow \\
a_2 & \longrightarrow & \longleftarrow \\
a_3 & \longrightarrow & \longleftarrow
\end{array}
$$

All of the eight combinations are equally probable, but the center groups of three are equivalent. Thus the (b) protons appear as a quartet with sub-areas in the ratio $1:3:3:1$. The total area of each multiplet remains in the ratio of $2:3$ as it must for two (b) protons and three (a) protons.

We can generalize these observations by stating that a proton with n equivalent protons on the neighboring carbon atom will be split by the n protons into $n + 1$ lines (a multiplet) with relative sub-areas given by the coefficients of the binomial expansion $(a + b)^n$. But what if the given proton finds neighboring protons on more than one neighboring carbon atom?

In propane, $CH_3CH_2CH_3$, the protons in the end methyl groups are equivalent; the six methyl protons split the methylene protons into a 7-membered multiplet, with sub-areas in the ratio of $1:6:15:20:15:6:1$. Nitropropane presents a more interesting problem:

$$
\begin{array}{ccccc}
 & H & H & H & O \\
 & | & | & | & \nearrow \\
H- & C- & C- & C- & N \\
 & | & | & | & \searrow \\
 & H & H & H & O \\
 & (a) & (b) & (c) &
\end{array}
$$

Coupling through more than three bonds is very inefficient, and is not normally observed, therefore the interpretation of the peaks for the (a) and (c) protons

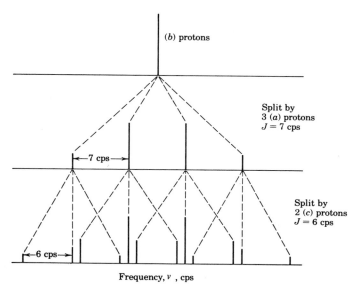

FIGURE 12-15. Double splitting of the methylene (b) protons in 1-nitropropane.

is straight-forward. Both are split into triplets by the two (*b*) protons. However, the (*b*) protons are split two-fold, once by the (*a*) protons and again by the (*c*) protons. Figure 12-15 is a diagram of the development of the splitting pattern; it makes no difference which splitting is considered first. (Try splitting into a triplet first!) The final pattern is a multiplet of 12 lines, but some of them are too weak to be seen in the actual spectrum given in Figure 12-16. Note that the triplets for the (*a*) and (*c*) protons appear to be distorted; the sub-areas are not precisely in the ratio 1:2:1. This behavior is a general phenomenon. As the chemical shifts of two kinds of protons become more nearly the same, the peak areas become distorted with the inner peaks increasing at the expense of the outer peaks. When the chemical shifts become identical, both multiplets merge into a singlet as shown in Figure 12-17. In other words, *equivalent protons do not split each other*.

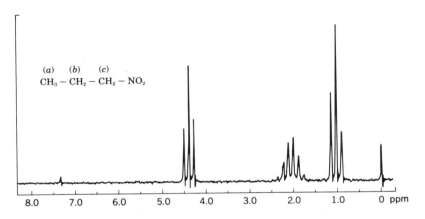

FIGURE 12-16. n.m.r. spectrum of 1-nitropropane. (Courtesy of Varian Associates.)

Let us recapitulate with a few rules and additional observations.

1. Spin-spin interactions are independent of the strength of the applied field. If a set of peaks cannot be identified as a multiplet or as a collection of several individual peaks, change the field. This does not change the coupling constant, but does change the chemical shift values (all measured in cycles per second).

2. Equivalent nuclei do not interact with each other to cause observable splitting.

3. Multiplicity is determined by the number of neighboring groups of equivalent nuclei. For protons, the multiplicity equals $n + 1$, provided $\Delta v \gg J$.

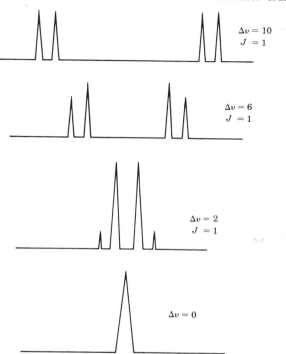

FIGURE 12-17. Behavior of peaks for two protons as the difference in chemical shift, Δv, approaches the coupling constant J.

4. Intensities of multiplets are symmetric (unless $\Delta v \approx J$) with relative intensities given by the coefficients of the terms in the expansion of $(a + b)^n$, where n is the number of equivalent neighbors causing the splitting.

5. Coupling constants decrease with distance; coupling is rarely observed at a distance greater than three bond lengths unless there is a charge delocalization as in conjugated or aromatic systems, or other special effects.

6. Coupling constants are the same in both multiplets of a pair which are interacting.

7. Coupling constants rarely exceed 20 cps, whereas chemical shifts vary over 1000 cps. For two coupled protons, if $\Delta v/J > 7$, the simple pattern of two doublets appears, but as $\Delta v \to J$ the inner peaks increase and the outer peaks decrease.

8. In undistorted multiplets, the chemical shift is measured at the center of the system of peaks. In distorted multiplets, the shift is measured at the "center of gravity."

The interpretation of spectra in which multiplets overlap requires a mathematical analysis and will not be considered here. However, with the information at hand, we make use of the splitting pattern and the coupling constants to help unravel the structure of an unknown compound. A number of coupling constants for pairs of protons, (*a*) and (*b*), are given in Table 12-4.

INTERPRETATION OF NMR SPECTRA

We are now ready to interpret some simple first order n.m.r. spectra. In this context the term "first order" means that $\Delta v \gg J$. The spectrum provides three kinds of information.

1. *Chemical shifts*, which identify the types of protons based on their electronic environment.

2. *Spin-spin splitting patterns*, which help to identify neighboring protons.

3. *Peak areas* (or intensities), which are proportional to the number of protons causing a given resonance line.

The spectra to be discussed were taken for 7% solutions of the compounds in a $CDCl_3$ solvent, using a Varian A-60 n.m.r. spectrometer.

We begin with the spectrum of acetaldehyde given in Figure 12-18. This molecule contains two types of protons, three in the methyl group and one aldehyde proton. The three methyl protons are split into a doublet by the aldehyde proton which in

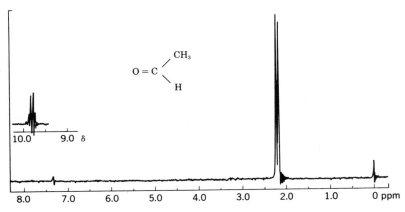

FIGURE 12-18.   n.m.r. spectrum of acetaldehyde. (Courtesy of Varian Associates.)

TABLE 12-4 PROTON SPIN-SPIN COUPLING CONSTANTS

Type	J_{ab}, cps	Type	J_{ab}, cps
H_a, H_b on C (geminal)	10–15	H_a, H_b on C=C (cis/trans vinyl)	6–12
H_a-C-CH_b	6–8	H_aC, CH_b on C=C	1–2
$H_aC-C-C-CH_b$	0	CH_a, H_b on C=C	4–10
H_aC-OH_b (no exchange)	4–6	CH_b, H_a on C=C	0–2
$H_aC-\overset{O}{\overset{\|}{C}}-CH_b$	2–3	$C=CH_a-CH_b=C$	9–12
$C=CH_a-\overset{O}{\overset{\|}{C}}H_b$	5–7	H_a, H_b on C=C ring	5 mem. 3–4 6 mem. 6–9 7 mem. 10–13
H_a, H_b on C=C	15–18		
H_a, H_b on C=C	0–2		

Type	J_{ab}, cps	Type	J_{ab}, cps
H_a —benzene— H_b	*ortho* 6–10 *meta* 1–3 *para* 0–1	thiophene (positions 2,3,4,5, S)	$J_{2\text{-}3}$ 5–6 $J_{3\text{-}4}$ 3.5–5 $J_{2\text{-}4}$ 1.5 $J_{2\text{-}5}$ 3.5
pyridine (positions 2,3,4,5,6, N)	$J_{2\text{-}3}$ 5–6 $J_{3\text{-}4}$ 7–9 $J_{2\text{-}4}$ 1–2 $J_{3\text{-}5}$ 1–2 $J_{2\text{-}5}$ 0–1 $J_{2\text{-}6}$ 0–1	pyrrole (positions 2,3,4,5, N-H_a)	$J_{a\text{-}2}$ 2–3 $J_{a\text{-}3}$ 2–3 $J_{2\text{-}3}$ 2–3 $J_{3\text{-}4}$ 3–4 $J_{2\text{-}4}$ 1–2 $J_{2\text{-}5}$ 2
furan (positions 2,3,4,5, O)	$J_{2\text{-}3}$ 1.5–2 $J_{3\text{-}4}$ 3–4 $J_{2\text{-}4}$ 0–1 $J_{2\text{-}5}$ 1–2		

turn appears as a quartet. In the spectrum, the center of the doublet appears at $\delta = 2.20$ ppm and the center of the quartet at $\delta = 9.80$ ppm. In saturated hydrocarbon molecules, the CH_3 resonance appears in the 0.7 to 1.3 ppm range. In acetaldehyde, the carbonyl group tends to deshield the methyl protons *both* by shifting electron density in the bond towards the partially positive carbon atom of the carbonyl *and* by anisotropic deshielding caused by the circulation of the carbonyl π electrons. As a result, the methyl protons resonate at lower field than in saturated hydrocarbons (i.e., δ is larger). The resonance at ~ 9.80 ppm is characteristic of aliphatic aldehydes.

The spectrum of a dilute solution of ethanol in $CDCl_3$ is shown in Figure 12-19. In dilute solutions of alcohols, proton exchange on the — OH group is so rapid that these protons do not spin-spin couple with neighboring protons and exhibit a singlet resonance line. The position of the OH resonance depends on the extent of dilution. In the spectrum in Figure 12-19, it appears at $\delta = 2.58$ ppm. The methylene protons split the methyl protons into a characteristic triplet at $\delta = 1.22$ ppm. The rapidly exchanging OH protons do not split the methylene proton resonance; however the methyl protons split the methylene signal into a quartet at $\delta = 3.70$ ppm. In ethanol, the — OH group is more electronegative than carbon and thus electron density is shifted away from the methylene group and diamagnetic deshielding results. Consequently, the methylene protons in ethanol resonate downfield from methylene protons in unsubstituted hydrocarbons ($\delta \sim 1.20$ to 1.35 ppm).

In the spectrum of α-chloropropionic acid, Figure 12-20, the single proton on the α carbon atom splits the methyl proton resonance into a doublet at $\delta = 1.73$ ppm. The resonance of the proton on the α carbon is split into a quartet by the

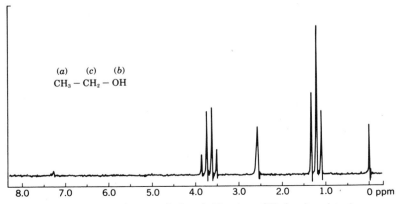

FIGURE 12-19.   n.m.r. spectrum of ethanol. (Courtesy of Varian Associates.)

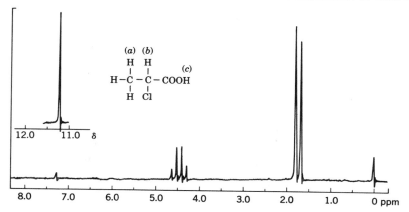

FIGURE 12-20. n.m.r. spectrum of α-chloropropionic acid. (Courtesy of Varian Associates.

methyl group at $\delta = 4.47$ ppm. The acidic proton resonance characteristically appears far downfield as a singlet at $\delta = 11.22$ ppm.

Ethyl acetate gives the spectrum shown in Figure 12-21. The (a) protons (labeled on the Figure) experience the greatest amount of diamagnetic shielding and appear as triplet at $\delta = 1.25$ ppm (split by methylene protons). The (b) protons are less shielded than the (a) protons due to the neighboring carbonyl group; as a result, the (b) protons resonate as a singlet at $\delta = 2.03$ ppm. The methylene protons (c) appear as a quartet at $\delta = 4.12$ ppm.

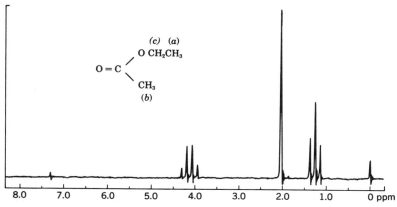

FIGURE 12-21. n.m.r. spectrum of ethyl acetate. (Courtesy of Varian Associates.)

252   Figure 12-22 gives the spectrum for α-methylbenzylamine. The amine protons (b) appear as a single resonance line at $\delta = 1.58$ ppm which shifts with dilution. The amine protons undergo rapid exchange and do not exhibit spin-spin interactions. The methyl protons (a) are split by the (c) proton and appear as a doublet at $\delta = 1.38$ ppm. The single proton (c) resonates considerably downfield at $\delta = 4.10$ ppm and is split into a quartet by the (a) protons. The (c) proton undergoes diamagnetic deshielding by the unsaturated ring and also experiences some anisotropic deshielding due to the circulating ring electrons. The benzene ring protons (d) resonate far downfield at $\delta = 7.30$ ppm. Benzene protons characteristically resonate in the 7 to 8 ppm region.

We have analyzed the n.m.r. spectra of some relatively simple compounds in an attempt to point out correlations between structure and the various types of resonance signals. The analysis of the spectra of more complex compounds often offers extremely challenging and difficult problems to the investigator. Nevertheless, the effort is well spent because the technique often provides structural information which is unobtainable using any other method. As a result, nuclear magnetic resonance spectroscopy has become an essential technique in the determination of the detailed structure of complex compounds.

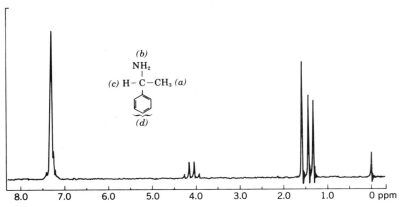

Figure 12-22.   n.m.r. spectrum of α-methylbenzylamine. (Courtesy of Varian Associates.)

ELECTRON SPIN RESONANCE SPECTROSCOPY

A chemical species with an odd number of electrons exhibits characteristic magnetic properties much like the nucleus. The spinning action of an unpaired electron generates a magnetic moment, μ, and in the presence of an applied magnetic field, the electron assumes orientations aligned with or against the field.

The energies of the two orientations correspond to $-\mu H_0$ and $+\mu H_0$; thus, the energy difference, ΔE, is $2\mu H_0$. Like an atomic nucleus, an electron in a magnetic field is able to absorb energy of the proper frequency, $\Delta E = h\nu$, and jump from the lower to upper energy level. This phenomenon is referred to as electron resonance, and the technique which is used to study this type of behavior is called *electron spin resonance* (e.s.r.) spectroscopy.

The magnetic moment of an electron is 9.284×10^{-19} erg-gauss^{-1}. From the relationship,

$$\Delta E = 2\mu H_0 = h\nu$$

the resonance frequency, ν, for free electrons in a typical e.s.r. field of 3400 gauss is 9500 Mc/sec. Consequently, electron spin resonance involves the absorption of radiation in the microwave region of the electromagnetic spectrum.

In a typical e.s.r. instrument, a klystron oscillator generates a microwave signal of approximately 9500 Mc. The permanent magnetic field is adjusted to approximately 3400 gauss. As in n.m.r. spectroscopy, provision is made to sweep the field in small increments around 3400 gauss. The area of an e.s.r. peak is directly proportional to the number of unpaired electrons in the sample investigated. In quantitative analysis, peak areas of the sample are compared with the peak area of a standard which contains a known quantity of unpaired electrons.

There is no phenomenon which parallels the n.m.r. chemical shift in e.s.r. studies. However, the e.s.r. spectra do exhibit hyperfine splittings which are caused by interactions between the spinning electrons and adjacent spinning magnetic nuclei. The "effective" magnetic field experienced by a given unpaired electron is represented by,

$$H_{\text{eff}} = H_0 \pm H_{\text{local}}$$

where H_0 is the applied magnetic field and H_{local} is the magnetic field generated by magnetically active neighboring nuclei. For the simplest case of one electron interacting with one hydrogen atom, the electron spin resonance signal consists of a doublet. In general the number of splittings caused by a 1 electron-1 nucleus interaction will equal $2I + 1$ where I is spin quantum number of the nucleus. When an electron interacts magnetically with n equivalent nuclei, the electron resonance signal is split into a $(2nI + 1)$ multiplet, with the relative peak areas equal to the coefficients of the binomial expansion, $(a + b)^n$.

Free radicals, molecules with triplet electronic states, and transition metal ions represent constituents which possess unpaired electrons and they may experience electron spin resonance. Electron spin resonance spectroscopy has proven most helpful in studying mechanisms of reactions which proceed through free radical intermediates. The technique is also being used to elucidate the electronic structures of complexes of transition metal ions and to examine molecular triplet electronic states.

12-1.   Predict what the high-resolution n.m.r. spectra of the following compounds would look like. Indicate the approximate δ values for the different groups of equivalent protons in these compounds.

      (a) acetone   (e) ethyl benzene

      (b) acetic acid   (f) n-propionamide

      (c) ethyl chloride   (g) 2-iodobutane

      (d) 1-bromo-3-chloropropane

12-2.   Interpret and discuss the n.m.r. spectra of the following compounds and suggest a structure for the compound. Indicate the nature of any additional spectroscopic information which would help you verify your prediction.

      (a) Compound (A) has the molecular formula C_4H_8O. The n.m.r. spectrum for this compound is presented in Figure 12-23.

      (b) Compound (B) has the molecular formula C_3H_8O. The n.m.r. spectrum is given in Figure 12-24.

      (c) Compound (C) has the molecular formula C_4H_8O. The n.m.r. spectrum is given in Figure 12-25.

      (d) Compound (D) has the molecular formula C_7H_8. The n.m.r. spectrum is given in Figure 12-26.

12-3.   The n.m.r. spectrum of a dichloro compound (Mol. Wt. 113) has a quintet with $\delta = 2.20$ and a triplet with $\delta = 3.70$. Assign the absorption peaks and identify the compound.

12-4.   The n.m.r. spectrum of $C_9H_{10}O_2$ shows three single peaks at $\delta = 7.29$ (area 84), $\delta = 5.00$ (area 34) and $\delta = 1.98$ (area 50). What is the structural formula of the compound?

12-5.   In very pure ethanol, $\underset{(c)}{CH_3} - \underset{(b)}{CH_2} - \underset{(a)}{OH}$, the (a) proton is coupled with the (b)

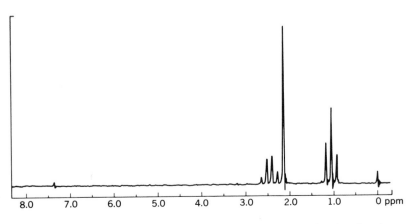

FIGURE 12-23.   n.m.r. spectrum of Compound A. (Courtesy of Varian Associates.)

proton, $J_{ab} = 5.0$ cps, and the (b) protons also couple with the (c) protons $J_{bc} = 7.2$ cps. Work out the splitting pattern for the (b) protons, similar to Figure 12-15.

12-6. If the radiofrequency oscillator has a constant frequency of 56.4 megacycles (Mc) per second, to what value must the applied magnetic field strength be adjusted for F^{19} resonance? For F^{19}, $I = \frac{1}{2}$ and $\mu = 1.329 \times 10^{-23}$ erg-gauss^{-1}.   *Ans.* 1.405×10^4 gauss.

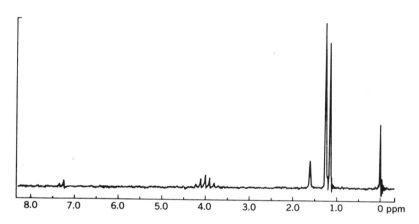

FIGURE 12-24. n.m.r. spectrum of Compound B. (Courtesy of Varian Associates.)

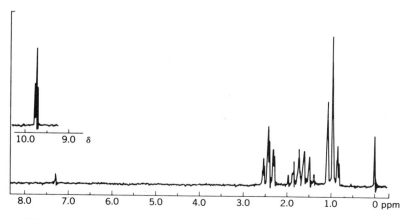

FIGURE 12-25. n.m.r. spectrum of Compound C. (Courtesy of Varian Associates.)

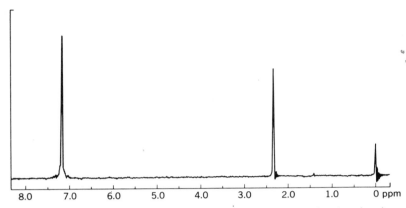

FIGURE 12-26.   n.m.r. spectrum of Compound D. (Courtesy of Varian Associates.)

REFERENCES

R. M. Silverstein and G. C. Bassler, *Spectrometric Identification of Organic Compounds*, 2nd ed., Wiley, New York, 1967; Chapter 4. Elementary theoretical discussion with comprehensive data; e.g., chemical shift charts, coupling constants, shielding constsnts, etc.

J. R. Dyer, *Applications of Absorption Spectroscopy of Organic Compounds*, Prentice-Hall, Englewood Cliffs, N. J., 1965. Paperback with good intermediate discussion of n.m.r.

L. M. Jackman, *Applications of Nuclear Magnetic Resonance Spectroscopy in Organic Chemistry*, Pergamon Press, New York, 1959. Short monograph with excellent discussions on the correlation of chemical shifts with molecular structure.

J. A. Pople, W. G. Schneider, and H. J. Bernstein, *High-Resolution Nuclear Magnetic Resonance*, McGraw-Hill, New York, 1959. Definitive detailed treatment. Considered by many to be the "bible" of n.m.r.

13 MASS SPECTROMETRY

In a mass spectrometer, the sample is bombarded with a beam of electrons which produces an ion-molecule or ionic fragments of the original species. The resulting assortment of charged particles is then separated according to their masses. The "spectrum" consists of a display of the various masses produced and their relative abundance. Although simple in principle, the mass spectrometer is a complex and expensive instrument. Nevertheless, it is becoming a common tool in the organic laboratory because (as Biemann has suggested) "it is probably correct to state that this technique, whenever applicable, gives the largest amount of specific information per microgram of sample."

Its use in determining atomic and molecular weights is no doubt familiar to the student. Equally as important are the characteristic fragmentation patterns of complex molecules which serve for identification and as a powerful aid in determining detailed structure. In this chapter we look at how a mass spectrometer operates and then consider the ionization and fragmentation processes, closing with a brief survey of some typical applications.

INSTRUMENTATION

Although there are many variations, all instruments include: (1) a device to introduce the sample, (2) ionization chamber, (3) ion separator, (4) ion collector, and (5) amplifier and readout. A typical arrangement for a 180° instrument is shown in Figure 13-1. Positive ions produced in the electron beam A are withdrawn by electrode B and accelerated in the electric field between B and C. Those ions which emerge through slit D traverse the evacuated tube E which is placed in a strong magnetic field H perpendicular to the plane of the diagram. Only those ions with the proper ratio of mass to charge (m/e) will pass through the exit slit F and strike collector plate G. The "spectrum" is obtained by varying the accelerating voltage on C.

Sample Handling Systems. Samples which are gases or liquids having a vapor pressure of at least 10^{-2} torr at ambient temperature are best introduced from a large (1- to 5-liter) reservoir through a pin-hole leak into the evacuated ionization chamber. Less volatile samples may be heated in the reservoir provided they are thermally stable. Still less volatile liquids and solids may be vaporized directly within the ionization chamber. What is required is a steady flow of sample into the ion beam during the course of the analysis.

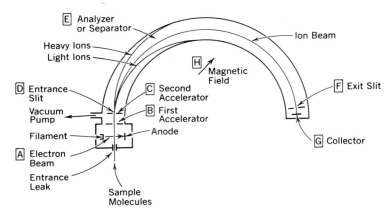

FIGURE 13-1. Schematic diagram of single deflection 180° mass spectrometer. Magnetic field is perpendicular to plane of the paper.

A sample size of about 1 μ mole is all that is required. Only a few percent of this will actually enter the ionization chamber, and of that which does, only about 0.1% is ionized. There is a further reduction of several orders of magnitude before the ions are collected. Since the ion collector can respond to a single ion, the problems of contamination should be obvious—we may easily analyze stopcock grease or the remains of the previous sample unless extreme care is used. Removal of contaminants by the "baking-out" of the apparatus may require many days, and is certainly one of the headaches of the technique.

The sample size and volatility required for mass spectrometry are essentially the same as for gas chromatography. Recall that a gas chromatograph is a powerful separator but a poor identifier. The mass spectrometer is a powerful identifier, but not well suited to complex mixtures. The combination of the two techniques is a "natural"; a small leak from the gas chromatographic column outlet to the mass spectrometer inlet provides an adequate sample. The large volume of carrier gas (hydrogen or helium) is of no concern provided the pumping system has sufficient capacity to maintain the required vacuum within the spectrometer. Alternatively, a substantial fraction of the carrier gas can be quickly removed by passage through a thin-wall glass tube which is permeable to helium, or a palladium tube permeable to hydrogen.

Ionization Chamber. A simple electron impact ion source is illustrated in Figure 13-2. The sample molecules stream in because of the difference in pressure across the inlet leak, from about 10^{-2} torr to 10^{-5} torr. An electrically heated

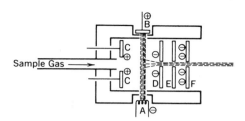

FIGURE 13-2. Schematic drawing of an electron-impact ion source.

filament *A* produces thermal electrons which are accelerated by anode *B*, thus creating a beam of electrons which intersects the flow of sample molecules. Positively charged ions are withdrawn by the electric field which exists between the repeller plate *C* and the first accelerator plate *D*. The intermediate plate *E* serves to focus the ion beam and the second accelerator plate *F* imparts a final acceleration to the ions.

The energy of the electron beam is controlled by the potential on anode *B*. The ionization potential of most organic compounds is about 10 V, and with this minimum energy the primary process is the production of singly charged molecular ions:

$$M + e^{\ominus} = M^{\oplus} + 2e^{\ominus}$$

giving a mass spectrum consisting almost entirely of a single peak corresponding to the mass of the original molecule (but see isotope effects to be discussed later). Increasing the energy of the electron beam will yield a more highly excited ion which will fragment if it is complex, or a second electron may be knocked out as shown in Figure 13-3 for argon atoms. For most applications the electron beam is given an energy of 50 to 70 eV, which yields the most reproducible spectra. Doubly charged ions are rare, even at this potential.

The difference in potential between *C* and *D* is only a few volts, sufficient only to remove the positive ions from the electron beam. Thus the positive ions reach electrode *D* with variable but relatively small kinetic energy.

Essentially all of the acceleration is accomplished between electrodes *D* and *F* which differ in potential from a few hundred to a few thousand volts. At a given accelerating voltage, all singly charged ions are given the same kinetic energy defined by the relation:

$$\text{Kinetic Energy} = \tfrac{1}{2}mv^2 = eV \qquad (13\text{-}1)$$

where *m* is the mass of the ion, *v* is its velocity, *e* is the electronic charge and *V*

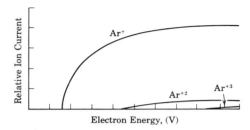

FIGURE 13-3.   Ion production efficiency for argon
as a function of electron beam energy.

is the accelerating potential. A monoenergetic beam of ions is essential for the
proper separation of the ions, and is a prime consideration in obtaining very
accurate mass measurements.

Ion Separators.   This part of the apparatus, sometimes called the analyzer,
must separate ions according to their masses with a very high differentiation
between masses. For example, a good high resolution instrument can distinguish
between $C_{16}H_{22}O_2$, Mol. Wt. 246.1620, and $C_{17}H_{26}O$, Mol. Wt. 246.1984; or
between CH, mass 13.0078 and C^{13}, mass 13.0034. A second requirement is a
high transmission of ions. Unfortunately, the two requirements are incompatible;
the narrower the slits are made, the better the resolution but the smaller the ion
current. As usual the designer must reach a compromise best suited for the
purpose. The different kinds of mass spectrometers differ mainly in the way
they sort out the ions.

Single-Focusing Magnetic Deflection.   This is the type of separation most
often described, and is the one shown in Figure 13-1. In the magnetic field H
the charged particles experience a magnetic force F:

$$F = Hev \qquad (13\text{-}2)$$

and a counterbalancing centrifugal force,

$$Hev = mv^2/r \qquad (13\text{-}3)$$

where r is the radius of the circular path. A combination and rearrangement of
Equations 13-1, 13-2, and 13-3 yields

$$m/e = H^2r^2/2V \qquad (13\text{-}4)$$

Equation 13-4 pertains to all ions, but only those with a particular path radius will
be collected. For most spectrometers, H and r are fixed, so that the mass which is
collected is inversely proportional to V. Some magnetic instruments employ a

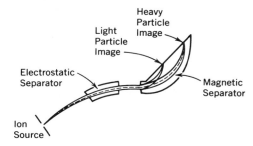

FIGURE 13-4. Schematic diagram of Mattauch-Herzog double-focusing mass spectrometer.

60° sector rather than the 180° bend depicted in Figure 13-1. If the geometry is correctly arranged, both of these types of magnets focus an imperfectly collimated ion beam on the exit slit and the collector placed immediately behind it.

Double-Focusing. In deriving Equation 13-4, it was assumed that all ions enter the magnetic field with the same kinetic energy; therefore, all ions with the same m/e ratio should have the same velocity. This is not strictly true because the ions vary in initial energy (Boltzmann kinetic energy distribution) and therefore leave the electron beam with variable energies. A much better focusing can be achieved if this energy spread is reduced before the ions enter the magnetic field. Mattauch and Herzog designed a "double-focusing" instrument in which a radial electrostatic field selects only those ions possessing a certain velocity, or kinetic energy. The geometry is shown in Figure 13-4. Since it can achieve such high resolution, the ion currents are extremely low. Double-focusing instruments are used whenever highest resolution is required, for example in the determination of precise molecular weights.

Cycloidal Focusing. Ions passing through crossed magnetic and electric fields will generate a cycloidal path as shown in Figure 13-5. The small radius of curvature permits the use of a smaller magnet without sacrificing range or resolution.

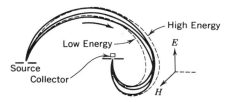

FIGURE 13-5. Schematic diagram of a cycloidal mass spectrometer.

Time-of-Flight. We have noted that all ions leave the acceleration field with the same kinetic energies but different velocities depending on their masses. With magnetic focusing the ions are separated by changing their directions. However, if they are left to float in a straight line through a field-free region they will take different times to travel a given distance. The measurement of this "time-of-flight" is the basis for the non-magnetic separator shown in Figure 13-6. If the ions were allowed to enter the drift tube continuously, there would be no possibility of measuring the time required for a given ion. This problem is solved

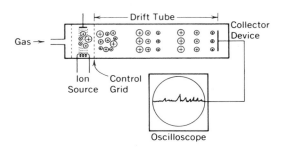

FIGURE 13-6.   Schematic diagram of a "Time-of-Flight" mass spectrometer.

by pulsing a control grid placed in the electron beam so that ions are produced in pulses lasting only about 0.25 μsec at a frequency of 10,000 times per second. The accelerating grid and collector device must also be pulsed in sequence. The time-of-flight, t, is proportional to the square root of the m/e ratio:

$$t = k\sqrt{m/e} \qquad (13\text{-}5)$$

where k is a proportionality constant which depends on the length of the flight path. If the distance traveled is 40 cm, e is measured in e.s.u., m in atomic mass units, and t in μsec, then k is nearly unity. Thus, for $N_2^{\oplus}$, $t = \sqrt{28} = 5.30$ μsec and for $O_2^{\oplus}$, $t = \sqrt{32} = 5.66$ μsec. Obviously, rather elaborate electronics are required to measure accurately these very short times. Oscilloscopes are commonly used to display the spectrum.

Other Types of Ion Separators.   There are several other kinds of instruments available, but space will not permit detailed descriptions. The "Omegatron" is based on the cyclotron principle of accelerating ions in a spiral path. The "radio-frequency" spectrometer, like the time-of-flight, separates on the basis of velocity, but the ions must make their way through a series of grids pulsed with an r-f signal set to allow only one velocity to get through. The "quadrupole" employs a four electrode system as shown in Figure 13-7, which gives a cross-sectional view. Oppositely placed electrodes are connected together. Both a d-c voltage and r-f alternating voltage are applied. Ions produced in a conventional source pass into the space between the electrodes in the Z-direction. The ions oscillate about the Z-axis and only those with a certain m/e ratio get through without striking an electrode. Quadrupole spectrometers require no magnet, so are more compact and less expensive than magnetic focusing instruments.

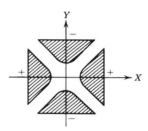

FIGURE 13-7. Cross section of analyzer tube of a quadrupole mass spectrometer. Ions travel perpendicular to plane of the page.

Ion Collectors. The ion beam currents which must be detected and measured are of the order of 10^{-15} to 10^{-9} amp. Historically, photographic plates served this purpose, but now Faraday cylinders, electron multipliers, and electrometers are more common. The collector electrode must be well shielded from stray ions and the amplifier must be stable and linear over 4 to 5 orders of magnitude. Recorders are often furnished with several pens each set at a different attenuation so that peaks of all sizes can be measured conveniently; at least one of the traces should always be at a convenient place on the chart.

In the "isotope-ratio" spectrometer, two detectors are used, placed in positions to catch ions which are identical except for the stable isotopes of one particular kind of atom. Thus the two isotopes are measured simultaneously and the ratio of the two can be determined very accurately. Compounds labeled with heavy isotopes are often used in tracer studies for biochemical work where radioactive tracers might cause objectionable side effects.

Vacuum System. Not the least of the complications of mass spectrometry is the high vacuum which must be maintained within the instrument. The inlet system is usually maintained at 10^{-2} torr, the ion source at 10^{-5} torr and the analyzer tube at 10^{-7} torr, or as low as possible. Mechanical, oil diffusion, and mercury diffusion pumps are used in various combinations. Obviously, a good part of the hardware around the spectrometer is involved in the vacuum system.

RESOLUTION

Any spectrometer can differentiate $NH_3^{\oplus}$ (mass 17) from $CH_4^{\oplus}$ (mass 16), but it would take a rather good one to differentiate $C^{12}H_3D^{\oplus}$ (mass 17.0376) from $C^{13}H_4^{\oplus}$ (mass 17.0347). The ability of a spectrometer to distinguish between two ions of nearly equal masses is called the "resolution" of the instrument.

Ideally, the spectrum consists of a series of narrow (zero width) peaks. This would represent infinite resolution. As seems to be inevitable in nearly every technique, there are a number of non-ideal processes causing peak broadening:

1. Distribution of kinetic energies produced in the electron beam.
2. Variations in the accelerating voltage.
3. Poorly collimated ion beam.
4. Variations in the magnetic field.
5. Width of the ion beam as determined by the slits.
6. Space charge of the ion beam. (The positive charges repel each other, thus broadening the beam. This effect is particularly noticeable at high concentrations.)

Resolution is expressed as $M/\Delta M$, where M is the nominal mass of a pair of closely spaced peaks of equal height, one at M and the other at $M + \Delta M$, with the stipulation that the signal at the valley minimum between the peaks must not exceed 10% of the height of the peak maximum. (Some authors use a 2% figure rather than 10%.) A resolution in excess of 10,000 is required to separate fragments having the same nominal mass, for example $N_2^{\oplus}$ (mass 28.0061) and $CO^{\oplus}$ (mass 27.9949).

THE MASS SPECTRUM

Molecular Ion or Parent Peak. With an electron beam energy of 9 to 15 eV, the principal ion is the molecular ion produced by the loss of a single electron. This gives a very simple mass spectrum with essentially all of the ions appearing in the "parent peak." With organic compounds, because of the small, but observable, natural abundance of C^{13} and H^2, there is generally a small peak appearing one mass unit higher than the parent peak (the $M+1$ peak); and if two heavy isotopes happen to be in the same molecule, there is an even smaller peak at $M+2$. Chlorine and bromine yield abnormally high $M+2$ peaks (Cl^{35}, 75.8%; Cl^{37}, 24.2%; Br^{79}, 50.5%; Br^{81}, 49.5%).

The stability of the molecular ion is increased if it contains a π-electron system which can more easily adjust to the loss of an electron than can a σ bond. Also, in a cyclic system the rupture of a bond does not split the molecule. The possibility of cleavage is related to both the bond strengths in the molecular ion and the stability of possible fragments. In general, the relative height of the parent peak decreases in the following order:

> Aromatics > conjugated olefins > alicyclics > sulfides > unbranched hydrocarbons > ketones > amines > esters > ethers > carboxylic acids > branched hydrocarbons and alcohols

The parent peak gives the exact molecular weight of the sample. It is not always easy to identify the parent peak; CCl_4, for example, does not give any parent peak.

Base Peak. With an electron beam energy of 70 eV, the original molecular ion splits into many fragments, and the parent peak is often quite small. The largest peak which is observed is called the "base peak," and all other peak heights are measured with respect to it. Thus ion abundances are given in terms of percent of the base peak, or as the percent of the total amount of ions produced.

Dissociation Processes. Under the usual conditions, the molecular ion originally produced is left with considerable excess energy. Both the energy and the charge are rapidly delocalized resulting in one or more *cleavages* with or without some rearrangements. One of the fragments retains the charge and the remaining fragments may be either stable molecules or radicals. The kinds of fragments obtained varies with the electron beam energy. The minimum voltage at which a given ion is observed in the spectrum is known as its "appearance potential." Fortunately, with electron beam energies of 50 to 80 eV, most organic molecules fragment in a reproducible manner. The relative abundance of the ions produced is related to the strength and chemical nature of the bonds which held the fragment to the rest of the molecule.

Cleavage is favored at branched carbon atoms as a consequence of the relative stability of the carbonium ions produced:

$$\text{tertiary } C^{\oplus} > \text{secondary } C^{\oplus} > \text{primary } C^{\oplus}$$

For example, side chains on saturated rings are cleaved at the α-bond. On the other hand, side chains on aromatic rings are cleaved at the β-bond, because of the relative stability of the resonance-stabilized benzyl ion, or the tropylium ion formed by rearrangement.

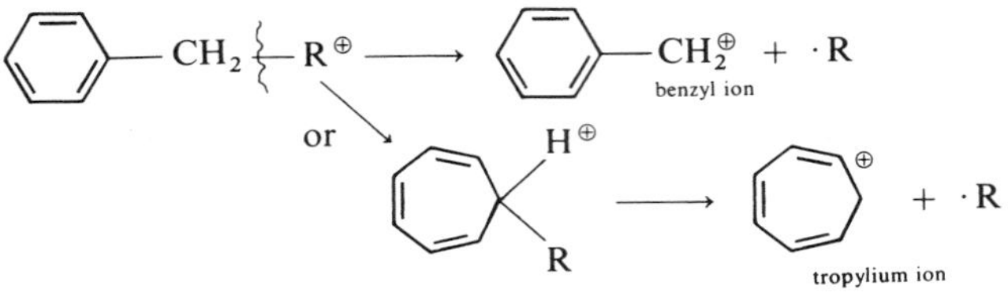

Cleavage is also favored by the formation of small stable molecules such as CO, CO_2, H_2O, NH_3, H_2S, HCN, ROH. The base (most abundant) peak often results from the loss of one of these molecules. For hydrocarbons, regardless of branching, the most intense peaks occur in the C_2 to C_5 range. In a homologous series, the extent of cleavage increases with molecular weight.

The influence of a heteroatom can be reasonably well predicted. Electronegative atoms such as N and O tend to lose one of their unshared electrons in the primary ionization process. Thus the electrons from neighboring bonds will be strongly attracted resulting in cleavage at the β bond:

$$R-CH_2 \wr CH_2-OR^{\oplus} \longrightarrow RCH_2 + CH_2^{\oplus}-OR$$
$$\updownarrow$$
$$CH_2 = OR^{\oplus}$$

It is customary to represent the movement of a single electron by a single barbed arrow (fish-hook), and the movement of an electron pair by a familiar doubly barbed arrow.

Rearrangement Ions. Sometimes fragments are observed which were not a part of the original molecule. In hydrocarbons, the rearrangements tend to be non-specific and unpredictable, while in molecules containing a hetero atom, the rearrangement is usually quite specific and may result in a very intense peak. Rearrangements are particularly favored where a stable fragment will result.

$$CH_3CH_2-X^{\oplus} \longrightarrow CH_3CH_2^{\oplus} + X$$
or
$$CH_3CH_2-X^{\oplus} \longrightarrow CH_2=CH_2^{\oplus} + HX$$

Metastable Ions. For the most part, fragmentation occurs within the ion source before the ions are accelerated into the analyzer tube. Ions resulting from a fragmentation after acceleration do not have a kinetic energy equal to that of the molecular ion from which they were formed, nor do they have a kinetic energy equal to ions of the same m/e originating before acceleration. Such ions are called metastable ions, and usually appear in the spectrum at non-integral mass numbers. The relationship between the apparent m/e of the metastable ion and its parent is given from the following formulation:

$$m_1^{\oplus} \longrightarrow m_2^{\oplus} + m_0$$

$$m^* = \frac{(m_2)^2}{m_1} \tag{13-6}$$

where m_1 = mass of parent ion
m_2 = mass of daughter (metastable) ion
m_0 = mass of neutral fragment
m^* = apparent mass of metastable ion

Metastable ions give peaks which are broad in comparison to regular peaks, and are also weaker in intensity. Such peaks are useful in studying the mechanism of fragmentation, but are not often used for the study of structure.

Multiply Charged Ions. The great majority of ions formed bear a single positive charge, but occasionally doubly charged ions are formed. These ions will appear at the same position as a singly charged ion of half the mass. Doubly charged ions of odd mass number must appear at half-integral masses and are easily recognized. Even numbered masses are more difficult to recognize when doubly charged.

The appearance potential for doubly charged ions is, of course, much higher than for singly charged ions—nearly always more than 30 eV. The removal of two electrons is much easier in the presence of a high π-electron density and in the absence of bonds which are easily broken. Therefore, it is more likely to be observed in heteroaromatic molecules.

Negative Ions. Although the most important ionization process produces positive ions, in about one out of a thousand collisions in the electron beam, the electron is captured by the molecule and forms a negative ion. They will not be observed with the usual mass spectrometers without considerable modification and are ignored except for special studies.

INTERPRETATION OF MASS SPECTRA

The interpretation of the mass spectrum requires an understanding of the ionization processes which occur before the ions reach the collector. Although some of these phenomena have been treated theoretically, by and large we must first observe the fragmentation patterns and then try to explain how and why they occurred. This empirical approach has been very fruitful in relating spectra to structure. A systematic description of this subject fills more than one book; all we can do here is to give some of the guiding principles and a few examples.

A complex organic compound will yield ions with almost every conceivable combination of its atoms, and its complete spectrum would be a nightmare to interpret. Fortunately, improbable fragments will have abundances too low to be observed. For most purposes, we need consider only major peaks (except in the region of the parent peak). In the case of unknowns, it is rare that we do not know, or cannot easily find out, something about the nature of the compound from other easily applied techniques.

In the following discussion we will first consider some general approaches used to arrive at the molecular formula, then explain the spectra of a few typical compounds, and finally reverse the procedure and try to identify compounds from their spectra. In order to simplify the discussion we will consider organic compounds containing only C, H, N, and O.

The Exact Molecular Weight. For a pure compound, it is usually not too difficult to determine the nominal (whole number) molecular weight from the identification of the parent peak. With a high-resolution instrument we can do much better and determine the molecular weight with considerable precision.

example / problem 13-1: We have found the molecular weight of an unknown compound to be 150.0681. Of the hundreds of molecules having the nominal value of 150, only $C_9H_{10}O_2$ has the exact value 150.0681. (This fact is quickly determined from Beynon's Tables; see reference.) This is only the beginning, because the *Handbook of Chemistry and Physics* lists 39 compounds with this molecular formula, but it is a long way toward solving the problem. Unfortunately, the precise data required ($C_9H_{10}O_2$ would have to be distinguished from $C_4H_{10}N_2O_4$, Mol. Wt. = 150.0641) are not easy to obtain, but suitable high-resolution instruments are now commercially available.

The Isotope Effect. A second approach to the molecular formula of a compound is through the distribution of naturally occurring isotopes. Molecules containing heavy isotopes will show up in peaks at m/e one or more units higher than normal; thus there will be small peaks at $M+1$ and $M+2$ (one and two units higher than the parent peak.) The relative abundances of heavy isotopes of C, H, N and O are well known.

For every 1000 C^{12} atoms, there are 11.2 C^{13} isotopes

"	"	"	H^1	"	"	"	0.16 H^2	"
"	"	"	N^{14}	"	"	"	3.8 N^{15}	"
"	"	"	O^{16}	"	"	"	0.4 O^{17}	"
"	"	"	O^{16}	"	"	"	2.0 O^{18}	"
"	"	"	S^{32}	"	"	"	7.8 S^{33}	"
"	"	"	S^{32}	"	"	"	44.0 S^{34}	"
"	"	"	Cl^{35}	"	"	"	320 Cl^{37}	"
"	"	"	Br^{79}	"	"	"	980 Br^{81}	"

Since the heavy isotopes occur in definite proportions, the probability of finding one or more in a given molecule can be calculated; thus we can predict the height of the $M+1$ peak relative to the parent peak.

example/problem 13-2: The parent peak for an unknown compound is at $m/e = 32$. The two most likely formulas are CH_4O and N_2H_4. What are the relative intensities of the $M+1$ peaks for these two molecules?

For every 100 molecules of CH_4O that have Mol. Wt. of 32, there will be 1.12 molecules having one C^{13} isotope. Since there are four H atoms in the molecule, the chances of finding a H^2 isotope are four times as great as if there were only one H atom in the molecule. For oxygen, only O^{17} will contribute to the $M+1$ peak; O^{18} contributes to the $M+2$ peak. In tabular form, for the two suggested formulas, we have

CH_4O			N_2H_4		
C^{13}	$1 \times 1.12\%$	$= 1.12\%$	N^{15}	$2 \times 0.38\%$	$= 0.76\%$
H^2	4×0.016	$= 0.06$	H^2	4×0.016	$= \underline{0.06}$
O^{17}	$1 \times \underline{0.04}$	$= \underline{0.04}$	$M+1$		$= \overline{0.82\%}$
	$M+1$	$= 1.22\%$			

Thus we could distinguish between the two compounds by measuring the $M+1$ peak.

Beynon has performed these calculations, and tabulated the results in an extensive table covering all reasonable combinations of C, H, N, and O, up to a molecular weight of 500. For each combination, an exact molecular weight is given, and the relative height to be expected for the $M+1$ and $M+2$ peaks. A $M+3$ peak would require three heavy isotopes in the same molecule—a very unlikely occurrence unless the molecule has been deliberately labeled. A portion of Beynon's Table for mass 150 is reproduced in Table 13-1.

In the first example, rather than measure the *exact* molecular weight, we might have measured the relative heights of the $M+1$ and $M+2$ peaks. Suppose that we had found that the $M+1$ peak was 10% and that the $M+2$ peak was 0.9% of the M peak. From Beynon's Tables we could have quickly decided that $C_9H_{10}O_2$ was the most likely formula. Beynon's Tables include many combinations which are not stable molecules but which can occur as fragment ions in the spectrum. This technique of making use of the distribution of isotopes is a general approach. In addition to Beynon's compilation, there are other useful observations. We have already noted that Cl and Br will give abnormally large $M+2$ peaks. Sulfur will do the same. On the other hand, F, I, and P have only a single isotope and will give abnormally low $M+1$ and $M+2$ peaks.

The Nitrogen Rule. All organic compounds having an even molecular weight must contain an even number (including zero) of nitrogen atoms, and all organic compounds with an odd molecular weight must have an odd number of nitrogen atoms. All *fragment* ions (formed by cleavage of one bond) have odd mass if they have an even number (0, 2, 4, ...) of N atoms, but even mass if they have an odd number of N atoms. The rule applies to compounds in which all bonds are covalent and includes molecules containing any combination of C, H, N, O, S, Si, As, P, halogens, and alkaline earth metals. The molecular weight to be used is the sum

TABLE 13-1 Masses and Isotopic Abundance Ratios for Various Combinations of C, H, N, and O

Formula	M^a	$M+1^b$	$M+2^c$
$C_4H_{10}N_2O_4$	0.0641	5.402	9.230
$C_4H_{14}N_4O_2$	0.1117	6.150	5.638
$C_5H_{12}NO_4$	0.0766	6.133	9.600
$C_6H_2N_2O_3$	0.0065	7.396	8.384
$C_6H_6N_4O$	0.0542	8.145	4.942
$C_7H_{10}N_4$	0.0905	9.250	3.840
$C_8H_8NO_2$	0.0555	9.233	7.797
$C_8H_{10}N_2O$	0.0793	9.607	6.138
$C_8H_{12}N_3$	0.1031	9.981	4.492
$C_9H_{10}O_2$	0.0681	9.964	8.447
$C_9H_{12}NO$	0.0919	10.338	6.816
$C_9H_{14}N_2$	0.1157	10.712	5.198
$C_{10}H_{14}O$	0.1045	11.069	7.547
$C_{11}H_{18}$	0.1408	12.175	6.769
$C_{12}H_6$	0.0469	13.062	7.832

a—Mass in excess of 150.0000,
b—Height of $M+1$ peak relative to $M = 100$,
c—Height of $M+2$ peak relative to $M = 1000$.
[After Beynon and Williams, *Mass and Abundance Tables for Use in Mass Spectrometry*, Elsevier, 1963]

of the most abundant isotopes. The rule is a consequence of the fact that the most abundant isotope of most elements of even valency has an even mass number, and vice versa. The only common exception is nitrogen.

The Ring Rule. Once the molecular formula is available, the number of "unsaturated sites" is apparent from the "ring rule." The number of unsaturated sites, R, is equal to the number of rings in the molecule plus the number of double bonds plus twice the number of triple bonds. For the molecule, $C_wH_xN_yO_z$:

$$R = w + 1 + \frac{y-x}{2} \qquad (13\text{-}7)$$

example/problem 13-3:   In benzene, C_6H_6

$R = 6 + 1 - 3 = 4$ (one ring, three double bonds)

In diethyl ether, $C_4H_{10}O$

$R = 4 + 1 - 5 = 0$ (no rings or double bonds)

In diethyl ketone, $C_5H_{10}O$

$R = 5 + 1 - 5 = 1$ (carbonyl group)

In cyclohexylamine, $C_6H_{11}NH_2$

$R = 6 + 1 - 6 = 1$ (one ring)

BEHAVIOR OF CLASSES OF COMPOUNDS

Paraffin Hydrocarbons.   The petroleum industry has made extensive use of mass spectrometry, so the behavior of the hydrocarbons is well known. The parent ion is intense in the C_1 to C_5 range, but falls off for higher homologs. The most intense peaks occur in the C_2 to C_5 range, with the general formula, $C_nH_{2n+1}^{\oplus}$ ($m/e = 29, 43, 57, 71,$ and 85). For long straight chain molecules, additional peaks will be observed at increments of 14 mass units (CH_2). At each of these prominent peaks there will be a smaller peak one unit higher for C^{13}, and peaks one and two units lower corresponding to the loss of hydrogen atoms. In highly branched molecules, random rearrangements (migration of hydrogen atoms) are common but not intense. The spectra of *n*-heptane and 2,2,3-trimethylbutane in Figure 13-8 illustrate many of these points.

Cycloparaffins are more likely to exhibit an intense parent peak although cleavage of the side chains at the ring is common. Fragmentation of the ring is observed as prominent peaks at $28(C_2H_4^{\oplus})$ and $29(C_2H_5^{\oplus})$.

Olefins.   Mono-olefins tend to rupture at the $C—C$ bond which is *beta* to the double bond (allylic cleavage) with the charge remaining with the group containing the double bond. Thus peaks should be expected at $m/e = 41, 55, 69,$ and 83—two units lower than for saturated compounds. For example, the most intense peak for 1-heptene is at 41 (Figure 13-8).

$$H_2C = CHCH_2 \overset{?}{\leftwedge} C_4H_9 \cdot\!\!\overset{\oplus}{} \longrightarrow H_2C = CHCH_2^{\oplus} + C_4H_9 \cdot$$
$$\boxed{m/e = 41}$$

Rearrangements are common, making it difficult to distinguish isomers.

Alkyl Benzenes.   The parent peak is usually large enough to allow measurement of the $M+1$ and $M+2$ peaks. The most common cleavage is the bond *beta* to the ring, giving a base peak at $91(C_6H_5CH_2^{\oplus})$ for short side chains, or at $92(C_6H_5CH_3^{\oplus})$ for long side chains. Peaks for naphthalene are all small except for the molecular ion (Figure 13-9).

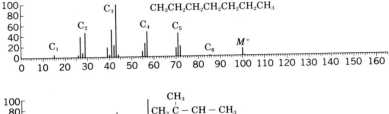

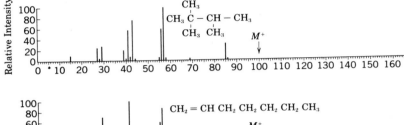

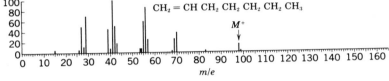

FIGURE 13-8. Mass spectra of *n*-heptane; 2,2,3-trimethyl butane and 1-heptene.

Alcohols. The parent peak is small, and may be absent for higher alcohols. The M—18 peak (loss of water) is easily mistaken for the parent peak. The loss of water which is especially prevalent for primary alcohols, yields the corresponding olefin ion which may fragment further in its characteristic manner. Generally, the bond *beta* to the oxygen atom is cleaved giving prominent peaks at $31(CH_2OH^{\oplus})$ for primary alcohols, at $45(CH_3CHOH^{\oplus})$ for secondary alcohols, and at $59((CH_3)_2COH^{\oplus})$ for tertiary alcohols.

$$R - \overset{\overset{\displaystyle H}{|}}{\underset{\underset{\displaystyle H}{|}}{C}} - \overset{..}{\underset{..}{O}} - H \xrightarrow{e^{\ominus}} R - \overset{\overset{\displaystyle H}{|}}{\underset{\underset{\displaystyle H}{|}}{C}} \overset{\oplus}{\underset{}{O}} - H \longrightarrow R - \overset{\overset{\displaystyle H}{|}}{\underset{\underset{\displaystyle H}{|}}{C}} = \overset{\oplus}{\underset{..}{O}} - H + \cdot H$$

31, 45, 59, 73

The spectra of *n*-hexanol and *n*-decanol, Figure 13-10, exhibit many of these features.

Aldehydes. There are a number of ways in which aldehydes cleave. Since these are typical of most carbonyl compounds, we will examine them in some detail.

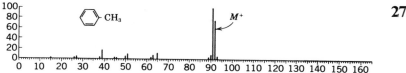

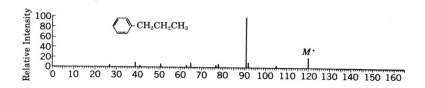

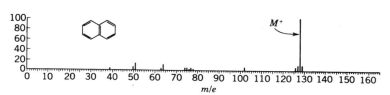

FIGURE 13-9.   Mass spectra of toluene; *n*-propyl benzene and naphthalene.

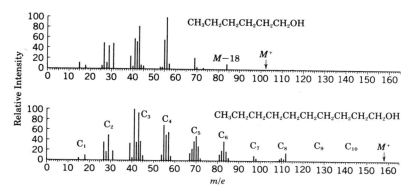

FIGURE 13-10.   Mass spectra of *n*-hexanol and *n*-decanol.

1. Elimination of small stable fragments

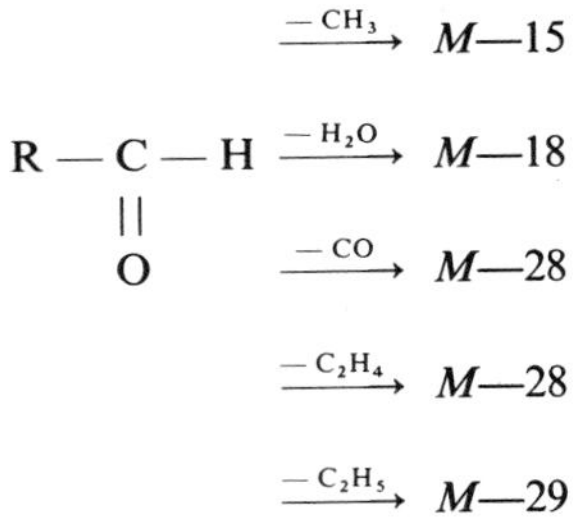

$$\xrightarrow{-CH_3} \quad M\text{—}15$$

$$R-\underset{\underset{O}{\|}}{C}-H \xrightarrow{-H_2O} \quad M\text{—}18$$

$$\xrightarrow{-CO} \quad M\text{—}28$$

$$\xrightarrow{-C_2H_4} \quad M\text{—}28$$

$$\xrightarrow{-C_2H_5} \quad M\text{—}29$$

2. α-Cleavage

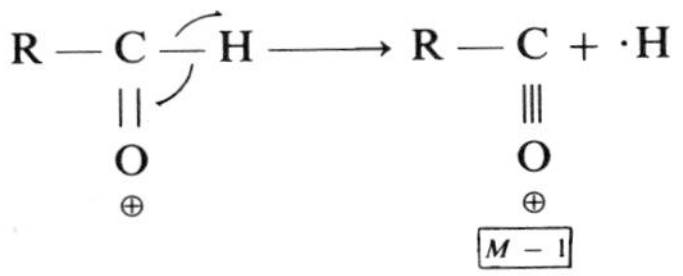

$$R-\underset{\underset{\overset{\oplus}{O}}{\|}}{C}\overset{\frown}{}H \longrightarrow R-\underset{\underset{\overset{\oplus}{O}}{\|\|}}{C} + \cdot H$$
$$\boxed{M-1}$$

or

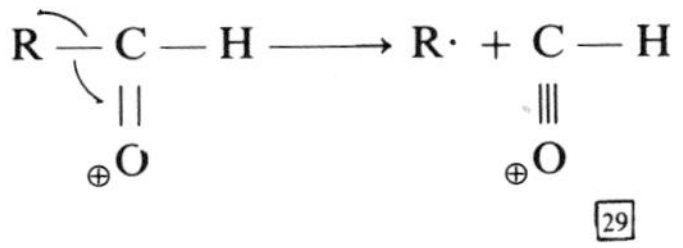

$$R\overset{\frown}{}\underset{\underset{\oplus O}{\|}}{C}-H \longrightarrow R\cdot + \underset{\underset{\oplus O}{\|\|}}{C}-H$$
$$\boxed{29}$$

or

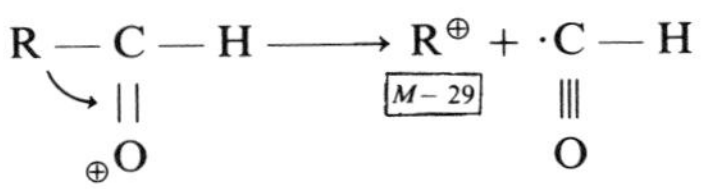

$$R-\underset{\underset{\oplus O}{\|}}{C}-H \longrightarrow R^{\oplus} + \cdot\underset{\underset{O}{\|\|}}{C}-H$$
$$\boxed{M-29}$$

3. β-Cleavage

$$R\overset{\frown}{}CH_2-\underset{\underset{\oplus O}{\|}}{C}-H \longrightarrow R^{\oplus} + \cdot CH_2-\underset{\underset{O}{\|}}{C}-H$$
$$\boxed{M-43}$$

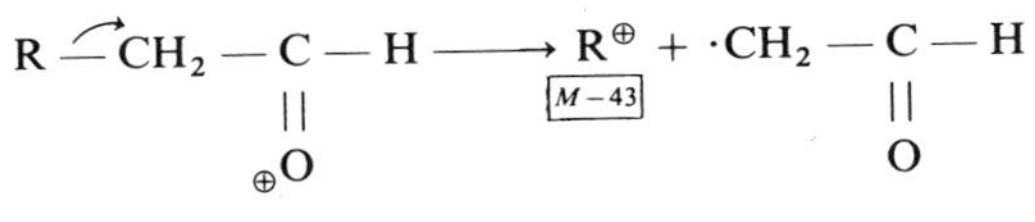

or

$$R\overset{\frown}{}CH_2-\underset{\underset{\oplus O}{\|}}{C}-H \longrightarrow R\cdot + \cdot CH_2-\underset{\underset{\oplus O}{\|}}{C}-H$$
$$\boxed{43}$$

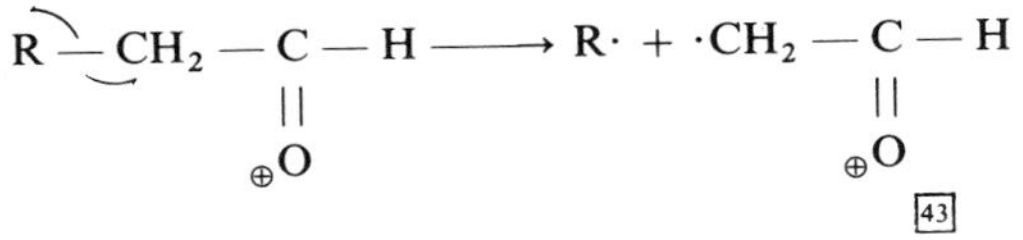

4. Rearrangement—a proton migration involving an intermediate ring structure.

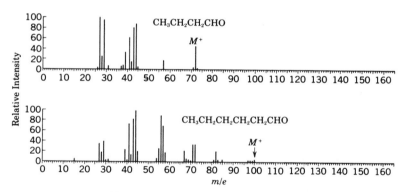

This rearrangement with β-cleavage is typical of aldehydes, ketones and esters. It is very prominent for straight chain aldehydes, often giving the base peak at 44, 58, 72, etc. Note that rearrangement peaks have even m/e ratios whereas all other peaks resulting from simple cleavage have odd numbers. The spectra for n-butyraldehyde and n-hexanal are given in Figure 13-11.

FIGURE 13-11. Mass spectra of n-butyraldehyde and n-hexanal.

Ketones. Parent peaks are usually prominent, and the base peak often results from cleavage of the C — C bonds adjacent to the carbonyl group. The spectra show the same cleavages as for aldehydes.

1. α-Cleavage on either side of the carbonyl group

$$R_1 \overset{\displaystyle \}{\underset{\displaystyle \|}{C}} R_2 \longrightarrow R_1^{\oplus} + \cdot C - R_2$$

$$\underset{\oplus O}{} \qquad \boxed{15,\ 29,\ 43,\ 57} \qquad \underset{O}{\|}$$

$$R_1 - \underset{\underset{\oplus}{\overset{\|}{O}}}{C} - R_2 \longrightarrow R_1\cdot \ + \ \underset{\underset{\oplus}{\overset{\|}{O}\ \boxed{43,\ 57,\ 71}}}{C} - R_2 \qquad \text{(favored if } R_1 > R_2\text{)}$$

$$\longrightarrow R_1 - \underset{\underset{\oplus}{\overset{\|}{O}}}{\underset{\boxed{43,\ 57,\ 71}}{C}} \ + \ \cdot R_2 \qquad \text{(favored if } R_1 < R_2\text{)}$$

$$\longrightarrow R_1 - \underset{\overset{\|}{O}}{C\cdot} \ + \ \overset{\oplus}{\underset{\boxed{15,\ 29,\ 43,\ 57}}{R_2}}$$

2. β-Cleavage on either side

$$R_1 - CH_2 - \underset{\underset{\oplus}{\overset{\|}{O}}}{C} - CH_2 - R_2 \longrightarrow \text{all four possible fragments}$$

3. Rearrangement

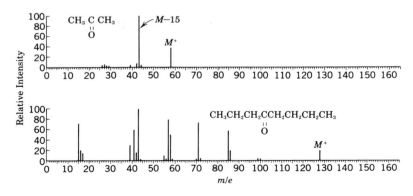

FIGURE 13-12.   Mass spectra of acetone and *n*-propyl-*n*-butyl ketone.

The spectra of acetone and *n*-propyl-*n*-butyl ketone, Figure 13-12, include these features.

Carboxylic Acids and Their Esters. The volatility of carboxylic acids is greatly enhanced by esterification. For example, methyl esters are often used to study carboxylic acids by mass spectrometry and gas chromatography. Esters follow the same pattern as for other carbonyl groups.

1. α-Cleavage

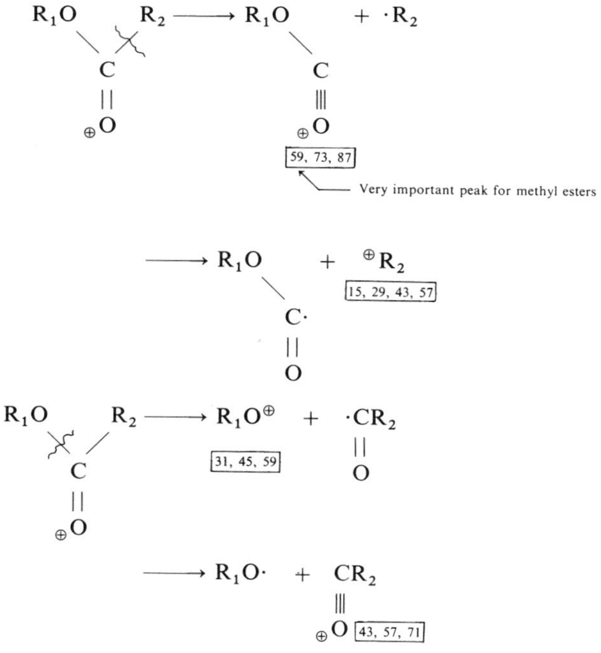

Very important peak for methyl esters

2. β-Cleavage

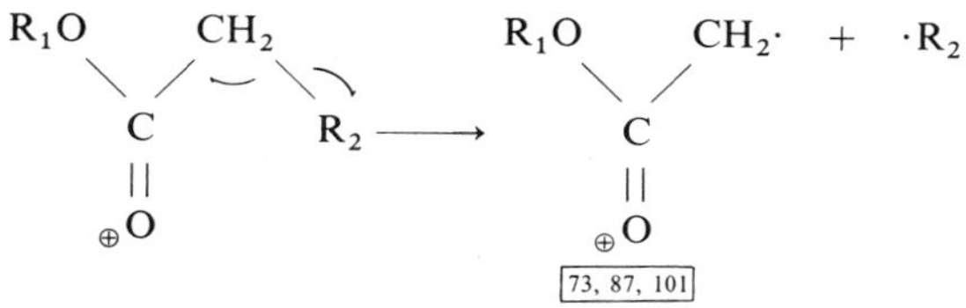

3. Rearrangement

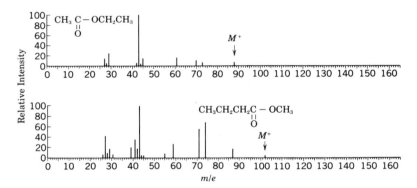

The rearrangement last given is very prevalent and often yields the base peak; for methyl esters, $R_1 = CH_3$ and $m/e = 74$, and for ethyl esters, $R_2 = C_2H_5$ and $m/e = 88$. Methyl butyrate and ethyl acetate, Figure 13-13, have most of these features.

FIGURE 13-13. Mass spectra of ethyl acetate and methyl butyrate.

Ethers. The formation of the molecular ion involves removal of a non-bonding electron from the oxygen atom which favors the cleavage of both the *alpha* and *beta* bonds. Therefore, the parent ion is weak and there are likely to be peaks at 29, 43, 57, 71, etc., from

$$R_1 - \overset{\displaystyle |}{\underset{\displaystyle |}{C}} - \overset{\displaystyle \oplus}{O}R_2 \longrightarrow R_1 - \overset{\displaystyle |}{\underset{\displaystyle |}{C}} \cdot \;\; + \;\; \cdot OR_2$$

as well as at 45, 59, 73, etc., from:

$$R_1 - \overset{\displaystyle +}{\underset{\displaystyle |}{C}} - \overset{\displaystyle \oplus}{O} - R_2 \longrightarrow R_1 \cdot \;\; + \;\; \overset{\displaystyle |}{C} = OR_2^{\oplus}$$

The prominent peaks of ethyl *sec*-butyl ether, Figure 13-14, show this behavior.

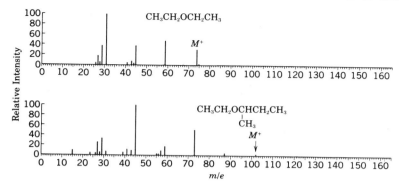

FIGURE 13-14.   Mass spectra of diethyl ether and ethyl *sec*-butyl ether.

Amines.   The parent peak of mono-amines occurs at an odd mass number and is weak for aliphatic amines and strong for aromatic amines. The most important process yielding the base peak is the rupture of the bond *beta* to the nitrogen atom, in which the loss of the largest hydrocarbon fragment is favored.

$$R_1 - \overbrace{CH_2} - \overset{\oplus}{N} - R_2 \longrightarrow \cdot R_1 + CH_2 = \overset{\oplus}{N} - R_2$$
$$\underset{R_3}{|} \qquad\qquad\qquad \underset{\boxed{30,\ 44,\ 58,\ 72,\ 86}}{\overset{|}{R_3}}$$

For primary amines, where R_2 and R_3 are H atoms, the base peak should be at 30. There is also a peak at 18 from the $NH_4^\oplus$ ion, which can be confused with a similar peak from $H_2O^\oplus$. Dimethyl amine and *n*-butyl amine (Figure 13-15) exhibit these features.

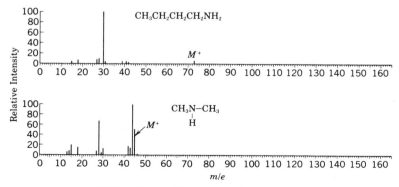

FIGURE 13-15.   Mass spectra of *n*-butylamine and dimethylamine.

IDENTIFICATION OF UNKNOWNS

It is much easier to predict or explain the spectrum of a known compound than it is to identify a compound from its observed spectrum. However, rarely does one have to work from the mass spectrum alone. The sample usually comes with a history which may give some clues. Other spectral data (infrared, n.m.r.) should be taken, chromatographic retention behavior noted (for polarity), melting point and boiling points should be observed, and in general every available bit of information should be considered. The interpretation will be greatly simplified if the compound is as pure as possible.

We have seen that the mass spectrometer provides several kinds of information:

1. *The molecular weight.* A low resolution instrument gives only the nominal (nearest whole number) value, while a high resolution instrument can give the exact molecular weight to several decimal places. From the latter, we can ascertain the empirical formula.

2. *The isotope distribution.* The relative heights of the $M+1$ and $M+2$ peaks (if available) help to select the most probable formula if only the nominal molecular weight is known. An abnormally small $M+1$ peak indicates fluorine, phosphorus or iodine. An abnormally large $M+2$ peak indicates chlorine, bromine or sulfur.

3. *The fragmentation pattern.* This is unique for each compound, so that if one has a large file of labeled spectra and a workable routine for comparison of unknown to the knowns, the solution is straightforward, although perhaps tedious without a computer.

There is nothing like experience—the beginner must expect to make many wrong guesses. For the major peaks, and all peaks near the parent peak, list not only the m/e of the charged fragment, but also the mass of the neutral fragment lost to give that peak. The rest is a matter of comparing peaks to common fragments (Tables 13-2 and 13-3), feeding in all other information as appropriate much the same as one solves a jig-saw puzzle. *Not all peaks need be identified.*

example / problem 13-4: Identify the compound whose spectrum is given in Figure 13-16A.

m/e	Rel. Intensity	Preliminary Remarks
26	21	CN
27	58	C_2H_3
28	69	C_2H_4, CO, N_2
29	100	C_2H_5, OCH_3
31	6	CH_2OH, OCH_3
39	4	
43	11	M-15, loss of CH_3
57	10	M-1, loss of H
58	38	Molecular ion

The molecular ion is intense; therefore, if it is an amine it must be aromatic. This is impossible because of the low molecular weight. Possible formulas involving C, H, and O are: $C_2H_2O_2$, C_3H_6O, and C_4H_{10}. Butane is unlikely because there are no peaks around $m/e = 15$, and an unexplainable peak at $m/e = 31$. For $C_2H_2O_2$, the ring rule gives $2 + 1 - 1 = 2$ sites of unsaturation, which makes the compound glyoxal, $OHC — CHO$. For C_3H_6O, the ring rule gives $3 + 1 - 3 = 1$ site of unsaturation leading to the following compounds: methyl vinyl ether, $CH_3OCH = CH_2$; propionaldehyde, CH_3CH_2CHO; propylene oxide, $\underset{\displaystyle O}{CH_2CHCH_3}$; acetone, CH_3COCH_3 and allyl alcohol, $CH_2 = CHCH_2OH$.

Methyl vinyl ether is a reasonable guess except for the peak at $m/e = 28$. The intense peaks around $m/e = 29$ do not fit acetone—in fact, we have already seen a spectrum for the latter compound, Figure 13-12, and it does not match. An alcohol should have a M-18 peak larger than the parent peak. Since this is not the case, we eliminate allyl alcohol and look at propionaldehyde. All peaks except $m/e = 26$ fit predictions for an aldehyde; therefore the best identification seems to be propionaldehyde.

TABLE 13-2 SOME COMMON FRAGMENTS

m/e	Ion	m/e	Ion
14	CH_2	44	CO_2, $C_2H_4NH_2$
15	CH_3	45	C_2H_4OH
16	O	46	NO_2
17	OH	55	C_4H_7
18	H_2O, NH_4	56	C_4H_8
19	F	57	C_4H_9, $C_2H_5C = O$
20	HF	58	$C_3H_6NH_2$
26	CN	59	$(CH_3)_2COH$, $COOCH_3$
27	C_2H_3	59	$CH_2OC_2H_5$
28	C_2H_4, CO, N_2	69	C_5H_9, CF_3
29	C_2H_5, CHO	70	C_5H_{10}
30	CH_2NH_2, NO	71	C_5H_{11}
31	CH_2OH, OCH_3	73	$OCOC_2H_5$
33	SH	77	C_6H_5
34	H_2S	79	Br
35	Cl	83	C_6H_{11}
36	HCl	84	C_6H_{12}
41	C_3H_5	85	C_6H_{13}
42	C_3H_6	91	$C_6H_5CH_2$
43	C_3H_7, $CH_3C = O$	92	$C_6H_5CH_3$

TABLE 13-3 SOME COMMON FRAGMENTS LOST

Parent Minus	Fragment Lost
1	H·
15	CH_3·
17	HO·
18	H_2O
19	F·
20	HF
26	$CH \equiv CH$, $·C \equiv N$
27	$CH_2 = CH$·, $HC \equiv N$
28	$CH_2 = CH_2$, CO
29	C_2H_5·, ·CHO
30	NH_2CH_2·, CH_2O, NO
31	·OCH_3, ·CH_2OH, CH_3NH_2
32	CH_3OH
33	HS·
34	H_2S
35	Cl·
36	HCl
37	H_2Cl
41	$CH_2 = CHCH_2$·
43	C_3H_7·, CH_3CO·
44	CO_2, $CH_2 = CHOH$
45	C_2H_5O·
57	C_4H_9·
58	NCS·
59	CH_3COO·
71	C_5H_{11}·

example/problem 13-5: Identify the compound whose spectrum is given in Figure 13-16B. Since we have neither the exact molecular weight nor the isotope distribution ($M+1$ and $M+2$ peaks) we must rely entirely on the nominal molecular weight and the fragmentation pattern.

m/e	Rel. Intensity	Preliminary Remarks
128	9	Parent peak
127	1	M-1, loss of H
113	4	M-15, loss of CH_3
99	35	M-29, loss of C_2H_5 or CHO
72	48	even m/e—rearrangement
71	36	C_5H_{11}
57	84	C_4H_9 or C_2H_5CO
43	100	C_3H_7 or CH_3CO
29	94	C_2H_5 or CHO

The compound appears not to contain N (no peaks typical of amines). Some likely formulas for molecular weight 128 include: $C_6H_8O_3$, $C_7H_{12}O_2$, $C_8H_{16}O$, C_9H_{20}, and $C_{10}H_8$. Next we propose reasonable structures for these formulas and see which of the predicted fragmentation patterns resemble the observed spectrum. For example, $C_{10}H_8$ (naphthalene) is aromatic and should give a very large parent peak (see Figure 13-9); therefore $C_{10}H_8$ can be eliminated. Likewise, C_9H_{20} is a saturated hydrocarbon which would not give the large rearrangement peak observed at $m/e = 72$ (see Figure 13-8).

The ring rule aids in composing structures, for example $C_6H_8O_3$ has $6 + 1 - 4 = 3$ rings or double bonds and we can invent corresponding structure such as:

$$CH_3CCH_2CCH_2CH \text{ or } HO-CH$$

Neither of these structures will give the observed spectra. We continue proposing and predicting, gradually narrowing down the possibilities. Other spectral data would be a great help at this point. Reference spectra might be available for some of the proposed compounds, and these should be compared with the given spectrum.

Lack of a $M-18$ and a $M-28$ peak makes an aldehyde doubtful. $C_7H_{12}O_2$ can be eliminated because it would most likely be a diketone or an unsaturated ester (neither of which would give a rearrangement peak at $m/e = 72$). This brings us to $C_8H_{16}O$ for which we can propose several ketones. There must be at least a three-carbon chain next to the carbonyl in order to get a rearrangement peak. The $m/e = 72$ peak indicates a five-carbon chain, for which we can propose several isomers, each of which satisfies the given spectrum.

$$C_2H_5C-(CH_2)_4-CH_3, \quad C_2H_5CCH_2CHC_2H_5, \quad C_2H_5CCH_2CH_2CHCH_3$$

This is as far as we can go with the data given; however, an n.m.r. spectrum would readily identify the compound. Compare this spectrum with Figure 13-12.

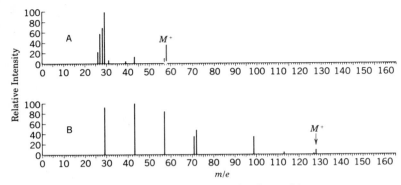

FIGURE 13-16. Mass spectra of unknown examples discussed in text.

ANALYSIS OF MIXTURES

We have seen that the interpretation of a spectrum of a pure compound is often a complex and sometimes doubtful process. The identification of compounds in a mixture from its mass spectrum is at least an order of magnitude more difficult. An experienced analyst may be able to recognize characteristic peaks, but it is a tedious process, unless there are enough peaks which are unique to each compound present.

If the identities of the compounds in the sample mixture are known, then quantitative analysis is fairly straight-forward. The general principle is that contributions to each peak are additive for each compound present; that is, one records the sum of the spectra, in which each compound acts independently of all others present. Fortunately, at the very low pressures used in the spectrometer, this is a good approximation. Thus the total ion currents at each peak, I_1, I_2, I_3, etc., can be represented as the sum of the currents resulting from each compound:

$$I_1 = i_{1a} p_a + i_{1b} p_b + i_{1c} p_c + \cdots$$

$$I_2 = i_{2a} p_a + i_{2b} p_b + i_{2c} p_c + \cdots$$

$$I_3 = i_{3a} p_a + i_{3b} p_b + i_{3c} p_c + \cdots$$

where the numerical subscripts refer to various mass numbers and the letter subscripts refer to the various compounds present, i.e., i_{2b} is the ion current at mass 2 due to component b at unit pressure (a calibration factor), and p_b is the actual partial pressure of component b in the sample. The values for i_{1a} etc. must be obtained from spectra of pure compounds at known pressures. Another equation is available by noting that the total pressure is equal to the sum of the partial pressures. A set of simultaneous equations (at least as many as there are unknowns) can be solved for the unknown partial pressures (percent composition)—an obvious job for a computer. Often the only reliable way to analyze a mixture is to separate the compounds by some other technique—gas chromatography is an obvious choice.

The presence of a mixture may be ascertained by noting the change in the spectrum with time. In the sample introduction device, the lighter molecules diffuse through the leak faster than the heavier; thus the ratio of light to heavy molecules will decrease with time.

SOME ADDITIONAL APPLICATIONS

Isotope Labeling. One of the most powerful means of determining the mechanism of a reaction or the structure of a complex compound is to use a reactant containing a labeled atom and then find out its exact location in the product. A radioactive isotope is easily spotted, but for many applications, particularly those in some biochemical systems, the radioactivity may be objectionable. In these cases, a stable heavy isotope can be used. The mass spectrometer can locate the position of the labeled isotope by the change it causes in the spectrum (some fragments will appear at a different mass number.) In some cases, it may suffice to detect which fragment is the heavy one. In other cases, it may be necessary to determine the resulting ratio of heavy to normal isotope—for this the isotope-ratio spectrometer is ideal.

Non-Volatile Substances. High polymers and many natural products have vapor pressures too low for ordinary mass spectrometry. Nevertheless, nearly all substances can be pyrolyzed and the decomposition products subjected to mass spectrometry. Such information may serve as a fingerprint and can be used for analytical purposes.

Physical Chemical Data. With high resolution spectrometers, the exact determination of the masses of nuclides can be done with an accuracy of about one part in 10^8. Thus the masses of isotopes are known very precisely from mass spectrometry, and the limitation on exact atomic weights (in the chemical sense) is the uncertainty of the relative abundance of the isotopes. Even the relative abundances have been accurately measured by mass spectrometry, and the final remaining limitation is the variation of the abundance in nature.

Ionization potentials and bond strengths can be estimated from the appearance potentials.

Electromagnetic Separation. Although a mass spectrometer can hardly be classsed as a preparative-scale machine, it is extremely useful in preparing small samples of pure isotopes of the elements. It is a very inefficient and expensive method, but it has been particularly valuable for this purpose in the atomic energy program.

QUESTIONS AND PROBLEMS

13-1. The mass spectrum of methane has a large peak (parent and base) at 16 for the $CH_4^{\oplus}$ ion, with smaller peaks at 15, 14, 13, and 12 for loss of H atoms and at 17 for the presence of C^{13} or H^2 ($=D$). An equimolar mixture of CH_4 and CD_4 has the same number of D atoms as the amount of CH_2D_2 but the spectrum of the mixture $CH_4 + CD_4$ differs markedly from that of CH_2D_2. Describe and explain these two spectra.

13-2. The isotope contributions to the $CH_3^{\oplus}$ peak result from the normal abundance of C^{13} and D^2. On the C-12 scale $H^1 = 1.007825$ and $C^{13} = 13.00354$. With ordinary resolution, only three peaks are seen at 15, 16, and 17. Calculate the relative heights of the peaks at 16 and 17 (height of the 15 peak $= 100$) from the following data:

Compound	Rel. Abundance
$C^{12}H^1H^1H^1$	98.882
$C^{13}H^1H^1H^1$	1.074
$C^{12}H^1H^1D^2$	0.040
$C^{13}H^1H^1D^2$	0.004

13-3. From the data given in Problem 13-2, determine what resolution ($M/\Delta M$) would be required to separate the $C^{13}H_3^1$ peak from the $C^{12}H^1H^1D^2$ peak.

13-4. Explain the origin of as many peaks as you can in the spectra for the following compounds: (R.I. is relative intensity)

(a) *Iso-butane*

m/e	14	15	26	27	39	41	42
R.I.	1.18	6.41	2.36	27.8	16.5	38.1	33.5

m/e	43	44	57	58	59
R.I.	100	38.1	3.00	2.73	0.11

(b) *Iso-octane (2,2,4-trimethyl pentane)*

m/e	15	27	28	29	29.5	39	41
R.I.	4.46	11.8	2.08	15.2	0.15	9.43	27.0

m/e	43	56	57	58	99	114
R.I.	23.0	32.2	100	4.34	4.56	0.02

(c) *n-Octane*

m/e	15	27	28	29	30	39	41
R.I.	3.00	29.2	6.29	34.5	0.74	13.5	38.1

m/e	42	43	44	55	56	57	70
R.I.	15.6	100	3.33	10.1	18.0	34.2	12.3

m/e	71	84	85	114	115	116
R.I.	23.3	5.96	29.5	6.74	0.55	0.03

(d) *Tert.-Butyl alcohol (2-methyl-2-propanol)*

m/e	15	27	28	29	31	39	41
R.I.	10.0	7.2	6.8	9.8	2.82	5.03	12.07

m/e	43	57	59	60	74
R.I.	12.1	8.7	100	3.4	0

(e) *Diisopropyl ether*

m/e	27	28	29	31	39	41	42	43
R.I.	6.90	1.39	1.67	2.82	5.03	12.07	3.37	40.65

m/e	44	45	46	59	69	87	102
R.I.	3.48	100	2.22	10.61	3.27	22.26	0.54

(f) *Methyl acetate*

m/e	29	31	42	43	44	59	74	75
R.I.	10.50	3.43	10.24	100	2.86	5.71	15.21	0.54

(g) *Ethyl formate*

m/e	26	27	28	29	30	31	43	45
R.I.	12.57	43.17	72.66	65.80	5.49	100	7.51	28.69

m/e	46	47	74
R.I.	5.17	5.98	7.07

(h) *n-propyl amine*

m/e	15	18	27	28	30	41	42	43
R.I.	3.11	2.99	6.65	12.7	100	5.21	3.12	2.12

m/e	44	59
R.I.	1.28	7.76

13-5. Using Equation 13-5, compute the theoretical mass range of a Time-of-Flight mass spectrometer (assume that $k = 1$). Commercial instruments seldom are able to exceed a mass range of 200. Comment on the discrepancy.   *Ans.* 10,000.

13-6. A monoamine has the mass spectrum given below. What is the structure of this amine?

m/e	R.I.
115	17
100	50
58	100

13-7. Anthraquinone ($C_{14}H_8O_2$) gives major fragmentation peaks at m/e 180 and 152 as well as the molecular ion base peak at m/e 208. In addition, two metastable ions are present at m/e 155.8 and 128.3. What can be said regarding the origin of the fragment peaks?

13-8. Centrally labeled (C^{13}) neopentane upon electron impact gives $C_4H_9^{\oplus}$ and $C_3H_5^{\oplus}$ ions that are 100% and 90% labeled, but $C_2H_5^{\oplus}$ is only 47% labeled. Neopentane-1-C^{13} gave $C_4H_9^{\oplus}$ ions that were 76% labeled; $C_3H_5^{\oplus}$, 52% labeled; and $C_2H_5^{\oplus}$, 36% labeled. Rationalize this behavior, using structures where necessary. (See data on page 288.)

m/e					R. I.
72	.	.	.	.	0.01
57	.	.	.	.	100.0
41	.	.	.	.	41.5
39	.	.	.	.	12.7
29	.	.	.	.	38.5
27	.	.	.	.	14.9

CH₃
|
CH₃ — C — CH₃
|
CH₃
neopentane

13-9. The mass spectra for several unknown compounds are given below in terms of the relative intensity of the peak heights. Assign as many fragments as you can and try to identify the compound.

m/e	14	15	17	18	26	27	28	29
A	5.9	30.5			4.9	7.5		
B					9.1	4.5	2.6	100
C					21.5	58.2	69.0	100
D		3.6	3.6	12.8		4.7		4.3
E		3.1		3.0		6.7	12.7	3.0

m/e	30	31	41	42	43	44	45	46
A				6.8	100			
B				9.2	26.7	45.7	1.24	0.10
C	5.7				11.2			
D	100	3.0	3.0	6.2	5.3	4.3		
E	100		5.2	3.1				

m/e	57	58	59	60	61
A		33.1	1.3	0.10	
B					
C	10.8	37.4	1.5	0.10	
D				2.4	0.10
E			7.8	0.32	

REFERENCES

R. M. Silverstein and G. C. Bassler, *Spectrometric Identification of Organic Compounds*, 2nd ed., Wiley, New York, 1967. Brief discussion in Chapter 2, and extensive reproduction of Beynon's Tables. Many spectra worked out in problems involving other methods as well.

K. Biemann, *Mass Spectrometry: Organic Chemical Applications*, McGraw-Hill, New York, 1962. Good discussion of instrumentation, fragmentation processes, and applications.

J. H. Beynon, *Mass Spectrometry and Its Applications to Organic Chemistry*, Elsevier, Amsterdam, 1960. Definitive but difficult, and not well organized for beginner.

H. Budzikiewicz, C. Djerassi, and D. H. Williams, *Mass Spectrometry of Organic Compounds*, Holden Day, San Francisco, 1967. Modern treatment of fragmentation of organic compounds.

R. W. Kiser, *Introduction to Mass Spectrometry and Its Applications*, Prentice-Hall, Englewood Cliffs, N. J., 1965. Heavy emphasis on instrumentation and handling of data. Many tables in Appendices.

J. H. Beynon and A. E. Williams, *Mass and Abundance Tables for Use in Mass Spectrometry*, Elsevier, Amsterdam, 1963. Tables for all reasonable combinations of C, H, N, and O with fragment masses up to 500. Data are based on the C-12 scale.

F. W. McLafferty, *Interpretation of Mass Spectra. An Introduction*, Benjamin, New York, 1966. A short, readable "self-study" text, including many example spectra to work on (with answers).

14 ELECTROCHEMICAL MEASUREMENTS

Chemical reactions in which one or more electrons are actually transferred from one species to another constitute the domain of electrochemistry. That species which gives up the electron is called the electron donor, or "reductant":

$$Red_1 = Ox_1 + ne^- \text{ (half-reaction for oxidation)} \quad \text{e.g., } Zn = Zn^{++} + 2e^-$$

That species which acquires the electron is called the electron acceptor, or "oxidant":

$$Ox_2 + ne^- = Red_2 \text{ (half-reaction for reduction)} \quad \text{e.g., } Fe^{+++} + e^- = Fe^{++}$$

The combination of these two "half-reactions" gives a complete "redox" reaction:

$$Zn + 2Fe^{+++} = Zn^{++} + 2Fe^{++}$$

In the complete reaction, zinc atoms donate electrons to ferric ions. The actual transfer can be done either by a direct collision between the two species, or by a "long distance" transfer through a wire. In the latter case, the two species are physically separated and the reaction can be carried out in an electrochemical cell. Fortunately, a wide variety of reactions can be studied in electrochemical cells. In this chapter we shall examine a number of kinds of electrodes and the factors which determine their potential. Although most of the applications we shall consider might be called "inorganic," the same principles are applied to more complicated "organic" examples. Water, with its high dielectric constant, is the most satisfactory solvent, but some organic solvents or mixed solvents are nearly as good. By far the most common use of electrochemical cells in analytical chemistry is to determine the concentration of one or more of the species involved in the reaction; for example, the determination of hydrogen ion with the pH meter.

ELECTROCHEMICAL CELLS

Figure 14-1 shows a typical cell (to be referred to as cell 1) which consists of two half-cells. One half-cell contains a solution of a zinc salt and a piece of metallic zinc; the other contains a solution of ferrous and ferric ion and a piece of platinum metal which serves as an inert electrode to supply or withdraw electrons from the solution.

291

In the zinc half-cell, zinc metal may dissolve as zinc ion, leaving the electrons behind to give the electrode a negative charge. Alternatively, zinc ion may deposit as zinc metal on the electrode, causing a deficiency of electrons on the electrode. For a given concentration of zinc ion, an equilibrium situation is established with a resultant charge on the electrode. Likewise in the ferrous-ferric half-cell, ferrous and ferric ions can exchange electrons with the platinum electrode establishing an equilibrium and a resultant charge on the platinum electrode. In this case, the charge on the zinc electrode is more negative than the charge on the platinum electrode. If the two electrodes are connected with a wire, electrons must flow from zinc to platinum and the reaction just described presumably will occur. However, we cannot increase the concentration of zinc ion or change the initial ratio of ferrous to ferric ion without disturbing the electroneutrality of the solutions. Since we cannot add electrical charge to either solution, the reaction cannot continue unless we provide a mechanism for transferring ions from one half-cell to the other. The salt bridge serves this function by allowing a small ion current to pass from one half-cell to the other in either direction with only negligible mixing of the two electrolytes.

As this cell operates, (*a*) zinc metal is oxidized and dissolves, (*b*) electrons are transferred to the platinum through the wire, (*c*) ferric ion is reduced by the electrons on the platinum electrode, (*d*) cations migrate from the zinc half-cell to the ferrous-ferric half-cell through the salt bridge, and (*e*) anions migrate in the reverse direction. By means of appropriate switches and resistances in the external circuit we can start or stop the cell reaction or control its rate. By means of appropriate

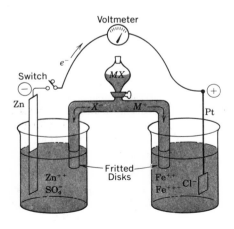

FIGURE 14-1. Schematic representation of cell 1.

meters we can measure its rate and the driving force (change in free energy) tending to make it go. With modern oscilloscopic and pulse techniques, we can also study the mechanisms and rates of fast electrode reactions.

The operation of a cell clearly requires a chemical reaction to take place. Thus the concentrations of the various species will necessarily change with time. For the most part we will be concerned only with cells that are not operating, i.e., essentially no current flowing. It is important to note that the charges on the electrodes are the result of chemical reactions; however, the amount of chemical reaction required to establish the charge is so slight that it cannot be measured and is safely neglected when compared to the total material in the cell. For example, a free charge of 10^{-17} mole of electrons will cause a potential of 1 volt at a distance of 1 cm. In these non-operating cells, we shall assume that each half-cell reaction is *in equilibrium with its own electrode*. A difference in potential between two electrodes implies that the two half-cell reactions are not in equilibrium with each other. In fact, the potential difference measures the force tending to drive the system toward equilibrium.

Some Typical Electrodes. In shorthand style, a half-cell is designated by listing the species taking part in the half-reaction, separating the electrode from the electrolyte by a vertical bar. A few examples will illustrate some of the conventions.

1. Metal-metal ion, in which the metal of the electrode takes part in the half-reaction:

$$Zn|Zn^{++} \text{ (as illustrated in Figure 14-1)}$$

2. Metal-complex ion, in which an excess of the complexing agent is added to regulate the particular form of the complex:

$$Cu|Cu(NH_3)_4^{++}, NH_3$$

3. Metal-saturated solution of one of its salts, in which the presence of the solid salt is inconsequential except to insure that the solution is saturated:

$$Ag|AgCl, Cl^-$$

4. Gas-ion, in which the solution is saturated at a given pressure with the gas as it is bubbled over the surface of an inert metal electrode:

$$Pt,H_2|H^+$$

5. Ion-ion, in which both the reduced and oxidized forms are soluble in the electrolyte, and an inert metal electrode (usually platinum) is used to make electrical contact between the electrolyte and the external circuit:

$$Pt|Fe^{+++}, Fe^{++} \text{ (as illustrated in Figure 14-1)}$$

6. Amalgam-ion, in which a reactive metal is amalgamated so that direct chemical reaction with the solvent is minimized:

$$Na(Hg)|Na^+$$

The order in which substances in the electrolyte are listed is irrelevant. When necessary to specify concentrations, this may be done within parentheses:

$$Pt|Cr^{+++}(0.5\ M),\ Cr_2O_7^=(0.1\ M),\ H^+(1.5\ M)$$

Finally, if two half-cells are combined to make a whole cell, the electrodes are listed first and last; for example, the cell in Figure 14-1 would be given as:

$$Zn|Zn^{++}||Fe^{+++},\ Fe^{++}|Pt$$

The double bar signifies the salt bridge between the two half-cells. Unless otherwise indicated, the solvent is assumed to be water and it is not listed as one of the cell ingredients even though it may take part in the reaction. In so far as practical, we shall write the predominant form of a species in the solution; e.g., Fe^{+++}, $Fe(OH)^{++}$, $FeCl_2^+$, HOAc, OAc$^-$, etc.

The following examples illustrate some typical cells and cell reactions. The direction in which half-reactions and the corresponding complete reaction are to be written is arbitrary and we shall return to this question shortly in the discussion of sign conventions. It should be apparent that for every cell there is a specific cell reaction. As a corollary, for every chemical reaction there should be a corresponding electrochemical cell, if we are clever enough to devise suitable electrode systems. In all of the examples there is oxidation and reduction at the electrodes, although some of the cell reactions would not normally be recognized as redox reactions.

Cell 2: $Pt,\ H_2|H^+||Cu^{++}|Cu$
$\quad\quad\quad$ *Right*: $Cu^{++} + 2e^- = Cu$
$\quad\quad\quad$ *Left*: $2H^+ + 2e^- = H_2$
$\quad\quad\quad$ *Cell*: $H_2 + Cu^{++} = Cu + 2H^+$

Cell 3: $Pt|Fe^{++},\ Fe^{+++}||Cr^{+++},\ Cr_2O_7^=,\ H^+|Pt$
$\quad\quad\quad$ *Right*: $Cr_2O_7^= + 14H^+ + 6e^- = 2Cr^{+++} + 7H_2O$
$\quad\quad\quad$ *Left*: $Fe^{+++} + e^- = Fe^{++}$
$\quad\quad\quad$ *Cell*: $Cr_2O_7^= + 6Fe^{++} + 14H^+ = 2Cr^{+++} + 6\ Fe^{+++} + 7H_2O$

Cell 4: $Pt,\ H_2|OH^-||H^+|H_2,\ Pt$
$\quad\quad\quad$ *Right*: $2H^+ + 2e^- = H_2$
$\quad\quad\quad$ *Left*: $2H_2O + 2e^- = 2OH^- + H_2$
$\quad\quad\quad$ *Cell*: $H^+ + OH^- = H_2O$

Cell 5: $Ag|AgCl,\ Cl^-||Cl^-,\ Hg_2Cl_2|Hg$

$Right$: $Hg_2Cl_2 + 2e^- = 2Hg + 2Cl^-$
$Left$: $AgCl + e^- = Ag + Cl^-$
$Cell$: $2Ag + Hg_2Cl_2 = 2AgCl + 2Hg$

Cell 6: Pt, $H_2|H^+||Cl^-$ Cl_2, Pt
$Right$: $Cl_2 + 2e^- = 2Cl^-$
$Left$: $2H^+ + 2e^- = H_2$
$Cell$: $H_2 + Cl_2 = 2H^+ + 2Cl^-$

Cell 7: $Cu|CuY^=, H_2Y^=, H^+||Cu^{++}|Cu$
$Right$: $Cu^{++} + 2e^- = Cu$
$Left$: $CuY^= + 2H^+ + 2e^- = Cu + H_2Y^=$
$Cell$: $Cu^{++} + H_2Y^= = CuY^= + 2H^+$

ELECTRODE POTENTIALS

The *charge* on an electrode results from an excess or deficiency of electrons on the metal. A large negative charge indicates the presence of a strong reducing agent (good electron donor).

The *potential* of an electrode is defined in an electrostatic sense. The absolute electric potential of a point is defined as the work needed to bring a unit of positive charge from an infinite distance in space to the point in question. Needless to say this is not a very practical measurement to make in the laboratory. We shall be concerned only with potential differences between two points; namely, the two electrodes of a cell. We should note that the point with the higher electric potential also has the higher positive charge. The potential difference thus compares the charge existing at two points, a relative measurement. We often use the term, "potential of an electrode," when we mean *potential difference relative to an arbitrary standard reference electrode*. Likewise, a "cell potential" is really the difference in potential between the two electrodes, and is more properly called the *cell voltage* or electromotive force (e.m.f. or EMF). We shall designate this term as E_{cell} rather than by ΔE or $\Delta \epsilon$.

Sign Conventions. The charge on an electrode, the electrode potential, the difference between two electrode potentials (cell voltage) and the direction of electron flow in a wire connecting the electrodes are all physical facts, independent of any arbitrary sign conventions. Nevertheless, since it is impossible to measure the charge or potential of a single electrode, we must select a consistent set of rules for writing reactions and computing electrode potentials. With more experience, there is no problem in working with any convention, in fact several are in common use. Some of these are discussed by Laitinen and by Licht and deBethune in the references given at the end of this chapter. For this text, we shall use only a minimum of arbitrary rules:

1. The potential of an electrode and the driving force (electromotive force) of the corresponding half-reaction are the same in magnitude and sign: both will be designated by the symbol E.

2. All half-reactions are written as reductions (electrons on the left).

3. E is a measure of:
   (a) The charge and electric potential of the electrode.
   (b) The tendency of a half reaction to go in the direction it is written.
   (c) The tendency of the system to accept electrons, that is, its power to oxidize some other species.

4. E for an electrode or a half-reaction is compared to and measured relative to E for the standard hydrogen electrode (SHE) to be described shortly. Thus the charge on the electrode and oxidizing power of the system may be either positive or negative, relative to the SHE.

5. The cell voltage, E_{cell}, is the algebraic difference taken in either direction, between the two electrode potentials. The potential of an electrode has a sign, but the cell voltage is given as an absolute value.

6. The corresponding *spontaneous cell reaction* is the one which occurs when the electrodes are connected with a wire and the cell is allowed to discharge. The spontaneous cell reaction is obtained by subtracting the half-reaction of the more negative electrode from that of the more positive. This follows because the half-reaction with the more negative potential contains the strongest reductant and supplies electrons to the electrode.

Obviously a cell reaction may be written in either direction; some authors relate the direction to geometry of the cell (right minus left or left minus right). We choose to relate the direction to that of the spontaneous reaction. The potentials of the electrodes used for the cells listed on page 294 are plotted in Figure 14-2. It is assumed that all concentrations are 1 M and all pressures 1 atm. Cell voltages are easily measured on the graph or computed by the subtractions indicated.

Standard Hydrogen Electrode. As we stated above, no one has yet measured a single electrode potential. Nor is it likely that anyone will ever do so, because a second electrode is always necessary in order to complete the electrical circuit. The voltmeter (or other voltage measuring device) can measure only *differences* in electrode potentials. But we can assign an arbitrary value to a selected electrode. If this so-called "primary standard" electrode is combined with some other electrode, we can then measure the potential of the second electrode with respect to the standard. Chemists have generally agreed to the arbitrary assignment of zero volt to the standard hydrogen electrode (SHE). Actually, this is a hypothetical electrode which is illustrated in Figure 14-3. As we will see later, we cannot give directions for preparing a solution with a hydrogen ion of unit *activity*, or measure

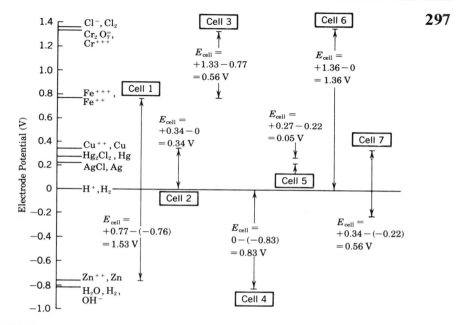

FIGURE 14-2. Electrode potentials and cell voltages for Example cells 1–7.

the *fugacity* of a real gas. In practice, the operation of obtaining a standard potential is performed by an extrapolation technique as described on page 306.

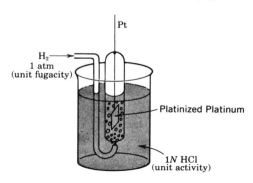

FIGURE 14-3. The (hypothetical) standard hydrogen electrode.

298   Any other electrode, once it has been calibrated against the SHE, will serve as a secondary standard. The silver-silver chloride electrode and the saturated calomel electrode described on pages 312-313 are often used as reference electrodes.

Effect of Concentration. Let us consider the ferrous-ferric electrode in more more detail. In Figure 14-4, the ferric ions and ferrous ions are in continuous motion and collide frequently with each other and with the electrode surface. For the ferric ions which reach the electrode surface, there is a finite probability

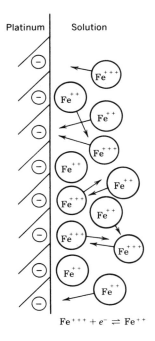

Platinum | Solution

$$Fe^{+++} + e^- \rightleftharpoons Fe^{++}$$

FIGURE 14-4. The dynamic equilibrium at the ferrous-ferric electrode.

that they will "pick up" an electron and become a ferrous ion. The degree of the probability depends on the electron affinity of the ferric ion and the "concentration" of electrons at the electrode surface. Similar considerations apply to the ferrous ions. Both processes occur simultaneously and for the most part cancel each other out. However, the equilibrium condition can be described by the ratio of the concentrations of the two ionic species and the "concentration" of electrons in the electrodes. The latter is more easily described as the charge or potential of the electrode. The mathematical expression which expresses the equilibrium situation is called the *Nernst equation*:

$$E = E^{\circ}_{Fe^{+++},Fe^{++}} - \frac{RT}{nF} \ln \frac{(Fe^{++})}{(Fe^{+++})} \qquad (14\text{-}1)$$

in which $E^{\circ}_{Fe^{+++},Fe^{++}}$ is a constant known as the standard potential, R the gas constant, T the absolute temperature, n the number of electrons transferred in the half reaction and F the Faraday constant. The Nernst equation can be derived from thermodynamic considerations or it can be obtained empirically as the best fit to the experimental data.

If the concentration of Fe^{++} is increased, there is a greater probability for their oxidation at the electrode surface, a higher density of electrons accumulates, and the electrode becomes more negative. The opposite is true for an increase in the ferric ion concentration. However, it is the *ratio* of concentrations that is important.

Standard Potentials. The constant term, E°, is the observed potential of the electrode when the concentrations of the two species, ferric and ferrous ion, are equal to each other; in which case their ratio is unity and the log term in Equation 14-1 is zero. E° expresses the inherent tendency of the system to accept electrons from the electrode and its value depends on the nature of the substances in the half-reaction. More accurately stated, the standard potential is the measured potential of an electrode (relative to the SHE) when all participating species are in their "standard states". Customarily, standard states for electrochemistry are defined as follows:

1. For all dissolved substances, concentration equal to one molar (more precisely, unit activity).

2. For all gases, partial pressure equal to one atmosphere (more precisely, unit fugacity).

3. For all pure liquids and pure solids, the most stable form at 25° C, which by definition has unit activity.

In principle, standard potentials are measured by means of cells such as cell 2:

$$Pt, H_2|H^+||Cu^{++}|Cu$$

with all species in their standard states; or by comparing the electrode to any secondary reference electrode which has been previously compared to the SHE. In practice, this procedure may not be as simple as it may seem. Some of the complicating factors to be considered in later sections include: (*a*) the difficulty of obtaining truly reversible electrode reactions, (b) the uncertainty of the junction potential between the two half cells, and (c) non-ideal behaviour of solutes. Some $E°$ values cannot be measured at all and are computed indirectly from other kinds of related thermodynamic data. The potentials plotted in Figure 14-2 are, of course, $E°$ values. A more complete list is given in Table 14-1. Extensive lists are available in the references by Latimer and by Clark, and in many texts and handbooks.

Use of the Nernst Equation. It is convenient to combine the constant factors in the log term of Equation 14-1 and convert natural logarithms (base e) to common logarithms (base 10). The simplified form of the Nernst equation is:

$$E = E° - \frac{0.059}{n} \log \frac{\text{(products)}}{\text{(reactants)}} \tag{14-2}$$

where 0.059 is valid for 25° C, 0.060 at 30° C, etc. The log term is set up much like the mass action expression for the reaction, but the numerical value is *not* equal to the equilibrium constant. Nernst equations for some of the electrodes used in cells 1 to 7 will serve as examples.

examples:

Pt, $H_2|H^+$ $\qquad\qquad\qquad 2H^+ + 2e^- = H_2$

$$E = 0 - \frac{0.059}{2} \log \frac{P_{H_2}}{(H^+)^2}$$

$Cu|Cu^{++}$ $\qquad\qquad\qquad Cu^{++} + 2e^- = Cu$

$$E = E°_{Cu^{++},Cu} - \frac{0.059}{2} \log \frac{1}{(Cu^{++})}$$

$Pt|Cr^{+++}, Cr_2O_7^=, H^+$ $\qquad Cr_2O_7^= + 14H^+ + 6e^- = 2Cr^{+++} + 7H_2O$

$$E = E°_{Cr_2O_7^=,Cr^{+++}} - \frac{0.059}{6} \log \frac{(Cr^{+++})^2}{(Cr_2O_7^=)(H^+)^{14}}$$

Pt, $H_2|OH^-$ $\qquad\qquad\qquad 2H_2O + 2e^- = 2OH^- + H_2$

$$E = E°_{OH^-,H_2} - \frac{0.059}{2} \log P_{H_2}(OH^-)^2$$

$Ag|AgCl, Cl^-$ $\qquad\qquad\qquad AgCl + e^- = Ag + Cl^-$

$$E = E°_{AgCl,Ag} - 0.059 \log (Cl^-)$$

In every case, the cell voltage is the algebraic difference between the two electrode potentials.

TABLE 14-1 STANDARD REDUCTION POTENTIALS IN AQUEOUS SOLUTIONS

$E°$, V	Couple
2.65	$F_2 + 2e^- = 2F^-$
2.07	$O_3 + 2H^+ + 2e^- = O_2 + H_2O$
1.77	$H_2O_2 + 2H^+ + 2e^- + 2H_2O$
1.695	$MnO_4^- + 4H^+ + 3e^- = MnO_2 + 2H_2O$
1.61	$Ce^{+4} + e^- = Ce^{+3}$
1.6	$H_5IO_6 + H^+ + 2e^- = IO_3^- + 3H_2O$
1.52	$BrO_3^- + 6H^+ + 5e^- = \frac{1}{2}Br_2 + 3H_2O$
1.51	$MnO_4^- + 8H^+ + 5e^- = Mn^{++} + 4H_2O$
1.36	$Cl_2 + 2e^- = 2Cl^-$
1.33	$Cr_2O_7^= + 14H^+ + 6e^- = 2Cr^{+++} + 7H_2O$
1.23	$MnO_2 + 4H^+ + 2e^- = Mn^{++} + 2H_2O$
1.229	$O_2 + 4H^+ + 4e^- = 2H_2O$
1.195	$IO_3^- + 6H^+ + 5e^- = \frac{1}{2}I_2 + 3H_2O$
1.065	$Br_2 + 2e^- = 2Br^-$
1.06	$ICl_2^- + e^- = \frac{1}{2}I_2 + 2Cl^-$
1.00	$VO_2^+ + 2H^+ + e^- = VO^{++} + H_2O$
0.87	$C_6H_5NO_2 + 7H^+ + 6e^- = C_6H_5NH_3^+ + 2H_2O$
0.799	$Ag^+ + e^- = Ag$
0.789	$Hg_2^{++} + 2e^- = 2Hg$
0.771	$Fe^{+++} + e^- = Fe^{++}$
0.73	$C_2H_2 + 2H^+ + 2e^- = C_2H_4$
0.699	$O = C_6H_4 = O + 2H^+ + 2e^- = HOC_6H_4OH$
0.682	$O_2 + 2H^+ + 2e^- = H_2O_2$
0.586	$CH_3OH + 2H^+ + 2e^- = CH_4 + H_2O$
0.564	$MnO_4^- + e^- = MnO_4^=$
0.536	$I_3^- + 2e^- = 3I^-$
0.5355	$I_2 + 2e^- = 2I^-$
0.521	$Cu^+ + e^- = Cu$
0.52	$C_2H_4 + 2H^+ + 2e^- = C_2H_6$
0.44	$HOOCCH = CHCOOH + 2H^+ + 2e^- = HOOCCH_2CH_2COOH$

(Continued)

TABLE 14-1 (Continued)

$E°$, V	Couple
0.361	$VO^{++} + 2H^+ + e^- = V^{+++} + H_2O$
0.36	$Fe(CN)_6^{-3} + e^- = Fe(CN)_6^{-4}$
0.337	$Cu^{++} + 2e^- = Cu$
0.31	$H_2C_2O_4 + 6H^+ + 6e^- = CH_3COOH + 2H_2O$
0.2676	$Hg_2Cl_2 + 2e^- = 2Hg + 2Cl^-$
0.222	$AgCl + e^- = Ag + Cl^-$
0.20	$CH_3COCOOH + 2H^+ + 2e^- = CH_3CHOHCOOH$
0.192	$CH_3CHO + 2H^+ + 2e^- = C_2H_5OH$
0.19	$HCHO + 2H^+ + 2e^- = CH_3OH$
0.17	$S_4O_6^= + 2e^- = 2S_2O_3^=$
0.17	$SO_4^= + 4H^+ + 2e^- = H_2SO_3 + H_2O$
0.15	$Sn^{+4} + 2e^- = Sn^{++}$
0.152	$Sb_2O_3 + 6H^+ + 6e^- = 2Sb + 3H_2O$
0.153	$Cu^{++} + e^- = Cu^+$
0.10	$TiO^{++} + 2H^+ + e^- = Ti^{+++} + H_2O$
0.1	$CO_2 + 6H^+ + 6e^- = CO(NH_2)_2 + H_2O$
0.095	$AgBr + e^- = Ag + Br^-$
0.056	$HCOOH + 2H^+ + 2e^- = HCHO + H_2O$
0.000	$2H^+ + 2e^- = H_2$
−0.118	$CH_3COOH + 2H^+ + 2e^- = CH_3CHO + H_2O$
−0.126	$Pb^{++} + 2e^- = Pb$
−0.13	$CrO_4^= + 4H_2O + 3e^- = Cr(OH)_3 + 5OH^-$
−0.136	$Sn^{++} + 2e^- = Sn$
−0.151	$AgI + e^- = Ag + I^-$
−0.196	$CO_2 + 2H^+ + 2e^- = HCOOH$
−0.255	$V^{+++} + e^- = V^{++}$
−0.276	$H_3PO_4 + 2H^+ + 2e^- = H_3PO_3 + H_2O$
−0.403	$Cd^{++} + 2e^- = Cd$
−0.41	$Cr^{+++} + e^- = Cr^{++}$
−0.44	$Fe^{++} + 2e^- = Fe$

TABLE 14-1 *(Continued)*

$E°$, V	Couple
−0.49	$2CO_2 + 2H^+ + 2e^- = H_2C_2O_4$
−0.50	$H_3PO_3 + 2H^+ + 2e^- = H_2PO_2 + H_2O$
−0.56	$Fe(OH)_3 + e^- = Fe(OH)_2 + OH^-$
−0.763	$Zn^{++} + 2e^- = Zn$
−0.828	$2H_2O + 2e^- = H_2 + 2OH^-$
−1.18	$V^{++} + 2e^- = V$
−1.66	$Al^{+++} + 3e^- = Al$
−2.25	$\frac{1}{2}H_2 + e^- = H^-$
−2.37	$Mg^{++} + 2e^- = Mg$
−2.714	$Na^+ + e^- = Na$
−3.045	$Li^+ + e^- = Li$

example / problem 14-1: What is the cell voltage for cell 3 if all concentrations are 0.1 M? For the ferric-ferrous electrode,

$$E = E°_{Fe^{+++},Fe^{++}} - 0.059 \log \frac{(Fe^{++})}{(Fe^{+++})}$$

$$= +0.77 - 0.059 \log \frac{0.1}{0.1} = +0.77 \text{ V}$$

For the dichromate-chromic electrode,

$$E = E°_{Cr_2O_7^=,Cr^{+++}} - \frac{0.059}{6} \log \frac{(Cr^{+++})^2}{(Cr_2O_7^=)(H^+)^{14}}$$

$$= +1.33 - \frac{0.059}{6} \log \frac{(0.1)^2}{(0.1)(0.1)^{14}} = +1.20 \text{ V}.$$

$$E_{cell} = 1.20 - 0.77 = 0.43 \text{ V}.$$

Note that E_{cell} is very sensitive to (H^+). For example if (H^+) were 0.001 M, other concentrations remaining 0.1 M, E_{cell} would be 0.14 V.

Activity Coefficients. Strictly speaking, the Nernst equation requires the use of activities rather than concentrations. The activity or effective concentration differs from the actual concentration because of interionic attractions and repulsions, as well as the finite space occupied by the various species and their solvation shells. To some extent, thermal motions modify the electrical effects. The activity coefficient expresses the ratio of activity to concentration

$$f_i = a_i/C_i \quad \text{or} \quad a_i = f_iC_i \tag{14-3}$$

where the subscript "i" stands for any given species. Although some may think f stands for "fudge factor," actually we know a great deal about this factor which measures the departure of real systems from ideal behaviour. There is, however, no way to be sure that we have included every possibility since there is no way to measure the activity coefficient of a single ion. Consider the problem of the activity coefficients in the following cell:

$$\text{Cell 8:} \quad \text{Pt, } H_2 | H^+, \, Cl^-, \, AgCl | Ag$$

This cell requires only a single electrolyte with both electrodes immersed in the same solution of HCl. The voltage for this cell is obtained from the two half-cell potentials:

$$\textit{Left: } E = E_H^\circ - \frac{0.059}{2} \log \frac{P_{H_2}}{(H^+)^2}$$

$$\textit{Right: } E = E_{AgCl,Ag}^\circ - 0.059 \log (Cl^-)$$

From Table 14-1, the right electrode is the more positive.

$$E_{cell} = E_{AgCl,Ag}^\circ + \frac{0.059}{2} \log P_{H_2} - 0.059 \log (H^+)(Cl^-) \tag{14-4}$$

Here we have the *product* of two activities. It is impossible to construct a cell in which there is only one ion in the cell reaction. While we can measure the *concentration* of each ion, we can measure only the *product of their activities* and thus only the product of their activity coefficients. If both ions have the same numerical charge, it is customary to assign the same value to each activity coefficient. This clearly must be the square root of the product, or the geometric mean. The *mean ionic activity coefficient* is thus defined:

$$f_\pm = \sqrt{f_+ \times f_-} \tag{14-5}$$

Although the *mean* ionic activity coefficient is the only one we can measure, the extended form of the Debye-Hückel limiting law provides a means to estimate the value of an *individual* ionic activity coefficient. In the original derivation of the Debye-Hückel law, ions were assumed to be point charges in a continuous medium of dielectric constant equal to that of the solvent. In the extended form of this law, the sizes of the ions are also considered. The extended Debye-Hückel law shows that the activity coefficient of an ion, f_i, depends on the total population of all ions, rather than on the concentration of the given ion.

$$-\log f_i = \frac{AZ_i^2 \sqrt{\mu}}{1 + Ba\sqrt{\mu}} \qquad (14\text{-}6)$$

where Z_i = the charge of the given ion

μ = ionic strength of the solution which is equal to one half of the sum of the concentration of each ion in the solution multiplied by the square of its charge, i.e.,

$$\mu = \tfrac{1}{2} \sum_i C_i Z_i^2 \qquad (14\text{-}7)$$

A = a constant which depends on the absolute temperature, T, and the dielectric constant, ϵ, of the solvent, e.g.,

$$A = 1.825 \times 10^6 \, (\epsilon T)^{-3/2}$$

for water, $A = 0.509$ at 25° C.

a = an adjustable parameter which is measured in angstrom units and roughly corresponds to the effective size of the hydrated ion.

B = a constant which also depends on the absolute temperature and the dielectric constant of the solvent, e.g.,

$$B = 50.3 \, (\epsilon T)^{-1/2}$$

$$B = 0.328 \text{ for water at 25° C.}$$

For an electrolyte $M_m X_x$ the mean ionic activity coefficient is given by

$$-\log f_\pm = \frac{AZ_m Z_x \sqrt{\mu}}{1 + Ba\sqrt{\mu}} \qquad (14\text{-}8)$$

where Z_m and Z_x are the charges on the anion and cation, respectively, without regard to sign. The mean activity coefficient has been determined experimentally for many electrolytes at various ionic strengths and the agreement with Equation 14-8 is very good. Single ion activity coefficients calculated by using Equation 14-6 are listed for several ions at various ionic strengths in Table 14-2.

example / problem 14-2: Calculate the mean ionic activity coefficient of 10^{-5} M HCl in a solution of 0.01 M Na_2SO_4.

The ionic strength consists primarily of the Na_2SO_4 and is computed from Equation 14-7:

$$\mu = \tfrac{1}{2}\Sigma C_i Z_i^2$$
$$= \tfrac{1}{2}(0.02 \times 1^2 + 0.01 \times 2^2) = 0.03$$

Then from Equation 14-8:

$$-\log f_\pm = \frac{AZ^2 \sqrt{\mu}}{1 + Ba\sqrt{\mu}}$$

$$= \frac{0.5 \times 1^2 \times \sqrt{0.03}}{1 + 0.328 \times 9 \times \sqrt{0.03}} = 0.0567$$

$$f_{\pm} = 0.88$$

TABLE 14-2 SINGLE ION ACTIVITY COEFFICIENTS

Ion Size, a	Ion	Ionic Strength			
		0.005	0.01	0.05	0.1
9	H^+	0.933	0.914	0.86	0.83
6	Li^+, $C_6H_5COO^-$	0.929	0.907	0.84	0.80
4	Na^+, IO_3^-, HSO_3^-, $H_2PO_4^-$	0.927	0.901	0.82	0.77
3	K^+, Cl^-, Br^-, CN^-, NO_3^-	0.925	0.899	0.81	0.76
2.5	Cs^+, NH_4^+, Ag^+	0.924	0.898	0.80	0.75
8	Mg^{++}, Be^{++}	0.755	0.69	0.52	0.45
6	Ca^{++}, Cu^{++}, Zn^{++}, Mn^{++}, $C_6H_4(COO)_2^=$	0.749	0.675	0.49	0.41
4	Hg_2^{++}, $SO_4^=$, $CrO_4^=$, $HPO_4^=$	0.740	0.660	0.445	0.355
9	Al^{+3}, Fe^{+3}, Cr^{+3}	0.54	0.445	0.245	0.18
4	PO_4^{-3}, $Fe(CN)_6^{-3}$	0.505	0.395	0.16	0.10
5	$Fe(CN)_6^{-4}$	0.31	0.20	0.05	0.02

[From Kielland, *J. Am. Chem. Soc.*, **59**, 1675 (1937).]

Let's use the definition of activity coefficients, Equations 14-3 and 14-5, in rewriting Equation 14-4:

$$E_{cell} = E^{\circ}_{AgCl,Ag} + \frac{0.059}{2} \log P_{H_2} - 0.059 \log C_{HCl}^2 - 0.059 \log f_{\pm}^2 \quad (14\text{-}9)$$

Now gather all measurable terms on the left:

$$E_{cell} - \frac{0.059}{2} \log P_{H_2} + 0.118 \log C_{HCl} = E^{\circ}_{AgCl,Ag} - 0.118 \log f_{\pm} \quad (14\text{-}10)$$

It is found from experiment that a plot of the left side of Equation 14-10 vs. $\sqrt{\mu}$ gives a straight line, Figure 14-5. At zero concentration, or zero ionic strength, $\log f_{\pm}$ also becomes zero, and the intercept gives the value of $E^{\circ}_{AgCl,Ag}$. *This is the fundamental method of measuring E° values.*

Now that E° has been determined we can use Equation 14-10 or Figure 14-5 to determine $f_{\pm}$ for HCl at any ionic strength.

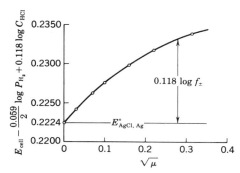

FIGURE 14-5. Plot of Equation 14-10 to yield the standard potential of the silver-silver chloride electrode at infinite dilution and the mean ionic activity coefficient of HCl.

For many of the discussions in this text, the distinction between activity and concentration is not important, and we will often use concentration where activity is more properly correct. Where the distinction is important, we will point this out and make such corrections as we can. In general, the use of parentheses will mean that activities should be used, but that concentrations will suffice. Where a distinction is required, we use the symbols a_i and C_i.

Liquid Junction Potential. Cell 8 is a special type of cell with only a single electrolyte and therefore no liquid junction (salt bridge). Most cells require two electrolytes with a junction between them. This introduces another uncertainty into our measurements. Whenever two solutions of different compositions are in contact, there is a tendency for diffusion of species from one solution to the other in order to equalize the concentrations. In general, the diffusion rates of the various species will not be the same and this will cause a slight separation of charges near the boundary between the two solutions. The electrical potential generated by this separation is called the *junction potential, E_j*. It will, of course, be included in the measured cell potential. In a few simple cases, the magnitude of this junction potential can be calculated from known diffusion coefficients. In general, the problem is too complex to handle. The junction potential can be reduced (but not altogether eliminated) by the use of a saturated solution of KCl in the salt bridge. This is so because the diffusion rates of K^+ and Cl^- are nearly equal. The effects of the diffusion of relatively large and nearly equal amounts of K^+ and Cl^- will overshadow the diffusion of the less concentrated constituents of the half-cells. Even so the uncertainty may be of the order of several millivolts. The use of $||$ indicates that we have reduced E_j to a minimum and will ignore it.

Reversibility. In the discussion of the Nernst equation, we have tacitly assumed that the electrode system behaves reversibly. By this we mean that the components within the half-cell system are always at equilibrium with the electrode. In other words, an infinitesimal change in the charge on the electrode results in an immediate change in concentrations to maintain the equilibrium; or, conversely, that an infinitesimal change in the concentrations results in an immediate change in charge on the electrode. This represents an ideal system; real systems approach this behaviour to varying degrees. A few of the soft metals (Ag, Hg, Pb, Zn, Cu, etc.) with their respective ions meet this criterion very well. Some others behave reversibly if the metal is amalgamated with mercury (Na, Cd, Bi, Tl, etc.). On the other hand, the mechanisms of most electrode reactions are very complicated indeed. The transfer of electrons between the electrode and electro-active species in solution can take place rapidly and reversibly only when the reduced and oxidized forms have essentially identical structures. Any rearrangement in the solvation shell or a transfer of atoms from one species to another will require promotion of the species to a higher energy state (activated complex). Under these circumstances the electrode reaction may take place very slowly and irreversibly or not at all, and the Nernst equation will be a poor approximation of the observed behavior. It is not surprising that many inorganic and most organic electrode reactions are irreversible. Many of these do, however, give reproducible behavior and are useful on an empirical basis.

Formal Potentials. Many redox reactions involve species other than those between which electrons are transferred. For example, many oxidants contain oxygen, requiring that hydrogen or hydroxyl ions and water appear in the reaction.

TABLE 14-3 FORMAL POTENTIALS

Couple	E°, V	E', V		
		1 F HClO$_4$	1 F HCl	1 F H$_2$SO$_4$
V^{+++}/V^{++}	-0.255	-0.21		
$H^+/\frac{1}{2}H_2$	0.000	0.005	0.005	
$Fe(CN)_6^{-3}/Fe(CN)_6^{-4}$	0.36	0.72	0.71	0.72
VO^{++}/V^{+++}	0.361			0.360
Fe^{+++}/Fe^{++}	0.771	0.732	0.700	0.68
Ag^+/Ag	0.7991	0.792	0.228	0.77
VO_2^+/VO^{++}	1.00	1.02	1.02	1.0
Ce^{+4}/Ce^{+3}	1.61	1.70	1.28	1.44

[After Swift, *A System of Chemical Analysis*, Prentice-Hall, 1940; p. 540.]

In other cases, complexing agents may be consumed or released. Consider, for example, the reaction between copper (I) and permanganate in hydrochloric acid:

$$10Cl^- + 5CuCl_2^- + MnO_4^- + 8H^+ = 5CuCl_4^= + Mn^{++} + 4H_2O$$

We can imagine this as a cell reaction and write each half-cell potential separately:

$$E_{Mn} = E^\circ_{MnO_4^-, Mn^{++}} - \frac{0.059}{5} \log \frac{(Mn^{++})}{(MnO_4^-)(H^+)^8} \tag{14-11}$$

$$E_{Cu} = E^\circ_{CuCl_4^=, CuCl_2^-} - 0.059 \log \frac{(CuCl_2^-)(Cl^-)^2}{(CuCl_4^=)} \tag{14-12}$$

When we use this reaction, we employ an excess of hydrochloric acid and its concentration stays relatively constant as the reaction proceeds. Under these conditions, (H^+) in Equation 14-11 is a constant and the log term can be separated:

$$E_{Mn} = \underbrace{E^\circ_{MnO_4^-, Mn^{++}} + \frac{0.059}{5} \log (H^+)^8}_{} - \frac{0.059}{5} \log \frac{(Mn^{++})}{(MnO_4^-)} \tag{14-13}$$

$$E_{Mn} = E'_{MnO_4^-, Mn^{++}} \qquad\qquad - \frac{0.059}{5} \log \frac{(Mn^{++})}{(MnO_4^-)} \tag{14-14}$$

Equations 14-13 and 14-14 define the *formal potential*, E', for this couple. E' is a constant which has a different value for each concentration of hydrogen ion. E' can be described as an effective or practical value of E°, and in this case it is seen that E' becomes more positive by $(8/5) \times 0.059$ V as (H^+) is increased tenfold. Thus changing the pH is a simple and powerful means for altering the oxidizing or reducing power of a reagent. This is a common situation for many inorganic and most organic reactions.

The same argument can be applied to define a formal potential for the copper half-cell which includes the effect of the concentration of Cl^-:

$$E_{Cu} = \underbrace{E^\circ_{CuCl_4^=, CuCl_2^-} - 0.059 \log (Cl^-)^2}_{} - 0.059 \log \frac{(CuCl_2^-)}{(CuCl_4^=)} \tag{14-15}$$

$$E_{Cu} = E'_{CuCl_4^=, CuCl_2^-} \qquad\qquad - 0.059 \log \frac{(CuCl_2^-)}{(CuCl_4^=)} \tag{14-16}$$

Formal potentials include the effects of ionic strength, complexation, hydrolysis, the pH effect and any other effect which can be attributed to the composition of the electrolyte other than the ratio of reduced to oxidized forms. A few formal potentials are listed in Table 14-3. Unfortunately, there are only a limited number of formal potentials available. The whole idea departs from the beauty of a simple tabulation of fundamental data, but in a practical sense, the answer obtained using a formal potential is more likely to be correct.

Biochemical Formal Potentials. The redox couples of interest to organic chemists, and especially to biochemists, often include hydrogen ion as a reactant or product. The potentials of such systems are thus a function of the pH of the medium, which in the case of biochemical systems is normally close to pH 7. In order to make comparisons of oxidizing or reducing power for biochemical purposes, it is convenient to set up a new table of "standard" potentials adjusted to pH 7. The conversion term is $0.059 (n_H/n_e) \log (H^+)$, where n_H and n_e are the number of protons and electrons respectively appearing in the half-reaction. In general, 1 proton and 1 electron are involved, so that the potential becomes approximately 0.41 V more negative (better reducing agents) at pH 7 than at pH 0. Typical "adjusted" potentials, symbolized by E_7, are found in Table 14-4.

TABLE 14-4 FORMAL POTENTIALS AT pH 7

Couple	$E°$, V	E_7', V
$H^+/\frac{1}{2}H_2$	0	−0.413
Riboflavin/leucoriboflavin	0.21	−0.20
Pyruvate/lactate	0.22	−0.19
Oxalacetate/malate	0.247	−0.166
Fumarate/succinate	0.444	0.031
Q/H_2Q	0.6994	0.286
O_2/H_2O	1.229	0.816

A simple example is the quinone-hydroquinone system:

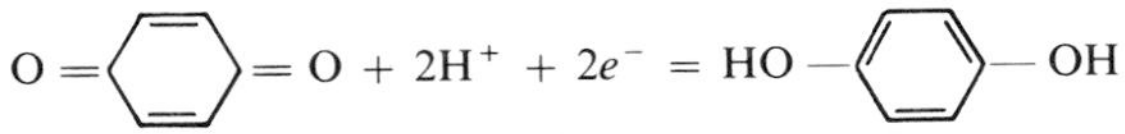

$$O = \text{⟨C_6H_4⟩} = O + 2H^+ + 2e^- = HO - \text{⟨C_6H_4⟩} - OH$$

or

$$Q \quad + 2H^+ + 2e^- = H_2Q$$

for which the Nernst equation is:

$$E = E° - 0.059/2 \log (H_2Q)/(Q)(H^+)^2 \tag{14-17}$$

or

$$E = \underbrace{E° + 0.059 \log (H^+)}_{E_7'\ \text{if}\ (H^+)\ =\ 10^{-7}\ M} - 0.059/2 \log (H_2Q)/(Q) \tag{14-18}$$

The quinone-hydroquinone system forms the quinhydrone electrode (vide infra) which measures pH. This follows from a different combination of terms in Equation 14-17:

$$E = \underbrace{E^\circ - 0.059/2 \log (H_2Q)/(Q)}_{E' \text{ for quinhydrone electrode used to measure } pH} + 0.059 \log (H^+) \qquad (14\text{-}19)$$

The pyruvate-lactate couple is another typical example:

or

$$\text{py} \quad + 2H^+ + 2e^- = \quad \text{lac}$$

for which: $E = \underbrace{E^\circ + 0.059/2 \log (H^+)^2}_{E_7' \text{ if } (H^+) = 10^{-7} M} - 0.059/2 \log (\text{lac})/(\text{py}) \qquad (14\text{-}20)$

The pyruvate-lactate couple is one of many couples in a long series of redox reactions associated with the metabolism of carbohydrates. Tables of E_7' data are far more convenient and pertinent to the study of these complex systems.

TYPES OF ELECTRODES

Electrodes are classified in two broad groups: indicator and reference electrodes. The reference electrode must be easy to construct, and must maintain a constant, reproducible potential even if small currents are passed. The indicator electrode must respond to changes in concentration of the species to be measured. Some electrodes are especially useful for one or both of these purposes.

The Hydrogen Electrode. Although this electrode is the standard of reference (see Figure 14-3 and related discussion), it is inconvenient to construct and difficult to maintain. A source of highly purified hydrogen is required, and its partial pressure within the cell must be regulated. The platinum surface must be coated with a thin layer of platinum black to increase its surface area and catalyze the electrode reaction. Traces of impurities in either the gas or solution may poison the electrode. The electrode responds to most other redox couples and therefore strong oxidants or reductants must not be present. Its use is limited mostly to calibrating other electrodes and to measuring hydrogen ion concentrations for solutions in which no other electrode will operate satisfactorily.

The Quinhydrone Electrode. The composition and function of this electrode have just been discussed, and it is only necessary to add that a solution containing equal concentrations of quinone and hydroquinone is easily prepared from solid quinhydrone, a molecular addition compound of quinone and hydro-quinone:

$$2QH = Q + H_2Q$$

Equation 14-19 then becomes

$$E = 0.6994 - 0.059\,pH \qquad (14\text{-}21)$$

Hydroquinone may be oxidized in the presence of strong oxidants and it will dissociate as a weak acid ($pK_a \sim 10$) in appreciable amounts above pH 8.5. Either of these processes will disturb the ratio of H_2Q/Q and give erroneous results for pH.

Smooth Platinum Electrode. A piece of smooth, bright platinum wire or plate responds to most redox couples when all species are present in the solution (including dissolved gases). In moderately strong acid solutions, we would expect the platinum to respond to pH (as in the SHE). However, with *smooth* platinum, the reduction of hydrogen ion is somewhat irreversible and the electrode is normally insensitive to pH. Very strong reductants, e.g., Cr^{++}, may be oxidized by hydrogen ion in the presence of platinum, giving erroneous redox potentials.

Saturated Calomel Electrode (SCE). This popular reference electrode is easily constructed from readily available materials. A solution is saturated with both calomel (mercurous chloride) and potassium chloride and placed over a layer of mercury which serves as the electrode. A commercial version of this electrode is shown in Figure 14-6.

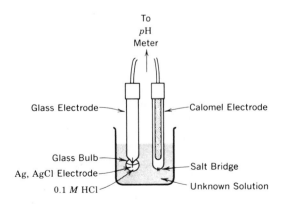

FIGURE 14-6. Schematic diagram of the glass and calomel electrodes.

$$\text{Hg} | \text{Hg}_2\text{Cl}_2, \text{KCl(sat)}$$

The potential can be derived from the primary reaction:

$$\text{Hg}_2^{++} + 2e^- = 2\text{Hg}$$

and the corresponding Nernst equation:

$$E = E_{\text{Hg}}^{\circ} - \frac{0.059}{2} \log \frac{1}{(\text{Hg}_2^{++})} \tag{14-22}$$

But the concentration of Hg_2^{++} is in turn controlled by the concentration of Cl^- which is essentially the same as the solubility of KCl. Chloride ion from Hg_2Cl_2 is negligible compared to that from KCl.

$$E = E_{\text{Hg}}^{\circ} - \frac{0.059}{2} \log \frac{(\text{Cl}^-)^2}{K_{\text{Hg}_2\text{Cl}_2}} \tag{14-23}$$

where $K_{\text{Hg}_2\text{Cl}_2}$ is the solubility product of Hg_2Cl_2.

Rearranging Equation 14-23, we define a new E° term for this electrode reaction:

$$E = \underbrace{E_{\text{Hg}}^{\circ} + \frac{0.059}{2} \log K_{\text{Hg}_2\text{Cl}_2}}_{E_{\text{Hg}_2\text{Cl}_2, \text{Hg}}^{\circ}} - 0.059 \log (\text{Cl}^-) = 0.242 \text{ v.} \tag{14-24}$$

The temperature coefficient of the SCE is practically the same as that of the solubility of KCl; viz.,

$$E_{\text{SCE}} = +0.242 - 7.6 \times 10^{-4} (t - 25), \tag{14-25}$$

where t is the temperature in $^{\circ}$C. Because the potential is controlled by a species that does not take part in the electrode reaction, this is known as an *electrode of the second order.*

Silver Chloride Electrode. A silver wire in contact with chloride ion is readily coated with a layer of AgCl. It is an excellent indicator for chloride ion concentration and a convenient reference electrode.

$$\text{Ag} | \text{AgCl}, \text{Cl}^-$$

$$E = E_{\text{Ag}^+, \text{Ag}}^{\circ} - 0.059 \log \frac{1}{(\text{Ag}^+)}$$

$$E = \underbrace{E_{\text{Ag}^+, \text{Ag}}^{\circ} + 0.059 \log K_{\text{AgCl}}}_{E_{\text{AgCl}, \text{Ag}}^{\circ}} - 0.059 \log (\text{Cl}^-) \tag{14-26}$$

Glass Electrode. No doubt the most common potentiometric measurement is the determination of hydrogen ion with the glass electrode and a *p*H meter. Figure 14-6 is a schematic representation of typical glass and calomel electrodes available commercially. Inside the glass electrode is a silver wire dipping into a solution of *ca.* 0.1 *M* HCl. The bulb at the tip of the electrode is made of a special glass composition. The inner surface of this glass membrane contacts the 0.1 *M* HCl solution and the outer surface contacts the solution in which the *p*H is to be measured. At each surface the glass membrane absorbs water forming a gel layer. The hydrogen ions from the solution can diffuse through the gel layer and replace (ion exchange) sodium or other metal ions in the glass structure. The net result of the diffusion and exchange processes is that a phase boundary potential is set up on each side of the glass membrane with the magnitude determined by the activity of hydrogen ion in the contacting solution.

The overall potential of the glass electrode consists of several parts: (*a*) the potential of the internal silver-silver chloride electrode, (*b*) the potential developed at the inner glass surface, (*c*) the asymmetry potential (caused by strains and imperfections in the glass membrane) and (*d*) the potential developed at the outer surface. However, potentials (*a*), (*b*), and (*c*) are all constant for a given electrode, and it is only (*d*) which changes with *p*H of the test solution. In practice, it is convenient to combine the constant potential terms and write the potential of the electrode in the usual Nernst form:

$$E = E'_G + 0.059 \log (H^+) \tag{14-27}$$

Equation 14-27 can be derived from Donnan membrane theory or simply stated as the observed response of the glass electrode.

The glass electrode is a most convenient electrode to use but it has a few drawbacks. The commercial version is moderately expensive and somewhat fragile— the sensitive tip is easily scratched and ruined. The electrical resistance of the glass membrane is exceedingly high (ca. 30 megohms) requiring the use of high impedance amplifiers (see below) and special care to prevent electrical leakages in other parts of the circuit. In highly alkaline solution, the concentration of H^+ is so low that other ions in the solution may interfere. For example, in strong NaOH solutions, the electrode may function as a sodium ion indicator electrode to some extent and a correction is necessary for accurate *p*H measurements. Special glass compositions with low sodium content are available at extra cost. Other special glasses with high sodium content have been developed specifically for measuring Na^+ concentrations, and glasses for measuring some other metal ions are on the market.

CELL VOLTAGE MEASUREMENTS

Ordinary voltmeters and ammeters require small but appreciable currents to deflect the needle. Since any current flowing through the cell will necessarily change the concentrations of the reacting species, the simple voltmeter is not a suitable device for accurately measuring a cell voltage. Two alternatives are available.

Electronic Voltmeter. Sometimes known as the vacuum tube voltmeter (VTVM), this meter incorporates an electronic amplifier so that only minute currents are required. In order to obtain highest accuracy and precision, an expensive complicated circuit is required. Electronic circuits are subject to drifting and aging, so the instrument must be standardized from time to time.

Potentiometer. The second approach makes use of an auxiliary variable voltage source which can be matched to the cell voltage to be measured. If the two voltages are identical and opposed to each other, no current will flow, and the null point can be detected by a simple galvanometer. The details of this circuit are shown in Figure 14-7. Although small currents are momentarily drawn in order to find the null point, the final measurement is made under no-flow conditions.

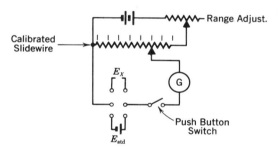

FIGURE 14-7. Simple potentiometer circuit.

Potentiometric Recorder. In addition to cell voltages, many phenomena of chemical interest can be readily converted to a voltage signal. Often the property of interest is changing with time, sometimes too rapidly for manual measurement. In any case, it is a great convenience to record voltage automatically. Basically, the recorder is a self-balancing potentiometer, with a pen drive coupled to the moving slide-wire contact so that its position can be automatically and continuously recorded on a paper chart. The chart is driven by a synchronous motor so that the pen traces a curve of voltage vs. time.

DEFINITION OF pH AND THE pH METER

We have deferred discussing this seemingly very elementary concept until we have developed the necessary background to present the practical scale of pH numbers. "*p*H" is one of the most used and misused terms in all of chemistry.

First of all, let us note the difference between concentration of total titratable hydrogen ion (including that of undissociated acids present), and the concentration of *free* hydrogen ion. The former can be determined by titration, but the latter cannot because any addition of base will cause further dissociation of any acids present. To determine free hydrogen ion concentration we must make the measurement without disturbing the existing equilibria. The term "*p*H" refers to free hydrogen ion concentration.

Operational Definition of pH. The definition employed should be capable of theoretical interpretation and practical measurement. Of all the techniques available to measure free hydrogen ion in a solution of unknown composition, none will measure either concentration or activity. The simple definitions, $pH = -\log C_H$ and $pH = -\log a_H$, are therefore not sufficient. Since pH is most often measured with a glass electrode and a pH meter, let us restrict our considerations to this technique. (The problems are similar with all other methods.) The cell to be used is represented:

$$\text{Cell 9:} \quad \text{Glass}|\text{H}^+||\text{SCE}$$

To compute the cell voltage, we will assume that the SCE is more positive than the glass electrode.

$$E_{\text{cell}} = \underbrace{E_{\text{SCE}} + E_j - E_G'} - 0.059 \log (\text{H}^+)$$

or

$$E_{\text{cell}} = \qquad E^* \qquad - 0.059 \log a_H$$
$$= \qquad E^* \qquad - 0.059 \log C_H f_H \qquad (14\text{-}28)$$

In our discussion of activity coefficients, it was shown that it is not possible to measure or compute f_H by itself. However, f_H is very nearly equal to $f_{\pm}$ which can be measured in cells such as Cell 8. (See page 304.)

$$\text{Cell 8:} \quad \text{Pt,H}_2|\text{H}^+,\text{Cl}^-,\text{AgCl}|\text{Ag}$$

Therefore, for practical purposes, pH is defined as:

$$pH = -\log C_H f_{\pm} \qquad (14\text{-}29)$$

or in terms of the voltage of either cell 8 or 9 just described

$$E_{\text{cell}} = E^* + 0.059 \, pH \qquad (14\text{-}30)$$

or

$$pH = \frac{E_{\text{cell}} - E^*}{0.059} \qquad \text{at } 25° \text{ C.} \qquad (14\text{-}31)$$

where E^* is a different constant for each cell.

Equation 14-31 is the *operational definition of pH*. Thus two approximations are tacitly included in the definition of *p*H: (*a*) the junction potential, E_j, remains constant, and (*b*) $f_H = f_{\pm}$. The second approximation is reasonably good in dilute aqueous solution, but the first is good only if the value of E_j is small (a few millivolts at most), as it should be with an effective salt bridge.

The pH Scale. The E^* term contains so many complications that it can only be determined empirically. A solution of known *p*H is required. Such a solution has been specified by the National Bureau of Standards using Equation 14-28 after a careful study of the most nearly ideal systems available. Actually several standard buffers have been specified, because no glass electrode follows the Nernst equation precisely over a wide range of *p*H values. Thus the working *p*H scale is an arbitrary set of numbers defined as described above. The *p*H value is close, but not exactly equal, to —log a_H. When one considers the approximations and experimental limitations, it is evident that it is very difficult indeed to reduce the error below ± 0.01 *p*H unit, although small changes in *p*H can be measured at the ± 0.001 level.

The pH Meter. The *p*H meter is basically an electronic voltmeter (or potentiometer) designed for use with a glass electrode system. From Equation 14-30 we see that 1 *p*H unit is equivalent to 59 mv at 25° C. Therefore, the same meter can be used with two scales to read either mv or *p*H units.

The basic circuit diagram of a typical *p*H meter is given in Figure 14-8. The

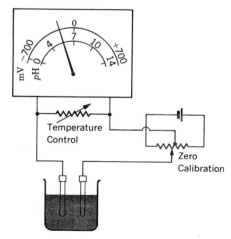

FIGURE 14-8.   Schematic diagram of a *p*H meter.

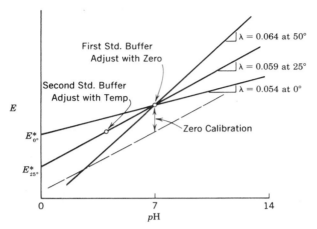

FIGURE 14-9. Plot of Equation 14-30, the basic equation of a pH meter. (Not to scale.) Zero calibration raises or lowers response line. Temperature control changes slope of response line.

sensitivity of the meter (scale divisions/mV) is adjustable by a temperature control knob to allow for a change in the 0.059 factor with temperature (or to allow for non-ideal response of the electrode). To read absolute mV rather than pH, the temperature control is disconnected entirely. The zero calibration knob changes the zero setting of the meter by introducing a bias voltage into the meter circuit so that the meter reading will correspond to the pH of the standard buffer.

pH meters are often constructed so that the true zero of the voltmeter is at or near pH 7 on the scale. In use, the meter should first be standardized with a pH 7 buffer, adjusting the zero calibration to give the correct reading. Then a second buffer, pH 4 or 10, is substituted and meter is adjusted to give the correct reading with the temperature control. This procedure establishes the correct linear relationship between mv and pH. At least two points are required to establish the line as shown in Figure 14-9, although for rough measurements, one point and the theoretical slope of 0.059 may be adequate for calibration.

THERMODYNAMICS OF CELLS

It is beyond the scope of this text to give a complete and rigorous discussion of thermodynamics. Nevertheless some of these relationships are of fundamental importance to the understanding of the operation and use of electrochemical cells.

Gibbs Free Energy. From a theoretical point of view, one of the most useful properties of a system is its free energy content. This is a composite of properties of state of the system. Basically, it is a combination of enthalpy content and entropy,

$$G = H - TS \qquad (14\text{-}32)$$

and if all substances are present in their standard states,

$$G^\circ = H^\circ - TS^\circ \qquad (14\text{-}33)$$

The free energy per mole of a substance is called its "chemical potential," symbolized by μ (not to be confused with ionic strength). The chemical potential of a substance is related to its reactivity, and in fact serves as a basis for the proper definition of activity:

$$G/\text{mole} = \bar{G} = \mu = \bar{G}^\circ + RT \ln a \qquad (14\text{-}34)$$

The free energy of a system is the summation of the free energy of its components. Whenever there is a possibility of a chemical reaction within a system, the total free energy must decrease or the reaction will not occur. Thus the driving force of a chemical reaction is measured by ΔG, the change in free energy, which is the difference between the free energy of the products and that of the reactants. At constant temperature and pressure:

$$\Delta G = \Delta H - T\Delta S = \Delta G^\circ + RT \ln a_{\text{products}} - RT \ln a_{\text{reactants}} \qquad (14\text{-}35)$$

Reactions will take place spontaneously only if $\Delta G < O$. If $\Delta G > O$, there will be a tendency for the reverse reaction to take place, and if $\Delta G = O$ the reaction is at equilibrium.

Derivation of the Nernst Equation. The change in free energy is also a measure of the maximum amount of electrical work that can be obtained from the cell if it is operated reversibly:

$$\Delta G = -W_{\text{elect.}} \qquad (\text{constant } P, T)$$

The electrical work, $W_{\text{elect.}}$, is the product of the charge times the potential difference through which it is transferred. The charge on one mole of electrons is the Faraday constant, F, and for n moles of electrons transferred, the work must be:

$$\Delta G = -W_{\text{elect.}} = -nFE_{\text{cell}} \qquad (14\text{-}36)$$

where E_{cell} represents a potential difference between two electrodes of a cell and ΔG is the change in free energy of that cell reaction. Combining Equations 14-35 and 14-36, we obtain:

$$-nFE_{\text{cell}} = \Delta G^\circ + RT \ln a_{\text{products}} - RT \ln a_{\text{reactants}}$$

or on rearranging:

$$E_{cell} = -\frac{\Delta G°}{nF} - \frac{RT}{nF} \ln \frac{(products)}{(reactants)} \qquad (14\text{-}37)$$

Equation 14-37 is identical in form to Equation 14-2, the Nernst equation. It should be clear that $E°$ in Equation 14-2 is the same as $-\Delta G°/nF$ in Equation 14-37.

In the conventions of this text, the cell voltage is computed by subtracting one electrode potential from the other, giving the voltage an absolute value only. In order to preserve the information available from the signs of the electrode potentials, we should state which of the two electrodes is the more positive. This additional information identifies the electrode at which *reduction* takes place when the cell operates spontaneously. To learn which direction is spontaneous for a given reaction, we must separate the reaction into half-reactions and measure or compute the half-cell potentials. The more positive potential corresponds to the system that will be reduced. If we insist that *the* cell reaction is to be written in the spontaneous direction, then ΔG is negative and E_{cell} is in fact positive according to Equation 14-36. The opposite set of statements is also true; i.e., for a reaction which is spontaneous in the reverse direction, ΔG is positive and E_{cell} is negative.

Equilibrium Constants. Another useful relation is obtained by considering a cell at equilibrium. As we have already observed, the half-cell reactions are always at equilibrium with the corresponding electrode, but the overall cell reaction, in general, is not at equilibrium, unless the cell voltage happens to be zero. Under these conditions (zero cell voltage) the ratio of activities of products to activities of reactants must satisfy the equilibrium constant, K, for the cell reaction and the following equations pertain:

$$E_{cell} = E°_{cell} - \frac{0.059}{n} \log \frac{(products)}{(reactants)}$$

At equilibrium,

$$E_{cell} = 0 \qquad and \qquad \frac{(products)}{(reactants)} = K$$

$$0 = E°_{cell} - \frac{0.059}{n} \log K$$

or

$$\log K = \frac{nE°_{cell}}{0.059} \qquad at\ 25°\ C. \qquad (14\text{-}38)$$

where E_{cell}° and K must correspond to the same reaction. If E_{cell}° is positive, then K is greater than unity, and vice versa. To avoid confusion over signs of E° values, remember that half-reactions (always written as reductions) should be subtracted in a direction to give the required whole reaction, and that E° values corresponding to these half-reactions must be subtracted in the same direction. Thus the equilibrium constant for a reaction can be calculated from a table of E° values (Table 14-1).

example | problem 14-3: Calculate the equilibrium constant for the reaction:

$$Fe^{++} + Ag^{+} = Ag + Fe^{+++}$$

The two half-reactions are:

$$Fe^{+++} + e^{-} = Fe^{++}; \qquad E_{Fe}^{\circ} = 0.771 \text{ V}$$

$$Ag^{+} + e^{-} = Ag; \qquad E_{Ag}^{\circ} = 0.799 \text{ V}$$

The reaction given is obtained by subtracting the first half-reaction from the second; $E_{react.}^{\circ}$ must be obtained in the same way:

$$E_{react}^{\circ} = E_{Ag}^{\circ} - E_{Fe}^{\circ} = 0.799 - 0.771 = 0.028 \text{ V}$$

$$\log K = \frac{nE^{\circ}}{0.059} = \frac{0.028}{0.059} = 0.475$$

$$K = 2.98$$

example | problem 14-4: Calculate the equilibrium constant for the reaction:

$$Fe^{++} + AgCl = Fe^{+++} + Ag + Cl^{-}$$

The two half-reactions are:

$$Fe^{+++} + e^{-} = Fe^{++} \qquad E_{Fe}^{\circ} = 0.771 \text{ V}$$

$$AgCl + e^{-} = Ag + Cl^{-} \qquad E_{AgCl}^{\circ} = 0.222 \text{ V}$$

Again, we must subtract the first from the second to obtain the given reaction

$$E_{react}^{\circ} = E_{AgCl}^{\circ} - E_{Fe}^{\circ} = 0.222 - 0.771 = -0.549 \text{ V}$$

$$\log K = \frac{-0.549}{0.059} = -9.30$$

$$K = 5.0 \times 10^{-10}$$

The negative value of E_{react}° and the very small K both show that the given reaction will be spontaneous in the reverse direction.

example | problem 14-5: The voltage of the following cell is 0.753 V with the left electrode more positive.

$$Ag|Ag^{+}(0.1 \ M)\|I^{-}(0.01 \ M), AgI|Ag$$

From this information, calculate the solubility product of AgI.

Left half-reaction: $Ag^{+} + e^{-} = Ag$

$$E_L = E^\circ_{Ag^+,Ag} - 0.059 \log 1/(Ag^+)$$

Right half-reaction: $Ag^+ + e^- = Ag$

where $(Ag^+) = K_{AgI}/(I^-)$,

$$E_R = E^\circ_{Ag^+,Ag} - 0.059 \log (I^-)/K_{AgI}$$

Because the left electrode is more positive (given), we know that reduction occurs at this electrode in the spontaneous reaction. Accordingly, we subtract the right half-reaction from the left and subtract potentials accordingly.

$$E_{cell} = E_L - E_R$$

$$0.753 = 0.059 \log (Ag^+) + 0.059 \log (I^-) - 0.059 \log K_{AgI}$$

$$\log K_{AgI} = -\frac{0.753}{0.059} + \log 0.1 + \log 0.01$$

$$= -12.8 - 1.0 - 2.0 = -15.8$$

$$K_{AgI} = 1.6 \times 10^{-16}$$

Alternatively, the solubility product can be obtained from the E° value for the half-reaction $AgI + e^- = Ag + I^-$ (Table 14-1) and the definition given in Equation 14-24. The details are left as an exercise for the student.

example/problem 14-6: Cell 4 is assembled with 0.0500 M HCl in the right half-cell and 0.0200 M NaOH in the left. The pressure of hydrogen is 0.923 atm at both electrodes.

$$Pt, H_2|OH^-\|H^+|H_2, Pt$$

The measured cell voltage is 0.6528 V with the right electrode more positive. From this information, calculate K_w.

The left half-cell reaction is:

$$2H_2O + 2e^- = 2OH^- + H_2$$

but it is equally correct to separate the half-reaction into two steps with the dissociation of water followed by the reduction of hydrogen ion:

$$2H_2O = 2H^+ + 2OH^-$$

$$2H^+ + 2e^- = H_2$$

With this approach we have the same electrode reaction occurring in both half-cells; therefore, the same Nernst equation but with two different values for the hydrogen ion concentration.

Left side: $E = E^\circ_H - \dfrac{0.059}{2} \log \dfrac{P_{H_2}}{(H^+)^2}$

$$= E^\circ_H - \frac{0.059}{2} \log \frac{P_{H_2}(OH^-)^2}{K_w^2}$$

$$= E^\circ_H - \frac{0.059}{2} \log P_{H_2} - 0.059 \log (OH^-)_{left} + 0.059 \log K_w$$

Right side: $E = E_H^\circ - \dfrac{0.059}{2} \log \dfrac{P_{H_2}}{(H^+)^2}$

$\qquad\qquad = E_H^\circ - \dfrac{0.059}{2} \log P_{H_2} + 0.059 \log (H^+)_{right}$

Since the right electrode is more positive, we subtract the left from the right to obtain E_{cell}. The E° terms and the hydrogen pressure terms cancel out.

$E_{cell} = 0.059 \log (H^+)_{right} + 0.059 \log (OH^-)_{left} - 0.059 \log K_w$

The data given justify using 0.05915 rather than 0.059.

$$\frac{0.6528}{0.05915} = \log 0.0500 \times 0.0200 - \log K_w$$

$$\log K_w = -11.03 - 3.00 = -14.03$$

$$K_w = 9.3 \times 10^{-15}$$

For many electrode systems, E° cannot be measured directly because many electrodes do not behave reversibly; however, various combinations of the relationships expressed above allow us to calculate E, E° or K from other thermodynamic data.

POTENTIOMETRIC TITRATIONS

In a potentiometric titration the course of the titration reaction is followed by measuring the concentration of one or more of the species potentiometrically. The titration beaker becomes one of the half-cells of an electrochemical cell, along with a convenient reference electrode for the other half-cell. It is not necessary that the titration reaction be a redox reaction as long as one of the species is, or can be made to be, a part of a redox couple.

It is important to distinguish between the titration reaction and the cell reaction. The reactants and products of the titration are all in the same half-cell, and the titration reaction is normally always at equilibrium. On the other hand the cell reaction consists of either of two possible half-reactions in the titration half-cell and the half-reaction in the reference half-cell. The cell reaction is normally not at equilibrium because it is not allowed to take place except for brief periods while balancing the potentiometer.

The Iron (II)-Cerium (IV) Titration. Let us study the titration of Fe^{++} with Ce^{+4}. The experimental features are shown in Figure 14-10 in which the cell is represented:

$$Hg|Hg_2Cl_2, KCl_{(sat)}||Fe^{++}, Fe^{+++}, Ce^{+4}, Ce^{+3}|Pt$$

Titration Half-cell: $Fe^{+3} + e^- = Fe^{+2}$;

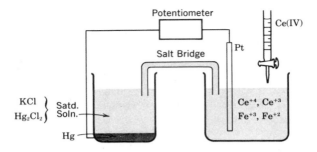

FIGURE 14-10. Apparatus for the potentiometric titration of iron(II) with cerium(IV).

$$E = E_{Fe}^{\circ} - 0.059 \log \frac{(Fe^{++})}{(Fe^{+++})} \tag{14-39}$$

or

$$Ce^{+4} + e^- = Ce^{+3};$$
$$E = E_{Ce}^{\circ} - 0.059 \log \frac{(Ce^{+3})}{(Ce^{+4})} \tag{14-40}$$

Reference Half-cell: $Hg_2Cl_2 + 2e^- = 2Hg + 2Cl^-$

Cell reaction: $2Fe^{+3} + 2Hg + 2Cl^- = 2Fe^{+2} + Hg_2Cl_2$
or

$$2Ce^{+4} + 2Hg + 2Cl^- = 2Ce^{+3} + Hg_2Cl_2$$

Titration reaction: $Fe^{+2} + Ce^{+4} = Fe^{+3} + Ce^{+3}$

If we perform the titration, measuring the cell voltage at many points along the way, the data are conveniently plotted as shown in Figure 14-11. Now we shall examine the theory which explains this curve and which would allow us to predict this curve without ever having to do the experiment. It is convenient to divide the titration into several regions.

1. *At the beginning* the solution contains only Fe^{++} plus traces of Fe^{+++} due to oxidation by air or hydrogen ion. If the concentration of Fe^{+++} were really zero, the Nernst equation would give us an infinitely negative value for the potential. This would indicate an infinitely powerful reducing agent which would surely reduce water. The initial potential can be measured but not calculated without knowing the extent of this extraneous oxidation. Since the initial potential is of no consequence to our titration, we will ignore the problem.

2. *Once the titration is begun,* all four species are present. However, up to the equivalence point, there remains an excess of Fe^{++} in the half-cell, and the

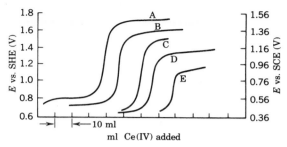

FIGURE 14-11. Potentiometric titration curves for iron(II) with cerium(IV) in various acids: A, Theoretical; B, HClO$_4$; C, HNO$_3$; D, H$_2$SO$_4$; E, HCl. (From Smith, *Cerate Oxidimetry*, Smith Chemical Co., 1942, p. 23.)

concentration of Ce^{+4} must remain extremely small as a consequence of the very large equilibrium constant for the titration reaction. In this region, the amount of Fe^{++} converted to Fe^{+++} is directly proportional to the amount of Ce^{+4} added. It is easy to calculate the ratio (Fe^{++})/(Fe^{+++}) from the volume of Ce^{+4} added, compared to the additional volume increment needed to reach the equivalence point.

3. *At the equivalence point,* there is no excess of either reactant. By definition, the same number of equivalents of both Fe^{++} and Ce^{+4} have been added. The large equilibrium constant indicates that each is converted essentially completely to Fe^{+++} and Ce^{+3}, respectively. But the equilibrium constant, though large, is not infinite, and therefore the concentrations of the Fe^{++} and Ce^{+4} cannot be zero. The concentrations of Fe^{++} and Ce^{+4} could be computed from the value of the equilibrium constant, but there is a more elegant way of calculating the potential without needing to know these concentrations. Remembering that both Nernst equations (Equations 14-39 and 14-40) are valid, we simply add the two together to obtain another equation which is true throughout the titration, but is especially useful at the equivalence point:

$$2E = E^{\circ}_{Fe} + E^{\circ}_{Ce} - 0.059 \log \frac{(Fe^{++})(Ce^{+3})}{(Fe^{+++})(Ce^{+4})} \qquad (14\text{-}41)$$

Equation 14-41 may resemble a Nernst equation, but it is only a bit of algebraic maneuvering performed with Equations 14-39 and 14-40. We combined the two Nernst equations in this manner only because it leads to a very simple expression for the equivalence point potential. At this point,

$$(Fe^{++}) = (Ce^{+4}) \quad \text{and} \quad (Fe^{+++}) = (Ce^{+3})$$

Thus we can cancel out all concentrations in Equation 14-41, leaving a value of unity for the concentration ratio and zero for the log term. Therefore,

$$E_{ep} = \tfrac{1}{2}(E^\circ_{Fe} + E^\circ_{Ce}) \qquad (14\text{-}42)$$

Observe that E_{ep} is independent of concentrations and equal to the arithmetic mean of the two standard potentials. A bit of reflection will show that if n_{ox} for the oxidant and n_{red} for the reductant in the titration reaction are not the same, we must modify our treatment. The two log terms of the individual Nernst equations cannot be combined unless the factor preceding the log is the same for both. The two factors can be made the same if we multiply the Nernst equation for the oxidant by n_{ox} and multiply that for the reductant by n_{red}. Thus the E_{ep} will become a weighted mean:

$$E_{ep} = \frac{n_{ox}E^\circ_{ox} + n_{red}E_r}{n_{red} + n_{ox}} \qquad (14\text{-}43)$$

For some unsymmetric titration reactions, e.g., those involving H^+ or complexing agents, not all concentrations will cancel. In these cases, E_{ep} will depend on the concentration of such species.

TABLE 14-5 TITRATION OF 50.00 ML OF 0.1 M Fe^{++} WITH 0.1 M Ce^{+4}

V, ml	f	(Fe^{++}) M	(Fe^{+++}) M	(Ce^{+3}) M	(Ce^{+4}) M	E vs. SHE, V
0	0	0.100	~0	0	0	—
1	0.02	0.096	0.002	0.002	2.3×10^{-19}	0.67
5	0.10	0.082	0.0091	0.0091	5.6×10^{-18}	0.71
10	0.20	0.067	0.0167	0.0167	2.3×10^{-17}	0.73
25	0.50	0.033	0.033	0.033	1.8×10^{-16}	0.77
40	0.80	0.011	0.045	0.045	1.0×10^{-15}	0.79
45	0.90	5.3×10^{-3}	0.047	0.047	2.3×10^{-15}	0.83
49	0.98	5.0×10^{-4}	0.049	0.049	2.5×10^{-14}	0.87
49.9	0.998	1.0×10^{-4}	0.050	0.050	1.4×10^{-13}	0.93
50	1.000	3.8×10^{-9}	0.050	0.050	3.8×10^{-9}	1.19
50.1	1.002	1.4×10^{-13}	0.050	0.050	1.0×10^{-4}	1.45
51	1.02	1.4×10^{-14}	0.050	0.050	9.9×10^{-4}	1.51
55	1.10	2.7×10^{-15}	0.048	0.048	4.8×10^{-3}	1.55
75	1.50	4.4×10^{-16}	0.040	0.040	2.0×10^{-2}	1.59
100	2.00	1.8×10^{-16}	0.033	0.033	3.3×10^{-2}	1.61

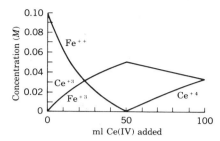

FIGURE 14-12. Actual concentration of species during the iron(II)-cerium(IV) titration.

4. *Beyond the equivalence point,* an excess of Ce^{+4} has been added. The amount of the excess is clearly that which has been added after the equivalence point has been reached, and its concentration can be easily calculated from the total volume of the solution. Likewise, the amount of Ce^{+3} in the solution can be calculated from the amount of Ce^{+4} required to reach the equivalence point—essentially all of it was reduced to Ce^{+3} by the Fe^{++} in the original solution.

The calculations for the titration curve, E vs. ml of titrant, are summarized in Table 14-5. The concentrations of the various species present have also been tabulated, although it is not necessary to know the concentrations of each in order to compute E. All species are present in the same volume; therefore, the ratio of concentrations is the same as the more readily calculated ratio of amounts. However, it is always very helpful to know what's in the beaker. As a visual aid in keeping track of "what's going on" during the titration, the concentration curves of Figures 14-12 and 14-13 should be carefully compared with the titration curves in Figure 14-11.

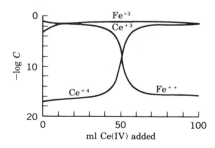

FIGURE 14-13. Logarithmic concentration of species during the iron(II)-cerium(IV) titration.

Notes on the calculations performed in Table 14-5.

1. Observe that 50 ml of Ce^{+4} are required to reach the equivalence point.

2. The concentrations at any point in the titration can be readily computed by introducing a new variable, f, the fraction titrated.

$f = V/50$, or volume added/volume required at the equivalence point

$$(Fe^{++}) = (1 - f) \times 0.1 \times \frac{50}{50 + V} \qquad 0 < f < 1$$

$$(Fe^{+++}) = f \times 0.1 \times \frac{50}{50 + V} \qquad 0 < f < 1$$

$$(Ce^{+3}) = (Fe^{+3}) \qquad \text{all } f$$

$$(Ce^{+4}) = (Ce^{+3})(Fe^{+3})/K(Fe^{+2}) \qquad 0 < f < 1$$

$$(Fe^{+2}) = (Ce^{+3})(Fe^{+3})/K(Ce^{+4}) \qquad f > 1$$

$$(Fe^{+++}) = 0.1 \times 50/(50 + V) \qquad f > 1$$

$$(Ce^{+4}) = 0.1(V - 50)/(50 + V) \qquad f > 1$$

3. E is computed in one of three ways (no concentrations are required).

$$E = E_{Fe}^{\circ} - 0.059 \log (1 - f)/f \qquad 0 < f < 1$$

$$E = \tfrac{1}{2}(E_{Fe}^{\circ} + E_{Ce}^{\circ}) \qquad f = 1$$

$$E = E_{Ce}^{\circ} - 0.059 \log 1/(f - 1) \qquad f > 1$$

The potentials listed in Table 14-5 refer to the platinum indicator electrode vs. the standard hydrogen electrode. In the actual cell, a saturated calomel electrode was used as the reference electrode. The conversion of one scale to the other is a simple matter of subtracting 0.24 V from the value vs. SHE to obtain the value vs. SCE; i.e., potentials measured vs. SCE are 0.24 V more negative than vs. SHE.

The theoretical titration curve is plotted in Figure 14-11 along with several actual titration curves obtained experimentally in different solutions. There are two important reasons why the actual curves differ from the theoretical curve. All four of the species involved in this titration readily form complexes and are subject to hydrolysis and dimerization. Furthermore, highly charged ions have activity coefficients which deviate greatly from unity. A different theoretical curve would have been obtained if we had used the appropriate formal potentials. A second cause of the difference between theoretical and actual curves is the irreversible behavior of many electrodes.

On the other hand, theoretical curves do approximate the actual curves in many important respects, and are useful in obtaining a graphical picture of what happens during a titration. The shape of a titration curve in the vicinity of the equivalence point, and in particular the slope of the curve at that point, tells us how sharp the end point will be, and within what range of potential we must stop in order to obtain a given accuracy.

Redox Indicator. It is not always necessary to set up the potentiometric equipment and actually measure an electrode potential in order to determine the end point of a titration. A redox indicator may be used to give a visual indication that this point has been reached. The color change takes place upon oxidation or reduction of the indicator itself. If the standard potential of the indicator system is close to the equivalence point potential of the titration reaction, the indicator will exist half in each form at the end point and display a color intermediate to the two forms.

Ferroin is a very stable, intensely red complex of 1,10-phenanthroline with Fe(II):

or $(Phen)_3Fe^{+2}$

When oxidized, the ferric complex is faintly blue:

$$\underset{\text{blue}}{(Phen)_3Fe^{+3}} + e^- = \underset{\text{red}}{(Phen)_3Fe^{+2}}; \qquad E' = 1.06 \text{ V in } 0.5 \text{ } M \text{ H}_2\text{SO}_4$$

$$E = 1.06 - 0.059 \log \frac{\text{(red form)}}{\text{(blue form)}}$$

With the Nernst equation, it is easy to show that this indicator exists 90% in the red form at $E = 1.00$ V, 50% in each form at $E = 1.06$ V, and 90% in the blue form at $E = 1.12$ V. The transition range is sufficiently close to the equivalence point potential (1.19 V) of the ferrous-ceric titration so that the end-point error is less than 0.1%. Most redox indicators exhibit complicated reaction mechanisms and do not exactly follow the Nernst equation. Nevertheless, a comparison of the formal potential of the indicator with the titration curve is very useful in choosing the best indicator. A few such indicators are listed in Table 14-6.

TABLE 14-6 TRANSITION POTENTIALS OF REDOX INDICATORS

Indicator	Transition Potential, V	Conditions
Phenosafranine	−0.25	$pH\,7$
	0.28	$pH\,0$
Indigo tetrasulfonate	−0.05	$pH\,7$
	0.36	$pH\,0$
Methylene blue	0.01	$pH\,7$
	0.53	$pH\,0$
Diphenylamine	0.76	$pH\,0$
Diphenylamine sulfonic acid	0.85	$pH\,0$
Ferroin	1.06	$pH\,0$
Nitroferroin	1.25	$pH\,0$

Stepwise Oxidation and Reduction. In a number of systems, it is possible to oxidize or reduce a substance in several stages in a fashion analogous to titrating protons one at a time from a polyprotic acid. Vanadium, for example, has stable oxidation states of (II), (III), (IV) and (V). Permanganate added in small increments to a solution of V(II) will oxidize the vanadium stepwise through each of the intermediate states. The composition and potential of the solution are represented in Figure 14-14. The curve is, of course, the titration curve one would

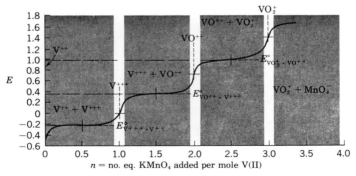

FIGURE 14-14. Potentiometric titration curve of vanadium(II) with permanganate.

obtain with a platinum indicator electrode. The details of the calculations will not be given, but it should be noted that up to 3 equivalents of permanganate added, the curve is independent of the nature of the oxidizing agent (titrant) used. In each of the first three regions, the potential is determined by the appropriate vanadium couple:

Eq. of MnO_4^- per mole of V	Appropriate Nernst Equation	
0–1	$E = E^\circ_{V^{+++}, V^{++}} - 0.059 \log (V^{++})/(V^{+++})$	(14-44)
1–2	$E = E^\circ_{VO^{++}, V^{+++}} - 0.059 \log (V^{+++})/(VO^{++})(H^+)^2$	(14-45)
2–3	$E = E^\circ_{VO_2^+, VO^{++}} - 0.059 \log (VO^{++})/(VO_2^+)(H^+)^2$	(14-46)
>3	$E = E^\circ_{MnO_4^-, Mn^{++}} - 0.059/5 \log (Mn^{++})/(MnO_4^-)(H^+)^8$	(14-47)

The calculation of E at exactly 1 and 2 equivalents added is perhaps not obvious. Consider the composition of the solution when exactly 1 equivalent of oxidant is added. The equilibrium constant for the reaction may be large but not infinite and therefore a small amount of V^{++} must remain. But since a total of 1 equivalent of oxidant was added, the V^{++} must be balanced by a like amount of VO^{++}. To put it another way, 1 equivalent of V^{++} was oxidized to V^{+++} which then partially disproportionated to V^{++} and VO^{++}:

$$2V^{+++} + H_2O = VO^{++} + V^{++} + 2H^+$$

Among other things, this indicates that at the first equivalence point:

$$(VO^{++}) = (V^{++}) \tag{14-48}$$

Now, Equations 14-44 to 14-47 are each valid throughout all regions and in particular at 1 equivalent. The trick is to add Equations 14-44 and 14-45, then substitute from Equation 14-48, yielding:

$$E_{n=1} = \tfrac{1}{2}(E^\circ_{V^{+++}, V^{++}} + E^\circ_{VO^{++}, V^{+++}}) + 0.059 \log (H^+)^2 \tag{14-49}$$

A similar argument applies to $E_{n=2}$.

In the vanadium system, the E° values of successive couples are separated by several tenths of a volt (see Table 14-1). The simple calculations described above must be modified for systems where the successive E° values are closer together than ~ 0.2 volt.

Coupled Reactions. The series of stepwise reactions in the vanadium system could be classified as coupled reactions. The product of the first step becomes a reactant in the second step, etc. The overall reaction has a tremendous driving force:

$$5V^{++} + 3MnO_4^- + 4H^+ = 5VO_2^+ + 3Mn^{++} + 2H_2O$$

$$E^\circ = 1.15 \text{ V}; \qquad K \sim 10^{290}; \qquad \Delta G^\circ = -4000 \text{ kcal}$$

In a series of stepwise processes, the free energy is utilized in smaller packages in a series of reactions:

$$V^{++} + VO^{++} + 2H^+ = 2V^{+++} + H_2O; \qquad \Delta G^\circ = -147 \text{ kcal}$$

$$V^{+++} + VO_2^+ = 2VO^{++}; \qquad \Delta G^\circ = -153 \text{ kcal}$$

$$5VO^{++} + MnO_4^- + H_2O = 5VO_2^+ + Mn^{++} + 2H^+; \quad \Delta G^\circ = -600 \text{ kcal}$$

When the three preceding reactions are multiplied by the proper coefficients (5, 10, and 3, respectively) and added, the same overall reaction is obtained with the same total ΔG° as above. Now, suppose we add other redox couples to the vanadium-permanganate system. Suppose Fe^{+++} is added to V^{++}. The Fe^{+++} is reduced to Fe^{++} by the V^{++}, forming Fe^{++} and V^{+++}. Now if permanganate is added, it makes no difference to the final result whether the MnO_4^- reacts with Fe^{++} or V^{+++}, since any VO^{++} formed will oxidize the Fe^{++} back to Fe^{+++}. The exact course of the reactions will depend on relative rates of the several possible reactions and the possible presence of specific catalysts.

Far more interesting and complicated examples of coupled reactions are found in the metabolic processes of living organisms. The tremendous oxidizing power of oxygen is transferred in a series of stepwise oxidative processes producing many intermediates between the original reducing agent (foodstuff) and the final products $(CO_2 + H_2O)$. In the complete oxidation of a mole of glucose, 688 kcal of energy are released. No organism could withstand the release of so much energy in one step. (It is something like touching a match to the gasoline tank of your car!) In metabolic processes, this energy is released in small packages, through a long series of reactions each of which involves small energy differences. The details of these are beyond the scope of this text, but the principles are essentially the same as in the vanadium system.

For example, in the respiratory chain of the mitochondrion, a series of compounds are intermediates in the oxidation of nicotinamide adenine dinucleotide (NAD). The direct oxidation of NAD with molecular oxygen would release 52.4 kcal per mole, all of which would be lost as destructive heat were it not for the sequential reactions of the respiratory chain. In the steps where ΔG is greater than 7 kcal, there is sufficient energy released to convert one molecule of adenosine diphosphate (ADP) to adenosine triphosphate (ATP) in a side reaction. Three of

TABLE 14-7 THE RESPIRATORY CHAIN

	E'_7, V	$-\Delta G$ kcal/mole

0.82 V

$O_2 + Cyt\ a_{red} \rightarrow H_2O + Cyt\ a_{ox}$ — 0.53 — 24.4*

0.29 V

.29 V

$Cyt\ a_{ox} + Cyt\ c_{red} \rightarrow Cyt\ a_{red} + Cyt\ c_{ox}$ — 0.03 — 1.4

0.26 V

0.26 V

$Cyt\ c_{ox} + Cyt\ b_{red} \rightarrow Cyt\ c_{red} + Cyt\ b_{ox}$ — 0.22 — 10.1*

0.04 V

0.04 V

$Cyt\ b_{ox} + Flpr_{red} \rightarrow Cyt\ b_{red} + Flpr_{ox}$ — 0.09 — 4.1

-0.05 V

-0.05 V

$Flpr_{ox} + NAD_{red} \rightarrow Flpr_{red} + NAD_{ox}$ — 0.29 — 12.4*

-0.32 V

*Steps with sufficient energy to convert ADP $\rightarrow$ ATP

Cyt = Cytochrome
Flpr = Flavoprotein

the sequential steps listed in Table 14-7 release enough energy to produce one ATP molecule each. Thus 3 × 7 kcal, or 21 kcal, of the 52 kcal released when one NAD molecule is oxidized are conserved by the simultaneous conversion of ADP to ATP. The ATP molecules so produced are the prime carriers of energy throughout living organisms. Each compound in the series listed in Table 14-7 participates in an electron transport sequence in which the end result is the transfer of electrons from NAD to oxygen.

334   *SOME OTHER ELECTROANALYTICAL TECHNIQUES*

This introduction to electrochemical cells, electrode potentials and potentiometry has covered only a small portion of electroanalytical chemistry. There are many other methods based on electrical measurements. Electrochemical methods are very useful because the measurements can be made quickly, easily and precisely, and are readily automated.

Electrolysis.   For potentiometry, the cell is not allowed to operate. With zero current, it is assumed that the electrode is in equilibrium with the solution and that concentrations do not change with time. Such cells, however, possess an e.m.f. whether or not they are operating, and are sources of electrical energy if the circuit is completed and current allowed to flow. With a finite current, the concentrations must change as the cell reaction proceeds. The e.m.f. gradually approaches zero as the concentrations approach the equilibrium state. Now let us add another component to the circuit. The cell in Figure 14-15 is connected to an external battery or power supply, E_{appl}, so that the two e.m.f.'s oppose each other. If E_{appl} is greater than E_{cell}, then the current is reversed. Likewise, the cell reaction is reversed from its normal spontaneous direction. Instead of copper metal dissolving into the solution, cupric ions are deposited on the electrode surface. The normal spontaneous cell reaction for this cell is:

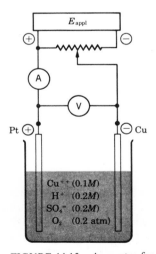

FIGURE 14-15.   Apparatus for the electrodeposition of copper. A is an ammeter, V is a voltmeter.

Pt Electrode: $O_2 + 4H^+ + 4e^- = 2H_2O$

Cu Electrode: $Cu^{++} + 2e^- = Cu$

Cell: $2Cu + O_2 + 4H^+ = 2Cu^{++} + 2H_2O$

with corresponding potentials:

$$E_{Pt} = E^\circ_{O_2, H_2O} - \frac{0.059}{4} \log \frac{1}{P_{O_2}(H^+)^4}$$

$$= 1.23 - \frac{0.059}{4} \log \frac{1}{(0.2)(0.2)^4} = 1.18 \text{ V}$$

$$E_{Cu} = E^\circ_{Cu^{++}, Cu} - \frac{0.059}{2} \log \frac{1}{(Cu^{++})}$$

$$= 0.34 - \frac{0.059}{2} \log \frac{1}{0.1} = 0.3! \text{ V}$$

$$E_{cell} = E_{Pt} - E_{Cu} = 1.18 - 0.31 = 0.87 \text{ V}$$

The cell voltage is often called the "back EMF". If E_{appl} just equals 0.87 V, the two e.m.f.'s cancel each other and no current flows. But if E_{appl} exceeds 0.87 V, the cell reaction is reversed, and *electrolysis* of the solution takes place. In actual cases, an E_{appl} slightly greater than E_{cell} is required to drive the cell reaction backwards. The extra voltage, called the *overvoltage*, is usually caused by the irreversibility of the electrode reactions. The basic equation for electrolysis is:

$$E_{appl} = E_{cell} + E_{ov} + iR \tag{14-50}$$

in which all quantities are considered to be positive. E_{ov} is the sum of the over-voltages (if any) at the electrodes, i is the current and R is the total resistance of the circuit. With current flowing, the concentrations change with time which results in changes in all three terms on the right side of Equation 14-50. There are many kinds of electrolysis which make use of Equation 14-50. One or more of the terms in this equation may be held constant giving rise to several special techniques which will be described briefly.

Electrodeposition. If the electrolysis of copper just described is continued for any length of time, the concentration of cupric ion in the electrolyte must decrease. In fact copper ion consumed at the cathode is being replaced by hydrogen ion produced in the anode reaction. The net result is that the cell voltage (back e.m.f.) must increase; therefore, the applied voltage must be increased in order to maintain the current flow. If the current is continued long enough to be sure that the cell reaction is essentially completed, the original concentration of copper ion can be determined from the increase in weight of the electrode. This has been the classical way to determine copper and a few other metals, but it finds little use in organic analysis.

Controlled Current Electrolysis. If E_{appl} is continuously adjusted to maintain a constant current, and if conditions are such that only a single electrode reaction takes place at the electrode (100% current efficiency), then it is not necessary to weigh the electrode. The amount of the reaction can be readily determined from Faraday's law:

$$F \times \text{equiv reacted} = i \times t \qquad (14\text{-}51)$$

where t is the time in seconds and F is the number of coulombs per equivalent (96493) or the Faraday constant. However, we have noted in the electrolysis of copper, that the cathode potential must be made more negative with time in order to continue the reduction of copper ion. Concurrently the hydrogen ion concentration is increasing, and eventually the cathode potential will be sufficiently negative to reduce hydrogen ion as well as copper ion. This is a typical situation—that is to say, it is rarely possible to maintain a single electrode reaction. The method, as such, finds little use, but is the basis for coulometric titrations to be described shortly.

example/problem 14-7: Copper is to be electroplated from a solution containing 0.1 M $CuSO_4$ and 0.1 M H_2SO_4 in a cell similar to Figure 14-15. The initial E_{appl} required must be at least 0.87 V. The overvoltage for deposition of soft metals at the cathode is usually very small, but the discharge of oxygen on the platinum anode may require an extra 0.4 V. If we wish to maintain a current of 0.25 amp and the total resistance is 0.2 ohms, the iR drop will require and additional 0.05 V.

$$E_{appl} = \underset{\text{back e.m.f.}}{0.87} + \underset{\text{overvoltage}}{0.4} + \underset{iR \text{ drop}}{0.05} = 1.32 \text{ V}$$

What concentration of copper ion remains in solution at the point when hydrogen ion begins to discharge? First we must note that the overvoltage required for the discharge of hydrogen on copper is ~ 0.4 V. Therefore, as a first guess, nearly all of the copper ion can be reduced before any hydrogen ion is reduced. But an equivalent amount of hydrogen ion is produced at the anode so that the concentration of H^+ increases to 0.2 (original) $+$ 0.2 (added) $= 0.4$ M. The potential required to discharge H^+ is

$$E_H = E_{ov} + E^\circ_{H^+,H_2} - \frac{0.059}{2} \log \frac{P_{H_2}}{(H^+)^2}$$

$$= -0.4 + 0 - \frac{0.059}{2} \log \frac{1}{(0.4)^2} = -0.4 \text{ V}$$

Note that the overvoltage always acts in a direction to make the process more difficult to perform. In this case H^+ is to be reduced which requires electrons from the electrode. Because of overvoltage, the potential of the electrode must be more *negative* by 0.4 V in order to reduce H^+ on copper; therefore, E_{ov} is given a negative sign.

The copper ion is in equilibrium with the same electrode at the same potential. Its concentration is obtained from:

$$E_H = E_{Cu} = E°_{Cu^{++},Cu} - \frac{0.059}{2} \log \frac{1}{(Cu^{++})}$$

$$-0.4 = 0.34 - \frac{0.059}{2} \log \frac{1}{(Cu^{++})}$$

$$(Cu^{++}) = 10^{-25} M$$

The fraction of the original copper remaining in solution is only $10^{-25}/0.1$ or $10^{-22}\%$.

Controlled Cathode (or Anode) Potential Electrolysis. If a (third) auxiliary reference electrode is placed within the electrolysis cell and connected through a voltage measuring device, then the potential of (either) one of the working electrodes can be monitored, as shown in Figure 14-16. The E_{appl} is then adjusted throughout the electrolysis to maintain a constant cathode or anode potential. In this way, we can be fairly sure that only a single reaction is taking place and that the number of coulombs passed is directly related to the substance to be determined. However, the current decreases with time and approaches zero asymptotically. Therefore, Equation 14-51 must be modified:

$$F \times \text{equiv reacted} = \int_0^t i \, dt \qquad (14\text{-}52)$$

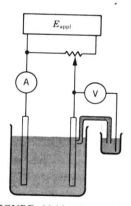

FIGURE 14-16. Apparatus for electrolysis with controlled cathode (or anode) potential. Signal from voltmeter may be used to adjust E_{appl} automatically as required.

In addition to analytical applications, controlled potential electrolysis is useful in identifying reaction products and the number of electrons taking part in a reaction. (These are not always obvious in complex organic reactions!) The method also serves as a preparative tool. The electrode acts as an oxidant or a reductant with a constant known potential of any value one desires. Some preparations for which no suitable reagents are available can be easily carried out.

Secondary Coulometric Titrations. The advantages of controlled potential and constant current can be combined if a reagent can be electrogenerated within the electrolysis cell. For example, consider the electrolytic oxidation of ferrous ion at a platinum anode. If the current is kept constant, the extent of the reaction is directly proportional to the time of the electrolysis, but the electrode potential must increase and another reaction will eventually take over. On the other hand, if the electrode potential is kept constant, only the desired reaction is likely to occur, but the rate of the reaction decreases exponentially. Both techniques have advantages and disadvantages. Now, if the solution also contains a large excess of cerous ion, the latter ion will be preferentially oxidized at the electrode and the ceric ion so produced will react immediately with the ferrous ion. The cerium acts as an intermediate and no significant amount of ceric ion remains until all of the ferrous ion is oxidized. The electrode potential is maintained nearly constant by the large excess of cerous ion; i.e., the ratio $(Ce^{+3})/(Ce^{+4})$ remains large and nearly constant. Thus we achieve a constant current with a constant electrode potential, and Equation 14-51 is applicable.

These methods are extremely sensitive and useful for determining traces of materials; for example, microgram quantities of pesticide residues which have been separated by gas chromatography. Coulometric titrations are also extremely precise—the ultimate limit of accuracy appears to be the value of the Faraday. Because of the ease of electrically generating acids, bases, oxidants, reductants and even some complexing agents, the electron may well become the universal primary standard for all titrations.

Polarography. If one of the electrodes in the electrolysis cell of Figure 14-15 is replaced with a micro-electrode, the current may become limited by the rate at which the reacting substance can reach the surface of the electrode. Such an electrode is said to be "polarized" because the current no longer depends on the potential, but rather on the diffusion rate of the electroactive species. The most commonly used micro-electrode is shown in Figure 14-17. It consists of small droplets of mercury issuing from a piece of small bore (inside diameter of about 0.06-0.08 mm) capillary tubing. Mercury is easily purified and in this arrangement its surface is continually renewed as the drop grows. An external reference electrode completes the electrolysis cell. The electrical circuit provides a source of continuously variable applied voltage and a device for measuring the very small

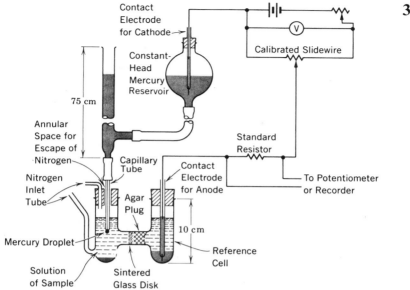

FIGURE 14-17.   Polarographic cell (after Lingane and Laitinen) and basic electrical circuit required to obtain current-voltage curves.

electrolysis currents (10^{-8} to 10^{-4} amp). On modern instruments, the contact is driven across the slide-wire by a synchronous motor which increases the applied voltage at a constant rate; and the current is measured by means of an automatic recorder.

Polarography is the study of the current-voltage relationships obtained with this apparatus. With the proper conditions, the "polarogram" (current vs. voltage) so obtained can be interpreted to yield both the nature and concentration of the reacting species. A typical polarogram for a solution containing 10^{-3} M Pb^{++} and 10^{-3} M Zn^{++} in 1 M KCl is shown in Figure 14-18. The presence of a large excess of a "supporting electrolyte" (1 M KCl) insures that the current will be determined by diffusion due to concentration gradients rather than by electrical forces of attraction, and it also reduces the electrical resistance of the solution. The steps in the polarogram are called "polarographic waves." Each wave is the result of a new electrode reaction. As the applied voltage is increased, a wave appears for each reducible substance when its decomposition potential is reached. The "half-wave potential," $E_{1/2}$, is unique for each electrode reaction and serves to

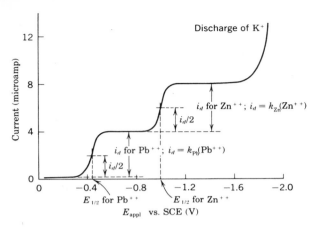

FIGURE 14-18. Polarogram for 1 mM Pb^{++} and 1 mM Zn^{++} in 1 M KCl.

identify the substance. The height of the wave, i_d (increase in current), is directly proportional to the concentration of the reacting substance, although the proportionality constant, k, varies slightly from one substance to another.

Polarography is especially adapted to trace analysis of metal ions, but is finding increasing use in organic and biochemical work. Because of the reproducible behavior of the dropping mercury electrode it is often used for fundamental studies of electrode reactions. There are many variations in the electrodes and circuits used which are described in more advanced and specialized texts.

QUESTIONS AND PROBLEMS

14-1. Describe the cell for which the following are cell reactions:

(a) $Ag^+ + Cl^- = AgCl$ *Ans.* $Ag|AgCl,Cl^-\|Ag^+|Ag$

(b) $Cd + 2Ag^+ = Cd^{++} + 2Ag$

(c) $6Ti^{+3} + Cr_2O_7^= + 2H^+ = 6TiO^{++} + 2Cr^{+++} + H_2O$

(d) $CH_3COO^- + H^+ = CH_3COOH$

(e) $2Ag + Hg_2Cl_2 = 2AgCl + 2Hg$

(f) $Cu^{++} + H_2 = Cu + 2H^+$

(g) $Cu^{++} + 4NH_3 = Cu(NH_3)_4^{++}$

14-2. If the concentrations of all soluble species in the cells of Problem 14-1 are 0.1 M and gases are at unit pressure, what is the voltage of each cell? Which electrode bears the positive charge?   *Ans.* (a) 0.459 V, (c) 1.22 V, (d) 0.222 V.

14-3. Write the cell reactions and compute the cell voltage for each of the following cells:

(a) $Cd|Cd^{++}(0.1\ M)\|Cd^{++}(0.5\ M)|Cd$

(b) $Pt|V^{+++}(0.1\ M),\ VO^{++}(0.01\ M),\ H^+(0.1\ M)\|SCE$

(c) $Ag|Ag^+(0.01\ M)\|Fe^{++}(0.1\ M),\ Fe^{+++}(0.01\ M)|Pt$

(d) $SCE\|H^+(10^{-7}\ M),\ \underset{Q\ =\ quinone}{Q(10^{-5}\ M)},\ H_2Q(10^{-5}\ M)|Pt$

(e) $Sb|Sb_2O_3,\ H^+(10^{-7}\ M)\|H^+(10^{-7}\ M)|H_2(1\ atm),\ Pt$

Ans. (a) 0.021 V, (c) 0.031 V, (e) 0.152 V.

14-4. Compute ΔG, ΔG° and K for each of the reactions in Problem 14-1 if all concentrations are 1 M and all pressures are 1 atm.

Ans. (a) $-10,700$ cal, $-13,400$ cal, 6×10^9; (c) $-169,000$ cal, $-170,000$ cal, 10^{125}.

14-5. If the saturated calomel electrode had been selected as the standard reference electrode, $E_{SCE} = 0$, what would be the standard potentials of each of the following couples?

(a) $Zn^{++} + 2e^- = Zn$

(b) $V^{+++} + e^- = V^{++}$

(c) $Sn^{+4} + 2e^- = Sn^{++}$

(d) $2H^+ + 2e^- = H_2$

(e) $Hg_2Cl_2 + 2e^- = 2Hg + 2Cl^-$ *Ans.* (a) -1.005 V, (c) -0.09 V.

14-6. Describe the experimental set-up required for the potentiometric titration of V^{++} with MnO_4^-.

14-7. An excess of silver metal is added to 250 ml of 0.01 M Fe^{+++}. What is the final Fe^{+++} in the solution if it contained in addition to the Fe^{+++}, (a) 1 M HNO_3 (b) 1 M HCl?   *Ans.* (a) $2.7 \times 10^{-4}\ M$, (b) $5 \times 10^{-12}\ M$.

14-8. Calculate the equilibrium constant for the reaction:

$$2H_2 + O_2 = 2H_2O\ (liq)$$

Describe the cell for which this would be the cell reaction. How would the cell voltage depend on the pH of the electrolyte?   *Ans.* 2.5×10^{83}.

14-9. On a single graph, plot the electrode potential vs. log C of the ionic species for the following

(a) $Ag|Ag^+$

(b) $Cu|Cu^{++}$

(c) $Pt,\ H_2|H^+$

(d) $Al|Al^{+++}$

(e) $Fe|Fe^{++}$

(f) $Ag|AgCl,\ Cl^-$

(g) $Zn|Zn^{++}$

(h) $Pt|Q,\ H_2Q,\ H^+$

14-10. A metal becomes a better reducing agent if the solution in contact with it contains a complexing agent capable of complexing the metal ion. Explain why this is so.

14-11. Cupric ion is an oxidizing agent and ferrous ion is a reducing agent. What happens when the two are mixed? Explain.

14-12. Compute E_7' for the MnO_4^-, Mn^{++}, and the $Cr_2O_7^=$, Cr^{+++} couples.

Ans. 0.85 V, 0.37 V.

14-13. Compute the solubility product for AgBr from the E° values in Table 14-1.

14-14. The complete reduction of picric acid to triaminophenol would require 18 electrons per molecule. In an electrolytic reduction at a mercury cathode held at a constant potential of -0.65 V vs. SCE, Lingane found that 65.7 coulombs were needed to reduce 0.0399

342   millimoles of picric acid. What was the product of the electrolysis under these conditions?

Ans.   HO —⟨benzene ring with NH$_2$, NH$_2$⟩— NH — NH —⟨benzene ring with NH$_2$, NH$_2$⟩— OH.

14-15. Compare the value for the mean ionic activity coefficient of 0.1 M HCl obtained from Figure 14-5 with that from Equation 14-8.

REFERENCES

J. J. Lingane, *Electroanalytical Chemistry*, 2nd ed., Interscience, New York, 1958. A very readable and definitive discussion of the theory and applications of potentiometry, various kinds of electrolysis and coulometry.

W. M. Latimer, *Oxidation Potentials*, 2nd ed., Prentice-Hall, New York, 1952. The most extensive and widely quoted source of standard potentials and related thermodynamic data. It includes much descriptive chemistry of the elements.

W. M. Clark, *Oxidation-Reduction Potentials of Organic Systems*, Williams and Wilkins, Baltimore, Md., 1960. An extensive discussion of theory as applied to organic chemistry with many tables of data.

W. C. Purdy, *Electroanalytical Methods in Biochemistry*, McGraw-Hill, New York, 1965. Elementary discussion of techniques applicable to biochemical problems.

A. L. Lehninger, *Bioenergetics*, Benjamin, New York, 1965. A lucid discussion of energy transport and storage in living systems.

T. S. Licht and A. J. deBethune, "Recent Developments Concerning the Signs of Electrode Potentials," *J. Chem. Educ.*, **34**, 433 (1957).

R. A. Durst, "Mechanism of the Glass Electrode Response," *J. Chem. Educ.*, **44**, 175 (1967).

H. A. Laitinen, *Chemical Analysis*, McGraw-Hill, New York, 1960; Chapters 15–17.

15 ACID-BASE EQUILIBRIUM CALCULATIONS IN WATER

The free hydronium ion concentration, (H_3O^+), dominates many chemical reactions. Wherever the hydronium ion is a reactant, product, catalyst, or in any way indirectly involved in the reaction, its concentration may determine the extent to which the reaction proceeds, the rate at which it goes, or the detailed mechanism of how it takes place. In living as well as in vitro physiological systems, for example, specific enzyme activity is often quite dependent on the concentration of free hydronium ion.

A facility and an intuition for handling the complex equilibria which are always present in acid-base systems is of paramount importance in many areas of chemistry and biochemistry. Careful study of this chapter will help the student to understand and use the concepts of acid-base equilibria in aqueous solution. The aim is to learn how to calculate the free hydronium ion concentration and to adjust or control it to the desired value.

MASS ACTION EXPRESSIONS

Consider a chemical reaction of the form,

$$aA + bB = cC + dD$$

which obeys the following relationship at equilibrium:

$$K^\circ = \frac{a_C^c a_D^d}{a_A^a a_B^b} \tag{15-1}$$

Equation 15-1 is the mass action expression for the reaction and K° is the thermodynamic equilibrium constant for the reaction at a specific temperature. The magnitude of the equilibrium constant provides an indication of the extent of the reaction. Recall that a_C, a_D, a_A, and a_B are the *activities* of the chemical species and are defined as follows:

Ions—the activity of an ion is equivalent to the "effective" or "free" concentration of the ion. In dilute solutions, ion activities are approximately equal to molar concentrations, i.e., $a_A \approx (A)$.

Molecules—the activity of a molecular species is essentially equal to the molar concentration.

Pure Solids or Liquids in Equilibrium with the Solution—activity is exactly equal to unity.

Gases in Equilibrium with the Solution—the activity is equal to the partial of the gas in atmospheres.

With molar concentrations, the mass action expressions take the form:

$$K^\circ = \frac{[f_C(C)]^c[f_D(D)]^d}{[f_A(A)]^a[f_B(B)]^b} \tag{15-2}$$

where f_C, f_D, f_B, and f_A are defined as the activity coefficients of the respective species and the terms inside parentheses are the molar concentrations. In moderately concentrated solutions ($0.1 < F < 1$), there is significant electrostatic attractive interaction between charged species; therefore, the activity of an ion is somewhat less than the molar concentration. The activity coefficient accounts for these electrostatic interactions and, consequently, it usually assumes values less than unity. However, in very dilute solutions all activity coefficients approach the value of unity and the mass expression takes the form:

$$K^\circ = \frac{(C)^c(D)^d}{(A)^a(B)^b} \tag{15-3}$$

The errors introduced by neglecting the activity coefficients in Equation 15-2 are often less than the experimental errors associated with equilibrium measurements. For most purposes, Equation 15-3 will yield satisfactory results.

ION PRODUCT OF WATER AND pH

The reaction of two water molecules to produce hydronium and hydroxide ions (autoprotolysis reaction) is one of the fundamental acid-base reactions in aqueous solution, i.e.,

$$H_2O + H_2O = H_3O^+ + OH^-$$

The mass action expression for this reaction is

$$K^\circ = \frac{(a_{H_3O^+})(a_{OH^-})}{(a_{H_2O})^2}$$

In dilute aqueous solutions the concentration of water is approximately 55.4 M and is constant. Therefore, at 25° C, we define a new constant:

$$K_w = (H_3O^+)(OH^-) = 1.008 \times 10^{-14} \quad \text{(at 25° C)} \tag{15-4}$$

From Equation 15-4, in any aqueous solution in which either (H_3O^+) or (OH^-) is known, the other may be calculated. In the following discussions, we will assume that $a_{H_3O^+} = (H_3O^+)$ and pH $= -\log (H_3O^+)$. Likewise pOH will be defined as $-\log (OH^-)$. From Equation 15-4,

$$p\text{H} = -\log (H_3O^+) = 14.00 - p\text{OH}$$

ACID-BASE EQUILIBRIA IN SIMPLE SYSTEMS

Solutions of Monoprotic Acids. The equilibrium reaction between a monoprotic acid and water is represented by

$$HB + H_2O = H_3O^+ + B^-$$

for which the mass action expression is:

$$K_a = \frac{(H_3O^+)(B^-)}{(HB)}$$

and K_a is the acid dissociation constant. The only other source of hydronium ion in this system is the autoprotolysis of water, i.e.,

$$H_2O + H_2O = H_3O^+ + OH^-$$

with the mass action expression:

$$(H_3O^+)(OH^-) = 1.00 \times 10^{-14} \qquad \text{(at } 25° \text{C)}$$

Strong acids are defined arbitrarily as molecules with K_a values larger than 1.0. The stronger the acid, the more completely dissociated it is in aqueous solution (i.e., K_a is very large). Perchloric acid, hydrochloric acid, nitric acid, and sulfuric acids are typical strong acids. As the K_a values become smaller, the acids are weaker, i.e., they are poorer proton donors to the solvent water molecules. A list of K_a values for various weak monoprotic acids is given in Table 15-1.

Let us consider the determination of the equilibrium ion concentrations in a solution of an acid, HB, of formal concentration, C_{HB}. To solve for four unknowns, four independent equations are needed. These equations are provided by the mass action expressions for the system and charge balance and material balance relationships.

From the electroneutrality principle, for every solution the sum of the positive charges must equal the sum of the negative charges. Therefore, for this system the charge balance is given by

$$(H_3O^+) = (B^-) + (OH^-)$$

The material balance is given by

ACID-BASE EQUILIBRIUM CALCULATIONS IN WATER

346

TABLE 15-1 MONOPROTIC WEAK ACID DISSOCIATION CONSTANTS
AT 25°C

Acid Name	Formula	K_a^*	pK_a
Acetic	CH_3COOH	1.75×10^{-5}	4.76
Benzoic	C_6H_5COOH	6.3×10^{-5}	4.20
Boric	HBO_2	5.8×10^{-10}	9.24
Chloroacetic	$ClCH_2COOH$	1.38×10^{-3}	2.86
Cyanic	$HOCN$	2.0×10^{-4}	3.70
Formic	$HCOOH$	1.77×10^{-4}	3.75
Glycolic	$HOCH_2COOH$	1.32×10^{-4}	3.88
Hydrocyanic	HCN	4.8×10^{-10}	9.32
Hydrofluoric	HF	6.75×10^{-4}	3.17
Hypochlorous	$HOCl$	2.95×10^{-8}	7.53
Lactic	$CH_3CHOHCOOH$	1.38×10^{-4}	3.86
Nitrous	HNO_2	5.1×10^{-4}	3.29
Phenol	C_6H_5OH	1.05×10^{-10}	9.98
Propionic	CH_3CH_2COOH	1.34×10^{-5}	4.87
Pyridine Hydrochloride	$C_5H_5NH^+Cl^-$	6.2×10^{-6}	5.21

*K_a values are given at zero ionic strength

$$C_{HB} = (HB) + (B^-)$$

which states that at equilibrium the *total* HB placed in the system, C_{HB}, must be present either in the form of HB or B^-. Therefore, the four independent equations which describe this system are:

$$\frac{(H_3O^+)(B^-)}{(HB)} = K_a \qquad (15\text{-}5)$$

$$(H_3O^+)(OH^-) = K_w \qquad (15\text{-}6)$$

$$(H_3O^+) = (B^-) + (OH^-) \qquad (15\text{-}7)$$

and

$$C_{HB} = (HB) + (B^-) \qquad (15\text{-}8)$$

When these four equations are solved simultaneously to determine (H_3O^+), the last step involves the solution of a cubic equation—a very difficult, time-consuming task. An exact solution is seldom necessary, and approximations are always in order if they can be justified. Approximations involve examining the independent relationships and making assumptions that some terms are negligible compared to others. Recall that the magnitude of an equilibrium constant is an indication of the extent to which the reaction proceeds. For example, if the K_a value for the acid is considerably larger than K_w (e.g., $> 10^{-11}$), the *principal* source of hydronium ion is the dissociation reaction of the acid HB. The *only* source of hydroxide ion is the autoprotolysis of water. Therefore, if $K_a \gg K_w$, $(H_3O^+) \gg (OH^-)$ and from Equation 15-7,

$$(H_3O^+) = (B^-) \tag{15-9}$$

From Equation 15-8,

$$(HB) = C_{HB} - (B^-) \tag{15-10}$$

Substituting from Equation 15-9 into Equation 15-10,

$$(HB) = C_{HB} - (H_3O^+) \tag{15-11}$$

Substituting from Equations 15-9 and 15-11 into Equation 15-5:

$$\frac{(H_3O^+)^2}{C_{HB} - (H_3O^+)} = K_a \tag{15-12}$$

Equation 15-12 contains only one unknown and may be solved either by successive approximations or by using the quadratic formula. The assumption that $(H_3O^+) \gg (OH^-)$ may be verified by substituting the calculated (H_3O^+) from Equation 15-12 into the K_w expression for water and solving for (OH^-). If (H_3O^+) were not significantly greater than (OH^-) a more exact cubic equation would have to be solved (or the problem would be put aside as having no practical interest!).

In most cases, Equation 15-12 may be further simplified. If C_{HB} is sufficiently large ($> 10^{-2}$) and K_a is small (e.g., $< 10^{-4}$), the extent of dissociation is quite small. In this case, $C_{HB} - (H_3O^+) \approx C_{HB}$ and

$$\frac{(H_3O^+)^2}{C_{HB}} = K_a \tag{15-13}$$

Equation 15-13 is easily solved for (H_3O^+). If (H_3O^+) is less than 10% of C_{HB}, the simplified calculation is normally satisfactory. Otherwise, the more exact expression (Equation 15-12) may be solved. Let us consider a few example problems which illustrate the principles we have just discussed.

example / problem 15-1: Calculate the hydronium ion and hydroxide ion concentrations of a solution which is 0.0300 M in HCl. Also determine the pH and pOH of this solution.

solution. HCl is a strong acid and is *completely* dissociated in aqueous solution, i.e., the reaction:

$$HCl + H_2O = H_3O^+ + Cl^-$$

has a very large K_a and proceeds essentially 100% from left to right. The only other source of hydronium ion is the autoprotolysis of water with the equilibrium constant 1.00×10^{-14}. Clearly the principal equilibrium is the dissociation of HCl and

$$(H_3O^+) = C_{HCl} = 0.0300 \ M = 3.00 \times 10^{-2} \ M$$

From K_w,

$$(OH^-) = \frac{1.00 \times 10^{-14}}{3.00 \times 10^{-2}} = 3.33 \times 10^{-13} \ M$$

Therefore,

$$pH = -\log (H_3O^+) = -(0.48 - 2.00) = 1.52$$

and

$$pOH = 14.00 - 1.52 = 12.48.$$

example / problem 15-2: Calculate the hydronium ion concentration and pH of a solution which is 0.0100 F in acetic acid, HOAc.

solution. The equilibrium expressions for this system are:

$$HOAc + H_2O = H_3O^+ + OAc^-$$

$$\frac{(H_3O^+)(OAc^-)}{(HOAc)} = K_a = 1.75 \times 10^{-5} \tag{15-14}$$

and

$$H_2O + H_2O = H_3O^+ + OH^-$$

$$(H_3O^+)(OH^-) = K_w = 1.00 \times 10^{-14}$$

What is the principal source of hydronium ion? From the relative values of the K_a for acetic acid and K_w, clearly the principal source of hydronium ion is the dissociation of acetic acid. For *every* molecule of acetic acid that dissociates, *one* hydronium ion and *one* acetate ion are formed. Therefore,

$$(H_3O^+) = (OAc^-)$$

and

$$(HOAc) = C_{HOAc} - (H_3O^+) = 0.0100 - (H_3O^+)$$

Substituting in Equation 15-14

$$\frac{(H_3O^+)^2}{0.0100 - (H_3O^+)} = 1.75 \times 10^{-5} \tag{15-15}$$

Trial solution of Equation 15-15: Assume that

$$0.0100 - (H_3O^+) \approx 0.0100$$

then

$$(H_3O^+)^2 = 1.75 \times 10^{-7}$$

and

$$(H_3O^+) = 4.2 \times 10^{-4} \ M$$

The percent error in making the simplifying assumption is,

$$\frac{0.0004}{0.0096} \times 100 = 4.2\%$$

Therefore, the simplifying assumption is acceptable.

Check of validity of original assumption that $(H_3O^+) \gg (OH^-)$:

From K_w, $\qquad (OH^-) = \dfrac{K_w}{(H_3O^+)} = \dfrac{1.00 \times 10^{-14}}{4.2 \times 10^{-4}} = 2.4 \times 10^{-10} \; M$

Therefore, the original assumption is valid and the $pH = -\log(4.2 \times 10^{-4}) = 3.38$

example / problem 15-3: Calculate the pH of a solution which is $1.34 \times 10^{-4} \; F$ in propionic acid, HOPr.

solution. The equilibrium expressions in this system are given by

$$\frac{(H_3O^+)(OPr^-)}{(HOPr)} = K_a = 1.34 \times 10^{-5}$$

and

$$(H_3O^+)(OH^-) = K_w = 1.00 \times 10^{-14}$$

Since $1.35 \times 10^{-5} \gg 1.00 \times 10^{-14}$, the principal equilibrium is the dissociation of propionic acid. Therefore,

$$(H_3O^+) = (OPr^-)$$

and

$$(HOPr) = C_{HOPr} - (H_3O^+) = 1.34 \times 10^{-4} - (H_3O^+)$$

Substituting into the K_a expression,

$$\frac{(H_3O^+)^2}{1.34 \times 10^{-4} - (H_3O^+)} = 1.34 \times 10^{-5} \qquad (15\text{-}16)$$

The assumption is made that,

$$1.34 \times 10^{-4} - (H_3O^+) \approx 1.34 \times 10^{-4}$$

Thus,

$$(H_3O^+)^2 = 1.80 \times 10^{-9}$$

and

$$(H_3O^+) = 4.24 \times 10^{-5} \; M$$

We see that (H_3O^+) is *not* insignificant compared to 1.34×10^{-4} ($\sim 32\%$ of this value). As a result, the more rigorous equation must be solved. Two alternative methods may be used.

quadratic solution. Rearranging Equation 15-16

$$(H_3O^+)^2 = 1.80 \times 10^{-9} - 1.34 \times 10^{-5} (H_3O^+)$$

and

$$(H_3O^+)^2 + 1.34 \times 10^{-5} (H_3O^+) - 1.80 \times 10^{-9} = 0$$

This is in the standard quadratic form, i.e.,

$$ax^2 + bx + c = 0; \qquad x = \frac{-b \pm \sqrt{b^2 - 4ac}}{2a}$$

Therefore, for this system,

$$(H_3O^+) = \frac{-1.34 \times 10^{-5} + \sqrt{1.80 \times 10^{-10} + 7.20 \times 10^{-9}}}{2}$$

$$= 3.62 \times 10^{-5} \ M$$

and

$$pH = 4.44.$$

successive approximations solution. In using successive approximations, approximate solutions are obtained and then these are substituted back into additive or subtractive terms in the original equation to obtain a more accurate solution. This process is continued until there is essentially no variation in the new solution. For example, in this problem,

$$\frac{(H_3O^+)^2}{1.34 \times 10^{-4} - (H_3O^+)} = 1.34 \times 10^{-5}$$

assuming $(H_3O^+) \ll 1.34 \times 10^{-4}$ and solving for (H_3O^+),

$$(H_3O^+)^2 = 1.80 \times 10^{-9}$$

$$(H_3O^+) = 4.24 \times 10^{-5} \ M$$

This value is substituted back into the denominator of the exact expression (Equation 15-16):

$$\frac{(H_3O^+)^2}{1.34 \times 10^{-4} - 4.24 \times 10^{-5}} = \frac{(H_3O^+)^2}{9.2 \times 10^{-5}} = 1.34 \times 10^{-5}$$

and

$$(H_3O^+) = 3.50 \times 10^{-5} \ M$$

Substituting this new value back into the denominator of the exact expression,

$$\frac{(H_3O^+)^2}{1.34 \times 10^{-4} - 3.50 \times 10^{-5}} = \frac{(H_3O^+)^2}{9.9 \times 10^{-5}} = 1.34 \times 10^{-5}$$

and

$$(H_3O^+) = 3.64 \times 10^{-5} \ M$$

Again, the new value is substituted back into the exact expression:

$$\frac{(H_3O^+)^2}{1.34 \times 10^{-4} - 3.64 \times 10^{-5}} = \frac{(H_3O^+)^2}{9.8 \times 10^{-5}} = 1.34 \times 10^{-5}$$

and

$$(H_3O^+) = 3.62 \times 10^{-5} \ M,$$

essentially the same answer as for the previous time. Therefore,

$$(H_3O^+) = 3.62 \times 10^{-5} \ M$$

and

$$pH = 4.44$$

Calculations similar to the ones illustrated in Example Problems 15-2 and 15-3 may be carried out for any weak acid system at any formal concentration of the acid. The results of these calculations for three systems are illustrated in Figure 15-1. Note that at very small concentrations, the $pH = 7.00$ and is independent of C_{HB}. At these concentrations, the principal source of hydronium ions is the autoprotolysis of water; as a result, $(H_3O^+) = (OH)$ and the pH is 7.00.

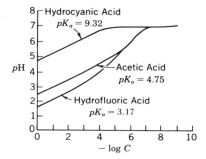

FIGURE 15-1. Variation of pH with the formal concentration of weak acids with different K_a values at 25° C. (From Butler, *Ionic Equilibrium*, Addison-Wesley, 1964, p. 117.)

Solutions of Bases. The determination of the equilibrium concentrations of the various constituents present in a solution of a base is analogous to that used for acid studies; however, the hydroxyl ion concentration is determined instead of the hydronium ion concentration.

The equilibrium reaction between a base and water is represented by

$$B^. + H_2O = BH^+ + OH^-$$

for which the mass action expression is

$$\frac{(BH^+)(OH^-)}{(B)} = K_b$$

where K_b is the base dissociation constant. Strong bases are defined as molecules which are completely dissociated in aqueous solution (e.g., sodium hydroxide). Weak bases are *incompletely* dissociated in aqueous solution. In basic solutions the only other source of hydroxide ion is the autoprotolysis of water. A list of various weak bases and their dissociation constants is given in Table 15-2.

TABLE 15-2 DISSOCIATION CONSTANTS OF WEAK BASES AT 25°C

Name	Formula	K_b	pK_b
Ammonia	NH_3	1.78×10^{-5}	4.75
Aniline	⬡—NH_2	4.2×10^{-10}	9.38
Dimethylamine	$(CH_3)_2NH$	1.18×10^{-3}	2.93
Ethylamine	$CH_3CH_2NH_2$	4.7×10^{-4}	3.33
Methylamine	CH_3NH_2	5.25×10^{-4}	3.28
Pyridine	⬡N	1.5×10^{-9}	8.82
Trimethylamine	$(CH_3)_3N$	8.1×10^{-5}	4.09

Let us consider the determination of the equilibrium ion concentrations in a solution of a base, B, of formal concentration C_B. The "unknowns" in this system are (B), (BH^+), (H_3O^+), and (OH^-); the "knowns" are K_b, K_w, and C_B. Analogous to an acid system, the four independent equations which describe this system are the two mass action expressions, the charge balance and the material balance.

$$\frac{(BH^+)(OH^-)}{(B)} = K_b \tag{15-17}$$

$$(H_3O^+)(OH^-) = K_w \tag{15-18}$$

$$\underset{\text{charge balance}}{(H_3O^+) + (BH^+) = (OH^-)} \tag{15-19}$$

and
$$\underset{\text{material balance}}{C_B = (B) + (BH^+)} \tag{15-20}$$

The hydroxide ion concentration can be determined by solving these four equations simultaneously. However, we may make approximations in order to avoid a cubic equation in (OH^-). If the K_b for the base is considerably larger than K_w (e.g. $> 10^{-11}$), the principal source of hydroxide ion is the dissociation reaction of the base B. The only source of hydronium ion is the autoprotolysis of water. Therefore, if $K_b \gg K_w$, $(OH^-) \gg (H_3O^+)$, and from Equation 15-19,

$$(BH^+) = (OH^-) \tag{15-21}$$

From Equation 15-20,

$$(B) = C_B - (BH^+) \tag{15-22}$$

Substituting from Equation 15-21 into Equation 15-22,

$$(B) = C_B - (OH^-) \tag{15-23}$$

Substituting from Equation 15-21 and 15-23 into Equation 15-17,

$$\frac{(OH^-)^2}{C_B - (OH^-)} = K_b \tag{15-24}$$

Equation 15-24 may be solved either by successive approximations or by using the quadratic formula. If C_B is large ($> 10^{-2} \, M$) and K_B is small ($< 10^{-4}$), the extent of dissociation is small and $C_B - (OH^-) \approx C_B$, and Equation 15-24 simplifies to

$$\frac{(OH^-)^2}{C_B} = K_b \tag{15-25}$$

Let us consider a few example problems, using base systems.

example/problem 15-4:   Calculate the hydronium ion and hydroxide ion concentrations, pH, and pOH of a solution which is $4.8 \times 10^{-5} \, M$ in $Sr(OH)_2$.

solution.   All alkali metal and alkaline earth hydroxides are strong bases and they completely dissociate in aqueous solution, thus the reaction

$$Sr(OH)_2 = Sr^{+2} + 2OH^-$$

proceeds essentially 100% to the right. The autoprotolysis of water is an insignificant source of hydroxide ion; therefore,

$$(OH^-) = 2C_B = 9.6 \times 10^{-5} \, M$$

and

$$pOH = -\log(9.6 \times 10^{-5}) = -(0.98 - 5.00) = 4.02$$

Therefore,

$$pH = 14.00 - 4.02 = 9.98$$

example/problem 15-5:   Calculate the pH of a solution which is $5.20 \times 10^{-2} \, F$ in trimethylamine, $(CH_3)_3N$.

solution.   The possible reactions in this system include

$$(CH_3)_3N + H_2O = (CH_3)_3NH^+ + OH^-$$

and

$$H_2O + H_2O = H_3O^+ + OH^-$$

The respective mass action expressions are

$$\frac{((CH_3)_3NH^+)(OH^-)}{((CH_3)_3N)} = K_b = 8.1 \times 10^{-5}$$

and

$$(H_3O^+)(OH^-) = K_w = 1.00 \times 10^{-14}$$

Clearly, the principal equilibrium is the dissociation of trimethylamine. Therefore, at equilibrium,

$$((CH_3)_3NH^+) = (OH^-)$$

and

$$((CH_3)_3N) = C_{(CH_3)_3N} - (OH^-) = 5.20 \times 10^{-2} - (OH^-)$$

From Equation 15-24,

$$\frac{(OH^-)^2}{5.20 \times 10^{-2} - (OH^-)} = 8.1 \times 10^{-5}$$

Again, we may solve by successive approximations or by application of the quadratic formula. However, if $(OH^-) \ll 5.20 \times 10^{-2}$, a simple solution is obtained:

$$(OH^-)^2 = 4.21 \times 10^{-6}$$

and

$$(OH^-) = 2.05 \times 10^{-3} \ M$$

This represents only a 4.2% error in the equilibrium concentration of trimethylamine and an even smaller error in the value of (OH^-). Consequently, the simple solution is satisfactory. Therefore,

$$pOH = -\log(2.05 \times 10^{-3}) = 2.69,$$

and

$$pH = 14.00 - pOH = 11.31$$

Solutions of Salts of Weak Acids. When alkali metal salts of weak acids are dissolved in water, the solution is found to be basic (i.e., the pH > 7). As a typical example, when sodium acetate is dissolved in water the ions in the crystals become hydrated sodium and acetate ions. If this was all that happened, the pH of the solution would be 7.00 because the only source of hydronium or hydroxide ions would be the autoprotolysis of water. However, the acetate ions react with water to some extent as follows,

$$OAc^- + H_2O = HOAc + OH^- \tag{15-26}$$

This is an acid-base reaction in which the acetate ion competes with the hydroxide ion for a proton. Since hydroxide ion is a much stronger base than acetate ion, we would expect the extent of this reaction (and thus the equilibrium constant) to be quite small. The mass action expression for the reaction shown in Equation 15-26 is given by

$$\frac{(HOAc)(OH^-)}{(OAc^-)} = K_{eq} = K_h \qquad (15\text{-}27)$$

The equilibrium constant, K_h, is often called the *hydrolysis constant*. Multiplying the left side of Equation 15-27 by $(H_3O^+)/(H_3O^+)$,

$$\frac{(H_3O^+)(HOAc)(OH^-)}{(H_3O^+)(OAc^-)} = K_h$$

we see that $K_h = K_w/K_a$.

example / problem 15-6: Calculate the concentration of OH^-, HOAc, OAc^-, and H_3O^+ in a solution which is 0.0100 F in sodium acetate, NaOAc.

solution. The mass action expressions are:

$$\frac{(HOAc)(OH^-)}{(OAc^-)} = \frac{1.00 \times 10^{-14}}{1.75 \times 10^{-5}} = 5.72 \times 10^{-10} \qquad (15\text{-}28)$$

and

$$(H_3O^+)(OH^-) = 1.00 \times 10^{-14}$$

Since $5.72 \times 10^{-10} \gg 1.00 \times 10^{-14}$, the principal equilibrium is the hydrolysis of acetate ion. Therefore,

$$(HOAc) = (OH^-)$$

and

$$(OAc^-) = C_{OAc^-} - (OH^-) = 0.0100 - (OH^-)$$

From Equation 15-28,

$$\frac{(OH^-)^2}{0.0100 - (OH)} = 5.72 \times 10^{-10}$$

Since K_h is so small, the extent of hydrolysis will also be small and we may assume that $0.0100 \gg (OH^-)$. Therefore,

$$\frac{(OH^-)^2}{0.0100} = 5.72 \times 10^{-10}$$

and

$$(OH^-) = 2.39 \times 10^{-6} \ M$$

The simplifying assumption that $0.010 \gg (OH^-)$ is valid since

$$0.010 \gg 2.39 \times 10^{-6}$$

Therefore,

$$(OH^-) = 2.39 \times 10^{-6} \ M$$

$$(OAc^-) = 0.0100 \ M$$

$$(HOAc) = 2.39 \times 10^{-6} \ M$$

and

$$(H_3O^+) = 4.19 \times 10^{-9} \ M$$

A general relationship for any system consisting of just a conjugate base salt is given by:

$$\frac{(OH^-)^2}{C_{M^+B^-} - (OH^-)} = K_h = \frac{K_w}{K_a^{HB}} \tag{15-29}$$

where $C_{M^+B^-}$ represents the formal concentration of the salt. Equation 15-29 may always be applied when $(OH^-) \gg (H_3O^+)$.

Solutions of Conjugate Acid Salts of Weak Bases. Solutions of ammonium chloride are acidic. Why? Chloride ions do not exhibit acid-base reactions with water; however, ammonium ions do react with water to some extent as follows:

$$NH_4^+ + H_2O = H_3O^+ + NH_3$$

The mass action expression for this reaction is represented by

$$\frac{(H_3O^+)(NH_3)}{(NH_4^+)} = K_{eq} = K_h \tag{15-30}$$

Even though K_h is often referred to as the hydrolysis constant for ammonium ion, it could just as well be called the acid dissociation constant for NH_4^+. By multiplying the left side of Equation 15-30 by $(OH^-)/(OH^-)$, it is demonstrated that

$$K_h = \frac{K_w}{K_b^{NH_3}} = K_a^{NH_4^+}$$

Thus equilibrium constants for weak bases may be listed in terms of the acid dissociation constants of the conjugate acids.

example/problem 15-7: Calculate the pH of a solution which is 0.0125 F in ammonium chloride.

solution. The mass action expressions are

$$\frac{(H_3O^+)(NH_3)}{(NH_4^+)} = K_h = \frac{1.00 \times 10^{-14}}{1.78 \times 10^{-5}} = 5.62 \times 10^{-10} \tag{15-31}$$

and

$$(H_3O^+)(OH^-) = K_w = 1.00 \times 10^{-14}$$

The principal source of hydronium ion is the hydrolysis reaction. As a result,

$$(NH_3) = (H_3O^+)$$

and
$$(NH_4^+) = C_{NH_4^+} - (H_3O^+) = 0.0125 - (H_3O^+)$$

Since the hydrolysis constant is so small, we can assume that $0.0125 - (H_3O^+) \approx 0.0125$. Therefore,

$$\frac{(H_3O^+)^2}{0.0125} = 5.62 \times 10^{-10}$$

and

$$(H_3O^+) = 2.65 \times 10^{-6} M$$

Thus,

$$pH = 5.58$$

A general expression which may be applied to any solution of the conjugate acid salt of a weak base, BH^+X^-, is

$$\frac{(H_3O^+)^2}{C_{BH^+X^-} - (H_3O^+)} = K_h = \frac{K_w}{K_b^B} = K_a^{BH^+X^-} \tag{15-32}$$

where $C_{BH^+X^-}$ represents the formal or analytical concentration of the conjugate acid salt. Equation 15-32 may always be applied when $(H_3O^+) \gg (OH^-)$.

Solutions Containing Both Weak Acids or Weak Bases and Their Corresponding Conjugate Base or Conjugate Acid Salts. Consider the general reaction,

$$HB + H_2O = H_3O^+ + B^-$$

From LeChatlier's principle, if a quantity of B^- is added to a solution of HB, the equilibrium reaction will be shifted to the left with a corresponding decrease in the equilibrium concentration of H_3O^+. Let us consider how this system is treated quantitatively in an example problem.

example / problem 15-8: In Example Problem 15-2, the hydronium ion concentration of a solution which is 0.0100 F in acetic acid, HOAc, was calculated to be $\sim 4.2 \times 10^{-4}$ M. Determine the hydronium ion concentration of a solution which is 0.0100 F in acetic acid *and* 0.0100 F in sodium acetate, NaOAc.

solution. Both the acid and the conjugate base are present. The acid dissociates to some extent according to the reaction,

$$HOAc + H_2O = H_3O^+ + OAc^-; \qquad K_a = 1.75 \times 10^{-5}$$

and the acetate ion hydrolyzes,

$$OAc^- + H_2O = HOAc + OH^-; \qquad K_h = 5.62 \times 10^{-10}$$

From the dissociation constant,

$$(H_3O^+) = K_a \frac{(HOAc)}{(OAc^-)} \tag{15-33}$$

Now the (HOAc) must equal C_{HOAc}, less that which dissociates, plus that which results from the hydrolysis of OAc^-. Furthermore, the (OAc^-) must equal C_{OAc^-} less that which hydrolyzes, plus that which results from the dissociation of HOAc. The extent of dissociation is measured by (H_3O^+) and the extent of hydrolysis of OAc^- is measured by (OH^-). Therefore, Equation 15-33 can be written as

$$(H_3O^+) = K_a \frac{C_{HOAc} - (H_3O^+) + (OH^-)}{C_{OAc^-} + (H_3O^+) - (OH^-)} \qquad (15\text{-}34)$$

Equation 15-34 can be readily simplified. If the solution is acidic, $(H_3O^+) > (OH^-)$ and (OH^-) can be neglected. If the solution is basic, $(OH^-) > (H_3O^+)$ and (H_3O^+) can be neglected. If the solution is nearly neutral, $(H_3O^+) \approx (OH^-)$ and the two cancel each other. In fact, in nearly all cases of interest, both C_{HOAc} and C_{OAc^-} are larger than either (H_3O^+) or (OH^-) and Equation 15-34 reduces to

$$(H_3O^+) = K_a \frac{C_{HOAc}}{C_{OAc^-}} \qquad (15\text{-}35)$$

Therefore,

$$(H_3O^+) = 1.75 \times 10^{-5} \frac{(0.0100)}{(0.0100)} = 1.75 \times 10^{-5} \ M$$

Buffer Solutions, Many chemical reactions generate free protons or free hydroxyl ions. If these ions remained in the system as free hydrated species, there would be significant changes in the pH. Buffer solutions contain constituents which react with both strong acids and strong bases in such a way that the free hydronium ion concentration of the system remains relatively constant. Buffers typically consist of weak acids and their conjugate bases. To illustrate how a buffer solution functions, consider the following problem.

example/problem 15-9: A certain solution is $0.100 \ F$ in sodium acetate and $0.100 \ F$ in acetic acid. An in vitro physiological chemical system generates 10.0 mmole of protons in one liter of the acetic acid-sodium acetate solution. (*a*) What was the original pH of the one liter solution? (*b*) What is the pH after the reaction? (*c*) What would be the pH after the reaction in a 1-liter solution of HCl which had an original pH equal to that of the $0.100 \ F$ acetic acid—$0.100 \ F$ sodium acetate solution?

solution. Part (*a*): To find the pH of the original acetic acid-sodium acetate solution we should recognize that this system is similar to the one discussed in Example Problem 15-8. That is, the system contains a weak acid and its salt. Applying Equation 15-35,

$$(H_3O^+) = K_a \frac{C_{HOAc}}{C_{OAc^-}} = 1.75 \times 10^{-5} \left(\frac{0.100}{0.100} \right) = 1.75 \times 10^{-5} \ M$$

and

$$pH = 4.76$$

Part (*b*): Here we have to consider what happens in the system when 10.0 mmoles of hydronium ions are added. A strong acid is being added to the system. Is there a stronger base than water present? Yes; acetate ion; e.g., for the reaction,

$$OAc^- + H_3O^+ = HOAc + H_2O$$

the mass action expression is,

$$\frac{(HOAc)}{(OAc^-)(H_3O^+)} = \frac{1}{K_a} = 5.72 \times 10^4$$

The large magnitude of this equilibrium constant indicates that the reaction essentially proceeds to completion. Now we have to determine how much acetate and acetic acid were in the original system and then how much of each of these species is present in the final system.

original mmole HOAc = (1000 ml)(0.100 mmole/ml) = 100.0 mmole

original mmole OAc⁻ = (1000 ml)(0.10 mmole/ml) = 100.0 mmole

final mmole OAc⁻ = 100.0 mmole − 10.0 mmole = 90.0 mmole
(used in reaction)

final mmole HOAc = 100.0 mmole + 10.0 mmole = 110.0 mmole
(generated in reaction)

Therefore, in the final solution the generated hydronium ion has been "absorbed" by the acetic acid-sodium acetate solution and the free hydronium ion concentration is again determined by the equilibrium concentrations of acetic acid and acetate ion. In the *final* solution,

$$C_{HOAc} = \frac{110.0 \text{ mmole}}{1000 \text{ ml}} = 0.1100 \ F$$

and

$$C_{NaOAc} = \frac{90.0 \text{ mmole}}{1000 \text{ ml}} = 0.0900 \ F$$

and

$$(H_3O^+) = 1.75 \times 10^{-5} \frac{(0.110)}{(0.0900)} = 2.14 \times 10^{-5}$$

and

$$pH = 4.67$$

So, even though a considerable amount of strong acid has been added to this system, there has been very little change in *pH*, only 0.09 unit.

Part (*c*): The 1-liter HCl solution of *pH* = 4.76 would have a concentration of 1.75×10^{-5} *M*, or $(H_3O^+) = 1.75 \times 10^{-5}$ *M*. If 10.0 mmole of H_3O^+ were added to this system, the total number of mmole of H_3O^+ would be,

$$(1000 \text{ ml})(1.75 \times 10^{-5} \text{ mmole/ml}) + 10.0 \approx 10.0 \text{ mmole}$$

and thus the H_3O^+ concentration would be

$$(H_3O^+) = \frac{10.0 \text{ mmole}}{1000 \text{ ml}} = 1.00 \times 10^{-2} \ M$$

and the final

$$pH = 2.00.$$

Thus, in this system, the addition of 10.0 mmole of hydronium ion would cause a significant change in *pH*, 2.76 units. The acetic acid-sodium acetate system is referred to as a buffered solution, whereas the HCl solution represents an unbuffered solution.

If free hydroxide ions are added to the buffer solution discussed in Example Problem 15-9, the hydroxide ion is absorbed by the system due to the reaction,

$$HOAc + OH^- = OAc^- + H_2O$$

The mass action expression for this reaction is given by

$$\frac{(OAc^-)}{(HOAc)(OH^-)} = K_{eq} = K_a/K_w = 1.75 \times 10^9$$

The magnitude of the equilibrium constant indicates that the reaction is essentially complete. Thus, when strong base is added to the buffer solution, the formal concentration of the conjugate base increases and the formal concentration of the weak acid decreases. However, the free hydronium ion concentration is still determined by the slight dissociation of the weak acid according to Equation 15-35. For a weak base buffer system, the hydronium ion concentration is given by

$$(H_3O^+) = K_a \frac{C_{BH^+} - (H_3O^+) + (OH^-)}{C_B + (H_3O^+) - (OH^-)} \qquad (15\text{-}36)$$

Recall that for a weak base, $K_a = K_w/K_b$; Equation 15-36 may be derived by applying the same approach as that used in the derivation of Equation 15-34. When (H_3O^+) and (OH^-) are much smaller than C_{BH^+} and C_B,

$$(H_3O^+) = K_a \frac{C_{BH^+}}{C_B} \qquad (15\text{-}37)$$

From Equations 15-35 and 15-37, for a system containing a weak acid and its conjugate base, or a weak base and its conjugate acid, (H_3O^+) depends only on the ratio of the concentrations. Thus, in a solution of acetic acid and sodium acetate, as long as the ratio of the concentration is 1.00, $(H_3O^+) = 1.75 \times 10^{-5}$ and the $pH = 4.76$. Exceptions to this statement occur when $C_{HB} \approx C_B \approx (H_3O^+)$, i.e., at *very low* concentrations. We can generalize the action of a buffer by noting that the final (H_3O^+) can be expressed as

$$(H_3O^+)_{final} = K_a \frac{VC_{HB}^\circ + n_{acid} - n_{base}}{VC_B^\circ + n_{base} - n_{acid}} \qquad (15\text{-}38)$$

where V is the volume of the buffer and n_{acid} and n_{base} are the number of equivalents of strong acid and/or strong base added.

Henderson-Hasselbalch Equations. The buffer Equation 15-35 may be written in logarithmic form; i.e.,

$$-\log(H_3O^+) = -\log K_a - \log \frac{C_{HB}}{C_{B^-}}$$

or

$$pH = pK_a + \log \frac{C_{B^-}}{C_{HB}} \qquad (15\text{-}39)$$

and for weak base,

$$pOH = pK_b + \log \frac{C_{BH^+}}{C_B} \qquad (15\text{-}40)$$

Equations 15-39 and 15-40 are referred to as *Henderson-Hasselbalch equations*. They are handy for determining the pH values for simple buffer solutions.

The most efficient buffer for any system consists of a 1:1 ratio of weak acid or weak base to its conjugate base. Therefore, if we wish to prepare a buffer solution of a certain pH, we try to select a weak acid with a pK_a value which is close to the desired pH value. If the pK_a does not exactly equal the desired pH, the C_{B^-}/C_{HB} ratio may be adjusted so that the value of $(pK_a + \log C_{B^-}/C_{HB})$ does equal the desired value. Let us consider some problems which illustrate how to prepare buffer solutions.

example / problem 15-10: Suggest a method of preparation of a 1-liter buffer with $pH = 5.00$ in which the *total acid + conjugate base* concentration is 0.200 F. Pick a system such that the acid and conjugate base concentrations are as nearly equal as possible.

solution. From Equation 15-39,

$$pH = pK_a + \log \frac{C_{B^-}}{C_{HB}}$$

if $C_{B^-} \approx C_{HB}$,

$$pH \approx pK_a$$

From Table 15-1, the weak acid with a pK_a closest to 5.00 is propionic acid ($pK_a = 4.87$). Therefore,

$$5.00 = 4.87 + \log \frac{C_{B^-}}{C_{HB}}$$

and

$$\log \frac{C_{B^-}}{C_{HB}} = 0.13$$

Therefore,

$$\frac{C_{B^-}}{C_{HB}} = 10^{0.13} = \frac{1.35}{1}$$

and

$$C_{B^-} = 1.35\, C_{HB}$$

But, from the stated problem,

$$C_{HB} + C_{B^-} = 0.200$$

Therefore,

$$2.35\, C_{HB} = 0.200$$

or

$$C_{HB} = 0.085\, F$$

and

$$C_{B^-} = 0.115\, F$$

So, to prepare the desired buffer take 0.115 mole of sodium propionate and 0.085 mole of propionic acid and dilute to one liter.

example/problem 15-11: How many grams of solid ammonium chloride must be added to 500 ml of 0.0200 F NH_3 to prepare a 1.000-liter buffer solution of $pH = 9.30$ after dilution with distilled water? Mol. Wt. $NH_4Cl = 53.49$.

solution. First, we must determine the concentration of ammonium ion required to attain pH 9.30 in the final solution. With a weak base, from Equation 15-40,

$$pOH = pK_b + \log \frac{C_{NH_4^+}}{C_{NH_3}}$$

From Table 15-2, pK_b for ammonia = 4.75

$$pOH = 14.00 - 9.30 = 4.70$$

Therefore,

$$4.70 = 4.75 + \log \frac{C_{NH_4^+}}{C_{NH_3}}$$

We know the concentration of NH_3, i.e., we started with 500 ml of 0.0200 F NH_3 and have diluted this to 1.000 liter. Therefore, the final NH_3 concentration is

$$C_{NH_3} = \frac{(500\ \text{ml})(0.0200\ \text{mmole/ml})}{(1000\ \text{ml})} = 0.0100\ F$$

$$\log \frac{C_{NH_4^+}}{C_{NH_3}} = -0.05$$

and

$$\frac{C_{NH_4^+}}{C_{NH_3}} = 0.89$$

Therefore,

$$C_{NH_4^+} = (0.89)(0.0100) = 0.0089\ F$$

Since the added NH_4Cl is the principal source of NH_4^+ in this solution, we must add (1 liter $\times$ 0.0089 moles/liter) = 0.0089 moles or 0.476 g solid NH_4Cl.

Buffer Capacity. Buffer solutions resist changes in pH upon the addition of strong acids or strong bases. For example, in Example Problem 15-9 the addition of 10 mmole of strong acid caused a change in pH of only 0.09 unit. The buffer capacity of a system often is defined as the moles of strong acid or strong base required to change the pH of 1 liter of the buffer solution by 1 unit. The larger the buffer capacity, the better the buffer, i.e., the more acid or base it can consume without significant changes in pH. Clearly, more concentrated buffer solutions have higher capacity than more dilute solutions. For example, even though a solution which is 0.0100 F in both acetic acid and acetate ion has the same pH as a solution which is 0.100 F in both of these constituents, the more concentrated solution can consume ten times as much strong acid or strong base for the same change in pH. Also, it can be shown that the minimum change of pH with an added increment of strong acid or strong base is achieved in a solution which has a 1:1 ratio of weak acid to conjugate base.

ACID-BASE TITRATIONS

One of the principal reasons for mastering pH calculations is to be able to use them in predicting and analyzing titration curves for acid-base reactions. A titration curve shows how the pH of a solution changes upon addition of acid or base; it is a plot of pH vs. volume of titrant added. Although our discussion of acid-base systems has been detailed and fairly rigorous, these refinements are seldom necessary for plotting theoretical curves. At most we need a half dozen points, and these can be selected for compositions which are simple to handle. Whenever possible, we select reagents and conditions yielding large equilibrium constants. Thus most of the simplified formulas for pH calculation are adequate.

Titration of a Strong Acid with a Strong Base. In a titration of an aliquot of a strong acid solution with a strong base titrant, the hydronium ion concentration prior to the equivalence point is determined by the excess strong acid which remains untitrated. At the equivalence point, the pH is 7.00 since there is no excess acid or base present and the only source of hydronium ion is the autoprotolysis of water. After the equivalence point, the hydroxide concentration is determined by the excess strong base which has been added and the pH is equal to $14.00 - pOH$. A theoretical titration curve for this system is calculated in Example Problem 15-12.

example / problem 15-12: A 50.00-ml aliquot of 0.100 N HCl is to be titrated with 0.100 N NaOH. Calculate the pH at the various points in the following titration.

(*a*) Before any base has been added

$$pH = -\log (H_3O^+) = -\log (0.100) = 1.00$$

(*b*) After 25.00 ml of base has been added. The excess acid is given by

$$(50.00)(0.100) - (25.00)(0.100) = 2.50 \text{ mmole}$$

Therefore,

$$(H_3O^+) = \frac{2.50 \text{ mmole}}{75.0 \text{ ml}} = 3.33 \times 10^{-2} \, M$$

and

$$pH = 1.48$$

(c) After 50.0 ml of base has been added. There is no excess acid or base. Therefore,

$$(H_3O^+) = (OH^-) = 1.00 \times 10^{-7}$$

and

$$pH = 7.00$$

(d) After 50.10 ml of base has been added,

$$\text{excess base concentration} = \frac{(0.10 \text{ ml})(0.100 \text{ mmole/ml})}{100.1 \text{ ml}} = 1.00 \times 10^{-4} \, M$$

$$pOH = 4.00 \quad \text{and} \quad pH = 10.00$$

Note: OH^- from autoprotolysis of water is negligible since $(H_3O^+) = 10^{-10} \, M$, (OH^-) from water $= 10^{-10} \, M$ which is $\ll 10^{-4} \, M$.

This titration is plotted in a normal titration curve in Figure 15-2. The equivalence point in

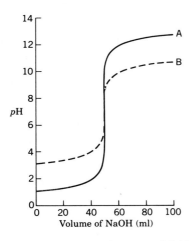

FIGURE 15-2.   Titration curves of 50.00 ml aliquots of HCl with NaOH titrant. In cruve A, the HCl aliquot concentration is 0.100 N and the titrant is 0.100 N NaOH. For curve B, the HCl aliquot concentration is $1.00 \times 10^{-3} \, N$ and the titrant is $1.00 \times 10^{-3} \, N$ NaOH.

a symmetrical titration reaction (A + B = C + D) coincides with the point of maximum slope of the titration curve. If a pH meter is available, this point is easily determined by adding small (preferably equal) increments of titrant as the equivalence point is approached. For each increment, Δ ml, the change in pH, ΔpH, is noted. The equivalence point is reached when ΔpH/Δ ml is at a maximum. A comparison of curves A and B in Figure 15-2 points out that when more dilute reactants are used, a smaller pH change occurs near the equivalence point.

Titration of a Weak Acid with a Strong Base. A weak monoprotic acid system may consist of the weak acid, the weak acid plus the conjugate base, or the conjugate base. The methods we have derived to determine the pH of these different systems also may be used to predict the pH during the course of a titration of a weak acid with a strong base.

example/problem 15-13: Calculate the titration curve for the titration of a 50.00-ml aliquot of 0.100 F acetic acid with 0.100 N NaOH.

solution.

(a) Calculation of pH before any base is added. The principal source of hydronium ion is the dissociation of the weak acid,

$$(H_3O^+) = (OAc^-)$$

and

$$\frac{(H_3O^+)}{C_{HOAc} - (H_3O^+)} = 1.75 \times 10^{-5}$$

assuming $(H_3O^+) \ll C_{HOAc}$,

$$(H_3O^+) = 1.32 \times 10^{-3} \ M$$

and

$$pH = 2.88$$

(b) Calculation of pH after 10.00 ml of base have been added. The reaction

$$HOAc + OH^- = OAc^- + H_2O$$

is essentially quantitative going left to right. Therefore, the number of millimoles of OAc^- in the solution equals the number of millimoles of OH^- added, and

$$C_{OAc^-} = \frac{(10.00 \ ml)(0.100 \ mmole/ml)}{60.0 \ ml} = \frac{1.00 \ mmole}{60.0 \ ml}$$

The new formal concentration of acetic acid is equal to the original number of mmole of HOAc minus the number of mmole of HOAc reacted with the NaOH divided by the total volume, i.e.,

$$C_{HOAc} = \frac{(50.0 \ ml)(0.100 \ mmole/ml) - (10.00 \ ml)(0.100 \ mmole/ml)}{60.0 \ ml}$$

$$C_{HOAc} = \frac{4.00 \ mmole}{60.0 \ ml}$$

Using Equation 15-39, i.e., $pH = pK_a + \log \dfrac{C_{OAc^-}}{C_{HOAc}}$

$$pH = 4.76 - 0.61 = 4.15$$

(c) Calculation of pH after 49.95 ml of base have been added. Using the same development as in part (b),

$$C_{OAc^-} = \frac{(49.95 \text{ ml})(0.100 \text{ mmole/ml})}{99.95 \text{ ml}} = 0.0500 \ M$$

and

$$C_{HOAc} = \frac{(50.00 \text{ ml})(0.100 \text{ mmole/ml}) - (49.95 \text{ ml})(0.100 \text{ mmole/ml})}{99.95}$$

$$= 5.0 \times 10^{-5} \ M$$

$$pH = pK_a + \log \frac{C_{OAc^-}}{C_{HOAc}} = 4.76 + 3.00 = 7.76$$

(d) Calculation of the pH after 50.00 ml of base have been added (at equivalence point). At this point, the system consists principally of the conjugate base OAc^- for which the pH is determined by the hydrolysis of the conjugate base; therefore,

$$\frac{(OH^-)^2}{C_{OAc^-} - (OH^-)} = K_h = 5.71 \times 10^{-10}$$

and mmole OH^- added = mmole OAc^- formed.

Therefore, $\qquad C_{OAc^-} = \dfrac{(50.0 \text{ ml})(0.100 \text{ mmole/ml})}{100.0 \text{ ml}} = 0.0500 \ M$

assuming

$$(OH^-) \ll 0.0500 \ M$$

$$(OH^-)^2 = 2.86 \times 10^{-11}$$

and

$$(OH^-) = 5.35 \times 10^{-6} \ M$$

Therefore,

$$pOH = 5.27 \quad \text{and} \quad pH = 8.73$$

(e) Calculation of pH after 50.05 ml of base have been added,

$$\text{excess } OH^- = (0.05 \text{ ml})(0.100 \text{ mmole/ml}) = 5.0 \times 10^{-3} \text{ mmole}$$

Since the hydrolysis constant for acetate is so small (5.71×10^{-10}), the principal source of hydroxide ion is the excess sodium hydroxide. Therefore,

$$(OH^-) = \frac{5.0 \times 10^{-3} \text{ mmole}}{100.05 \text{ ml}} = 5.0 \times 10^{-5} \ M$$

Thus,

$$pOH = 4.30 \quad \text{and} \quad pH = 9.70$$

(f) After 60.00 ml of base have been added, again the pH is determined by the excess base concentration; i.e.,

$$(OH^-) = \frac{(60.00 \text{ ml})(0.100 \text{ mmole/ml}) - (50.00 \text{ ml})(0.100 \text{ mmole/ml})}{(110.0 \text{ ml})}$$

and

$$(OH^-) = 9.09 \times 10^{-3} M$$

Therefore,

$$pOH = 2.04 \quad \text{and} \quad pH = 11.96$$

Table 15-3 provides a more complete listing of the pH variation in this titration as strong base is added.

TABLE 15-3 pH Variations in the Titration of 50.0 ml of 0.100 N Acetic Acid with 0.100 N NaOH

Volume NaOH Added, ml	pH
0.0	2.88
10.0	4.15
25.0	4.76
40.0	5.36
49.0	7.45
50.0	8.73
50.1	10.0
51.0	11.00
60.0	11.96
75.0	12.30
100.0	12.52

The titration curve derived from the data in Table 15-3 is plotted in Figure 15-3 and compared with the strong acid-strong base titration curve. Note that the pH change near the equivalence point is considerably smaller in the weak acid titration than in the strong acid case. The magnitude of the pH break depends on both the concentration of the reactants and the dissociation constants of the weak acid or weak base being titrated. Titration curves for acids and bases with various dissociation constants are illustrated in Figures 15-4 and 15-5. These curves clearly indicate that if the K_a or K_b is smaller than 10^{-8}, there will be difficulty in locating the equivalence point even with a pH meter. Weak acids and weak bases, with K_a's or K_b's smaller than 10^{-8}, are best titrated in non-aqueous solvents (to be discussed in Chapter 16).

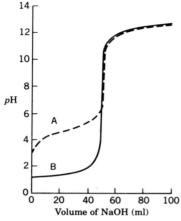

FIGURE 15-3. Titration curves for the titrations of 50.0 ml of 0.100 F acetic acid with 0.100 N NaOH (curve A) and 50.0 ml of 0.100 N HCl with 0.100 N NaOH (curve B).

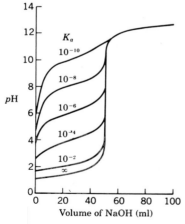

FIGURE 15-4. Titration curves for acids with different dissociation constants. Each curve corresponds to the titration of 50.0 ml of 0.100 F acid with 0.100 N NaOH.

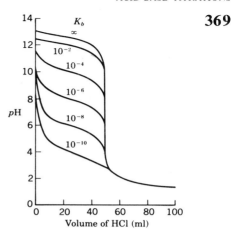

FIGURE 15-5. Titration curves for bases with different dissociation constants. Each curve corresponds to the titration of 50.0 ml of 0.100 F base with 0.100 N HCl.

POLYPROTIC ACIDS

Compounds with more than one acidic proton are referred to as polyprotic acids. The dissociation of each proton from a polyprotic acid consists of a separate equilibrium; consequently, the number of equilibrium constants corresponds to the number of acidic protons. The dissociation constants for a number of polyprotic acids are listed in Table 15-4.

Phosphoric Acid System. The dissociation of phosphoric acid is represented by the three dissociation equilibria,

$$H_3PO_4 + H_2O = H_3O^+ + H_2PO_4^- ; \quad K_1 = \frac{(H_3O^+)(H_2PO_4^-)}{(H_3PO_4)} = 5.89 \times 10^{-3}$$

$$(15\text{-}41)$$

$$H_2PO_4^- + H_2O = H_3O^+ + HPO_4^{-2}; \quad K_2 = \frac{(H_3O^+)(HPO_4^{-2})}{(H_2PO_4^-)} = 6.16 \times 10^{-8}$$

$$(15\text{-}42)$$

TABLE 15-4 Polyprotic Acid Dissociation Constants at 25° C

Acid Name	Formula	K_1 (pK_1)	K_2 (pK_2)	K_3 (pK_3)	K_4 (pK_4)
Carbonic acid	$CO_2 + H_2O$	4.46×10^{-7} (6.35)	5.62×10^{-11} (10.25)		
Hydrogen sulfide	H_2S	1.00×10^{-7} (7.00)	1.20×10^{-13} (12.92)		
Oxalic acid	HOOCCOOH	5.62×10^{-2} (1.25)	5.25×10^{-5} (4.28)		
Tartaric acid	HOOCCHOHCHOHCOOH	9.1×10^{-4} (3.04)	4.26×10^{-5} (4.37)		
Succinic acid	$HOOC(CH_2)_2COOH$	6.45×10^{-5} (4.19)	3.31×10^{-6} (5.48)		
Adipic acid	$HOOC(CH_2)_4COOH$	3.80×10^{-5} (4.42)	3.89×10^{-6} (5.41)		
Phthalic acid	$C_6H_4(COOH)_2$	1.12×10^{-3} (2.95)	3.89×10^{-6} (5.41)		
Phosphoric acid (ortho)	H_3PO_4	5.89×10^{-3} (2.23)	6.16×10^{-8} (7.21)	4.79×10^{-13} (12.32)	
Citric acid	OH | HOOCCH$_2$C CH$_2$COOH | COOH	1.15×10^{-3} (2.94)	7.25×10^{-5} (4.14)	1.51×10^{-6} (5.82)	
Ethylene-diamine-tetra-acetic acid (EDTA)	$[(HOOCCH_2)_2NCH_2-]_2$	1.01×10^{-2} (1.99)	2.13×10^{-3} (2.67)	6.90×10^{-7} (6.16)	5.47×10^{-11} (10.26)

and

$$HPO_4^{-2} + H_2O = H_3O^+ + PO_4^{-3}; \quad K_3 = \frac{(H_3O^+)(PO_4^{-3})}{(HPO_4^{-2})} = 4.79 \times 10^{-13}$$

(15-43)

The structure of phosphoric acid is represented by,

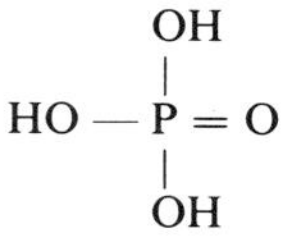

$$\begin{array}{c} OH \\ | \\ HO - P = O \\ | \\ OH \end{array}$$

with the phosphorus atom located in the center of a tetrahedral arrangement of oxygen atoms. When one of the protons is removed, the remaining anion has one negative charge which is delocalized over all four of the oxygen atoms. As a result, the removal of a second proton from an oxygen which assumes a partially negative charge is more difficult, and the removal of the third proton from the dinegatively charged species is even more difficult. These trends are reflected in the values of the successive dissociation constants ($K_1 = 5.89 \times 10^{-3}$, $K_2 = 6.16 \times 10^{-8}$, $K_3 = 4.79 \times 10^{-13}$) which differ by large amounts. On the other hand, for a molecule like succinic acid, $HOOC - CH_2 - CH_2 - COOH$, the two acidic protons are far removed from each other and the negative charge formed when the first proton leaves is not delocalized into the vicinity of the other proton. As a result, the dissociation constants are nearly the same ($K_1 = 6.45 \times 10^{-5}$ and $K_2 = 3.31 \times 10^{-6}$).

Polyprotic Acid Distribution Diagrams. The molecular or anionic forms which a polyprotic acid assumes in aqueous solution depend upon the pH of the system or, conversely, the pH of a polyprotic acid system is determined by the forms of the polyprotic acid which are present. A plot of the fraction of the total polyprotic acid present as each species vs. pH is referred to as a distribution diagram. This graphic representation of a polyprotic system is extremely helpful in understanding the nature of the equilibria which are involved. A distribution diagram for the phosphoric acid system is derived in Example Problem 15-14.

example/problem 15-14: Determine the fraction of the total phosphoric acid which is present as H_3PO_4, $H_2PO_4^-$, HPO_4^{-2} and PO_4^{-3} as a function of pH.

solution. The mass action expressions for the three dissociations are given in Equations 15-41 through 15-43. The material balance for this system is

$$C_{PO_4} = (H_3PO_4) + (H_2PO_4^-) + (HPO_4^{-2}) + (PO_4^{-3})$$

where C_{PO_4} is the *total analytical concentration* of all phosphate species. The fraction of each species is equal to the concentration of that species divided by the total analytical concentration. The fraction is denoted by the symbol α (alpha) with a numerical subscript corresponding to the number of acidic protons on the species, e.g.,

$$\alpha_3 = \frac{(H_3PO_4)}{C_{PO_4}}, \quad \alpha_2 = \frac{(H_2PO_4^-)}{C_{PO_4}}, \quad \alpha_1 = \frac{(HPO_4^{-2})}{C_{PO_4}}, \quad \text{and } \alpha_0 = \frac{(PO_4^{-3})}{C_{PO_4}}$$

Clearly, $\alpha_3 + \alpha_2 + \alpha_1 + \alpha_0 = 1.00$.

Determination of α_3:
From the material balance expression,

$$\alpha_3 = \frac{(H_3PO_4)}{(H_3PO_4) + (H_2PO_4^-) + (HPO_4^{-2}) + (PO_4^{-3})}$$

The right side of this equation has four unknowns. Simplifying the denominator by using the appropriate mass action expressions,

$$\alpha_3 = \frac{(H_3PO_4)}{(H_3PO_4) + \dfrac{K_1(H_3PO_4)}{(H_3O^+)} + \dfrac{K_1K_2(H_3PO_4)}{(H_3O^+)^2} + \dfrac{K_1K_2K_3(H_3PO_4)}{(H_3O^+)^3}}$$

Further simplification gives,

$$\alpha_3 = \frac{(H_3PO_4)}{\dfrac{(H_3O^+)^3(H_3PO_4) + K_1(H_3O^+)^2(H_3PO_4) + K_1K_2(H_3O^+)(H_3PO_4) + K_1K_2K_3(H_3PO_4)}{(H_3O^+)^3}}$$

Therefore,

$$\alpha_3 = \frac{(H_3O^+)^3}{(H_3O^+)^3 + K_1(H_3O^+)^2 + K_1K_2(H_3O^+) + K_1K_2K_3} \tag{15-44}$$

Determination of α_2:
From Equation 15-41,

$$(H_2PO_4^-) = \frac{K_1(H_3PO_4)}{(H_3O^+)}$$

Therefore,

$$\alpha_2 = \frac{(H_2PO_4^-)}{C_{PO_4}} = \frac{K_1\dfrac{(H_3PO_4)}{(H_3O^+)}}{C_{PO_4}}$$

and since $(H_3PO_4) = \alpha_3 C_{PO_4}$,

$$\alpha_2 = \frac{K_1\alpha_3}{(H_3O^+)} \tag{15-45}$$

Determination of α_1:
From Equation 15-42,

$$(HPO_4^{-2}) = \frac{K_2(H_2PO_4)}{(H_3O^+)}$$

Therefore,

$$\alpha_1 = \frac{(HPO_4^{-2})}{C_{PO_4}} = \frac{\dfrac{K_2(H_2PO_4^-)}{(H_3O^+)}}{C_{PO_4}}$$

Since $(H_2PO_4^-) = \alpha_2 C_{PO_4}$,

$$\alpha_1 = \frac{K_2\alpha_2}{(H_3O^+)} = \frac{K_1K_2\alpha_3}{(H_3O^+)^2} \tag{15-46}$$

In a similar manner it may be shown that

$$\alpha_0 = \frac{(PO_4^{-3})}{C_{PO_4}} = \frac{K_3\alpha_1}{(H_3O^+)} = \frac{K_1K_2K_3\alpha_3}{(H_3O^+)^3} \tag{15-47}$$

Therefore, Equations 15-44 through 15-47 may be used to derive the distribution curves for the phosphoric acid system. These are shown in Figure 15-6.

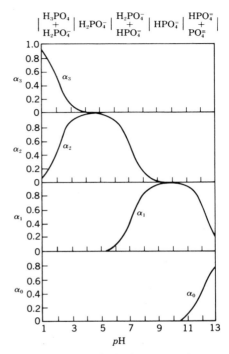

FIGURE 15-6. Distribution curves for the phosphoric acid system.

For any general polyprotic acid system where H_nB represents the *most* protonated form of the acid,

α_n = the fraction of the *total* "B" existing as the *most* protonated form, H_nB

$$\alpha_n = \frac{(H_3O^+)^n}{(H_3O^+)^n + K_1(H_3O^+)^{n-1} + K_1K_2(H_3O^+)^{n-2} + K_1K_2K_3(H_3O^+)^{n-3}}$$

(15-48)

α_{n-1} = the fraction of the total "B" existing as $H_{n-1}B$

$$\alpha_{n-1} = \frac{K_1(H_3O^+)^{n-1}}{(H_3O^+)^n + K_1(H_3O^+)^{n-1} + K_1K_2(H_3O^+)^{n-2} + K_1K_2K_3(H_3O^+)^{n-3}}$$

(15-49)

α_{n-2} = the fraction of the total "B" existing as $H_{n-2}B$

$$\alpha_{n-2} = \frac{K_1 K_2 (H_3O^+)^{n-2}}{(H_3O^+)^n + K_1(H_3O^+)^{n-1} + K_1 K_2(H_3O^+)^{n-2} + K_1 K_2 K_3(H_3O^+)^{n-3}}$$

$$(15\text{-}50)$$

α_{n-3} = the fraction of the total "B" existing as $H_{n-3}B$

$$\alpha_{n-3} = \frac{K_1 K_2 K_3 (H_3O^+)^{n-3}}{(H_3O^+)^n + K_1(H_3O^+)^{n-1} + K_1 K_2(H_3O^+)^{n-2} + K_1 K_2 K_3(H_3O^+)^{n-3}}$$

$$(15\text{-}51)$$

Although the equations just given may appear to be complex, they give a complete description of a polyprotic acid system in terms of the dissociation constants and a single variable, the pH of the solution. Analogous equations are used to describe stepwise complex ion dissociation equilibria.

The distribution curves shown in Figure 15-6 can be used to determine both the relative amounts of species needed to prepare a solution of a given pH, and to predict the pH of the system, given the amounts of the various species. The curves in Figure 15-6 indicate that at a given pH there are a maximum of two *principal* phosphate species present. This is true in any polyprotic acid system in which the successive dissociation constants differ by a factor of $\sim 10^3$ or more. The fraction of each species at a particular pH is determined as follows. At pH = 3.00, α_1 and α_0 are negligible; therefore $\alpha_3 + \alpha_2 = 1.00$. From the graph, $\alpha_3 = 0.127$ and $\alpha_2 = 0.873$. Therefore, if it is desired to prepare a solution of pH = 3.00 for which the total phosphate concentration is 0.1000 F, the solution is made up so that $(H_3PO_4) = 0.0127\ F$ and $(H_2PO_4^-) = 0.0873\ F$. At pH = 7.21, α_3 and α_0 are insignificantly small and $\alpha_2 + \alpha_1 = 1.00$. At pH = 7.21, both α_2 and α_1 equal 0.500; thus, an equimolar mixture of $H_2PO_4^-$ and HPO_4^{-2} has a pH of 7.21 (neglecting activity effects, which, unfortunately, are important in phosphate systems).

The general equations 15-48 through 15-51, representing the fractional distribution of species of a polyprotic acid system apply no matter what the dissociation constant values and no matter what the magnitude of their differences.

When the polyprotic acid dissociation constants are significantly different (i.e., K_1/K_2 and $K_2/K_3 > 10^3$), the system may be treated essentially the same as if the various species behave as independent monoprotic acids of much different strengths. Example problems which illustrate this are now presented.

example / problem 15-15: Calculate the pH of 50.0 ml of a solution which is 0.100 F in H_3PO_4.

solution. The possible equilibria are:

$$H_3PO_4 + H_2O = H_3O^+ + H_2PO_4^-; \quad K_1 = 5.89 \times 10^{-3}$$
$$H_2PO_4^- + H_2O = H_3O^+ + HPO_4^{-2}; \quad K_2 = 6.16 \times 10^{-8}$$
$$HOH + HOH = H_3O^+ + OH^-; \quad K_w = 1.00 \times 10^{-14}$$

From the magnitude of the equilibrium constants, the principal equilibrium is the dissociation of H_3PO_4. The $H_2PO_4^-$ ions in this system result from the partial dissociation of H_3PO_4 and the extent of dissociation of $H_2PO_4^-$ is relatively small. This is graphically illustrated in the distribution curves in Figure 15-6 which demonstrate that the amount of HPO_4^{-2} in a system containing H_3PO_4 and $H_2PO_4^-$ is insignificant. Water autoprotolysis is also negligible. Therefore, the mass action expression,

$$\frac{(H_3O^+)(H_2PO_4^-)}{(H_3PO_4)} = 5.89 \times 10^{-3} \tag{15-52}$$

is used to determine the pH. Since the dissociation of H_3PO_4 is the only source of $H_2PO_4^-$,

$$(H_3O^+) = (H_2PO_4^-)$$

and

$$(H_3PO_4) = C_{PO_4} - (H_3O^+) = 0.100 - (H_3O^+)$$

Substituting into Equation 15-52,

$$\frac{(H_3O^+)^2}{0.100 - (H_3O^+)} = 5.89 \times 10^{-3} \tag{15-53}$$

If we assume that $0.100 \gg (H_3O^+)$,

$$(H_3O^+)^2 = 5.89 \times 10^{-4}$$

and

$$(H_3O^+) = 2.42 \times 10^{-2} \, M$$

Therefore, (H_3O^+) is not $\ll 0.100$ and Equation 15-53 must be solved rigorously. Rearranging terms,

$$(H_3O^+)^2 = 5.89 \times 10^{-4} - 5.89 \times 10^{-3}(H_3O^+)$$

and

$$(H_3O^+)^2 + 5.89 \times 10^{-3}(H_3O^+) - 5.89 \times 10^{-4} = 0$$

A quadratic solution yields,

$$(H_3O^+) = 2.13 \times 10^{-2} \, M$$

and

$$pH = 1.67$$

example / problem 15-16: Calculate the pH of the solution which results from the addition of 30.0 ml of 0.100 N NaOH to 50.0 ml of 0.100 F H_3PO_4.

solution. There are originally (50.0 ml)(0.100 mmole/ml) = 5.00 mmole of H_3PO_4 before the base is added. Since OH^- is a *much* stronger base than $H_2PO_4^-$, the reaction $H_3PO_4 + OH^- = H_2O + H_2PO_4^-$ is essentially quantitative. Therefore, in the final solution there are 2.00 mmole of H_3PO_4 left and 3.00 mmole of $H_2PO_4^-$ formed since (30.0 ml)(0.100 mmole/ml) = 3.00 mmole of base were added. The possible equilibria are:

$$H_3PO_4 + H_2O = H_3O^+ + H_2PO_4^-; \quad K_1 = 5.89 \times 10^{-3}$$

$$H_2PO_4^- + H_2O = H_3O^+ + HPO_4^{-2}; \quad K_2 = 6.16 \times 10^{-8}$$

$$HOH + HOH = H_3O^+ + OH^-; \quad K_w = 1.00 \times 10^{-14}$$

In this solution the principal source of hydronium ions is the slight dissociation of phosphoric acid, or $H_3PO_4 + H_2O = H_3O^+ + H_2PO_4^-$. However, there are now two sources of $H_2PO_4^-$, the amount formed from the base reaction and the amount contributed from the dissociation of H_3PO_4. Therefore,

$$(H_3PO_4) = \frac{2.00 \text{ mmole}}{80.0 \text{ ml}} - (H_3O^+)$$

and,

$$(H_2PO_4^-) = \frac{3.00 \text{ mmole}}{80.0 \text{ ml}} + (H_3O^+)$$

Substituting into the mass action expression for K_1,

$$\frac{(H_3O^+)\left[\dfrac{3.00}{80.0} + (H_3O^+)\right]}{\dfrac{2.00}{80.0} - (H_3O^+)} = 5.89 \times 10^{-3} \tag{15-54}$$

Considering the value of the equilibrium constant, (H_3O^+) will *not* be $\ll 2.00/80.0$. Therefore, Equation 15-54 must be rearranged and solved by successive approximations or quadratically. Using successive approximations, assuming $(H_3O^+) \ll 2.00/80.0$,

$$(H_3O^+) = 5.89 \times 10^{-3}\left(\frac{2}{3}\right) = 3.93 \times 10^{-3} \, M$$

This value is substituted into the additive and subtractive terms on the left side of Equation 15-54 and again solving for (H_3O^+),

$$(H_3O^+) = 5.89 \times 10^{-3}\left(\frac{2.20 \times 10^{-2}}{4.05 \times 10^{-2}}\right) = 3.20 \times 10^{-3} \, M$$

Again substituting into Equation 15-54 and solving,

$$(H_3O^+) = 5.89 \times 10^{-3}\left(\frac{2.18 \times 10^{-2}}{4.07 \times 10^{-2}}\right) = 3.16 \times 10^{-3} \, M$$

3.16×10^{-3} is reasonably close to 3.20×10^{-3} and so we stop here. Therefore,

$$pH = 2.50$$

example / problem 15-17: Calculate the *p*H of a solution which is 0.0500 *F* in NaH_2PO_4 and 0.0600 *F* in Na_2HPO_4.

solution. The possible equilibria in this system include:

$$H_2PO_4^- + H_2O = H_3O^+ + HPO_4^{-2}; \quad K_2 = 6.16 \times 10^{-8}$$

$$HPO_4^{-2} + H_2O = H_3O^+ + PO_4^{-3}; \qquad K_3 = 4.79 \times 10^{-13}$$

and

$$H_2O + H_2O = H_3O^+ + OH^-; \qquad K_w = 1.00 \times 10^{-14}$$

Since $10^{-8} \gg 10^{-13}$ and 10^{-14}, the principal equilibrium is the dissociation of $H_2PO_4^-$. Therefore,

$$(H_2PO_4^-) = C_{H_2PO_4^-} - (H_3O^+) \qquad \text{and} \qquad (HPO_4^{-2}) = C_{HPO_4^{-2}} + (H_3O^+)$$

From the K_2 mass action expression,

$$\frac{(H_3O^+)(0.0600 + (H_3O^+))}{0.0500 - (H_3O^+)} = 6.16 \times 10^{-8}$$

Making the assumption that $(H_3O^+) \ll 0.0500$

$$(H_3O^+) = 6.16 \times 10^{-8}\left(\frac{0.0500}{0.0600}\right) = 5.14 \times 10^{-8} \, M$$

Therefore the above assumption is valid and $pH = 7.29$

example / problem 15-18: Calculate the pH of a solution which is 0.0400 F in Na_2HPO_4 and 0.0500 F in Na_3PO_4.

solution. The important equilibria in this solution include:

$$HPO_4^{-2} + H_2O = H_3O^+ + PO_4^{-3}; \qquad K_3 = 4.79 \times 10^{-13}$$
$$\text{(dissociation)}$$

$$PO_4^{-3} + H_2O = HPO_4^{-2} + OH^-; \qquad K_h = 2.09 \times 10^{-2}$$
$$\text{(hydrolysis)}$$

and

$$H_2O + H_2O = H_3O^+ + OH^-; \qquad K_w = 1.00 \times 10^{-14}$$

Clearly, the hydrolysis equilibrium represents the principal source of OH^- in this solution. Therefore,

$$(PO_4^{-3}) = C_{PO_4^{-3}} - (OH^-)$$

and

$$(HPO_4^{-2}) = C_{HPO_4^{-2}} + (OH^-)$$

Substituting into the hydrolysis mass action expression,

$$\frac{(0.0400 + (OH^-))(OH^-)}{0.0500 - (OH^-)} = 2.09 \times 10^{-2}$$

The magnitude of the hydrolysis constant is such that (OH^-) is not significantly smaller than 0.0400. Consequently, the hydrolysis expression has to be solved exactly. Simplifying and rearranging,

$$(OH^-)^2 + 0.0609 \, (OH^-) - 1.05 \times 10^{-3} = 0$$

Solving quadratically,

$$(OH^-) = 1.41 \times 10^{-2} \, M$$

Therefore,

example / problem 15-19:   Calculate the pH of a solution which is prepared by dissolving 9.84 grams of Na_3PO_4 in 250 ml of water and diluting to 500.0 ml with distilled water. Molecular weight, $Na_3PO_4 = 164.0$.

solution.   There are only two possible equilibria in this solution,

$$PO_4^{-3} + H_2O = \underset{\text{hydrolysis}}{HPO_4^{-2}} + OH^- ; \qquad K_h = 2.09 \times 10^{-2}$$

and

$$H_2O + H_2O = H_3O^+ + OH^- ; \qquad K_w = 1.00 \times 10^{-14}$$

Since $10^{-2} \gg 10^{-14}$, the hydrolysis reaction represents the principal equilibrium. Because the only source of HPO_4^{-2} in the solution is the hydrolysis reaction,

$$(HPO_4^{-2}) = (OH^-)$$

and

$$(PO_4^{-3}) = C_{PO_4^{-3}} - (OH^-)$$

$$C_{PO_4^{-3}} = \frac{9.84 \text{ g}}{164.0 \text{ g/mole}} \times \frac{1}{0.500 \text{ liter}} = 0.120 \ F$$

From the hydrolysis mass action expression,

$$\frac{(OH^-)^2}{0.120 - (OH^-)} = K_h = 2.09 \times 10^{-2}$$

The value of K_h indicates that (OH^-) is not $\ll 0.120$. Simplifying and rearranging,

$$(OH^-)^2 + 2.09 \times 10^{-2}(OH^-) - 2.51 \times 10^{-3} = 0$$

Solving quadratically,

$$(OH^-) = 4.08 \times 10^{-2} \ M$$

Thus,

$$p\text{OH} = 1.39 \qquad \text{and} \qquad p\text{H} = 12.61$$

To summarize, in Example Problems 15-15 through 15-19 above, we have considered a typical polyprotic acid system in which the stepwise dissociation constants differ by factors of 100 or more. Example calculations were worked out in detail for several combinations of constituents:

1. A solution with *only* H_3PO_4, the most protonated form, present. The equilibrium concentrations are calculated on the basis of a simple first step dissociation using the K_1 mass action expression.

2. A solution containing *both* H_3PO_4 and $H_2PO_4^-$. The equilibrium concentrations are calculated using the mass action expression which contains both

of these species, K_1. Because K_2 is so much smaller than K_1, the extent of dissociation of $H_2PO_4^-$ is negligible compared to the extent of the dissociation of H_3PO_4.

3. A system containing *both* $H_2PO_4^-$ and HPO_4^{-2}. The equilibrium concentrations are calculated using the mass action expression which includes both of these species, K_2. The extent of dissociation of HPO_4^{-2} is considered to be small compared to that of $H_2PO_4^-$.

4. A solution containing *both* HPO_4^{-2} and PO_4^{-3}. The principal equilibrium is that for the hydrolysis of PO_4^{-3}. The mass action expression for this reaction, K_w/K_3, contains both of the species which are present.

5. A solution containing *only* PO_4^{-3}, the unprotonated form of the acid. The hydrolysis of PO_4^{-3} is the principal equilibrium in this system. The hydrolysis constant is used with the approximation that $(OH^-) = (HPO_4^{-2})$ to determine the equilibrium ion concentrations.

SOLUTIONS OF INTERMEDIATE SALTS OF POLYPROTIC ACIDS

The remaining polyprotic acid systems which we have not yet treated are solutions which contain only an intermediate salt of the acid (e.g., $H_2PO_4^-$ *or* HPO_4^{-2}). Let us therefore consider these types of systems with two example problems.

example / problem 15-20: Calculate the hydronium ion concentration in a solution which is $0.100\ F$ in NaH_2PO_4.

solution. The possible equilibria are:

$$H_2PO_4^- + H_2O = H_3O^+ + HPO_4^{-2}; \qquad K_2 = 6.16 \times 10^{-8}$$
$$\text{dissociation}$$

$$H_2PO_4^- + H_2O = H_3PO_4 + OH^-; \qquad K_h = 1.70 \times 10^{-12}$$
$$\text{hydrolysis}$$

$$H_2PO_4^- + H_2PO_4^- = H_3PO_4 + HPO_4^{-2}; \qquad K' = K_2/K_1 = 1.05 \times 10^{-5}$$
$$\text{disproportionation}$$

and
$$H_2O + H_2O = H_3O^+ + OH^-; \qquad K_w = 1.00 \times 10^{-14}$$

For charge balance,

$$(Na^+) + (H_3O^+) = (H_2PO_4^-) + 2(HPO_4^{-2}) + (OH^-)$$

Since NaH_2PO_4 is completely dissociated in aqueous solution,

$$(Na^+) = C_{H_2PO_4^-}$$

Substituting into the charge balance equation,

$$C_{H_2PO_4^-} + (H_3O^+) = (H_2PO_4^-) + 2(HPO_4^{-2}) + (OH^-) \qquad (15\text{-}55)$$

For material balance,

$$C_{H_2PO_4} = (H_2PO_4^-) + (H_3PO_4) + (HPO_4^{-2}) \qquad (15\text{-}56)$$

Subtracting Equation 15-56 from Equation 15-55,

$$(H_3O^+) = (HPO_4^{-2}) + (OH^-) - (H_3PO_4) \qquad (15\text{-}57)$$

Equation 15-57 is simplified by expressing all terms in the form of equilibrium constants, $(H_2PO_4^-)$ and (H_3O^+). This is appropriate since the magnitude of the equilibrium constants for the possible reactions in this system indicates that $(H_2PO_4^-) \approx C_{NaH_2PO_4}$. Therefore,

$$(H_3O^+) = \frac{K_2(H_2PO_4^-)}{(H_3O^+)} + \frac{K_w}{(H_3O^+)} - \frac{(H_3O^+)(H_2PO_4^-)}{K_1}$$

Simplifying,

$$K_1(H_3O^+)^2 = K_1K_2(H_2PO_4^-) + K_1K_w - (H_3O^+)^2(H_2PO_4^-)$$

Rearranging terms,

$$(H_3O^+)^2 = \frac{K_1K_2(H_2PO_4^-) + K_1K_w}{K_1 + (H_2PO_4^-)} \qquad (15\text{-}58)$$

When $(H_2PO_4^-) \gg K_1$, and $K_1K_w \ll K_1K_2(H_2PO_4^-)$,

$$(H_3O^+)^2 = K_1K_2; \qquad (H_3O^+) = \sqrt{K_1K_2} \qquad (15\text{-}59)$$

Thus under these conditions the hydronium ion concentration is independent of the concentration of $H_2PO_4^-$. Using Equation 15-59,

$$(H_3O^+)^2 = 3.63 \times 10^{-10} \quad \text{and} \quad (H_3O^+) = 1.91 \times 10^{-5} \, M$$

In the same manner as above, it may be shown that for a solution of Na_2HPO_4,

$$(H_3O^+)^2 = \frac{K_2K_3(HPO_4^{-2}) + K_2K_w}{K_2 + (HPO_4^{-2})} \qquad (15\text{-}60)$$

For this system K_2K_w is not $\ll K_2K_3(HPO_4^{-2})$ and since (HPO_4^{-2}) is always $\gg$ K_2, Equation 15-60 simplifies to,

$$(H_3O^+)^2 = K_2K_3 + \frac{K_2K_w}{(HPO_4^{-2})} \qquad (15\text{-}61)$$

The use of Equation 15-61 requires that $(HPO_4^{-2}) \approx C_{Na_2HPO_4}$.

When the successive dissociation constants of a polyprotic acid differ by a factor of a hundred or less, the "alpha approach" simplifies the calculations. An example problem of such a system is given below.

example / problem 15-21: How many milliliters of 0.200 N sodium hydroxide must be added to 500 ml of 0.100 F tartaric acid to produce a buffer of $pH = 4.00$?

solution. For tartaric acid, H_2Tar,

$$K_1 = 9.1 \times 10^{-4} \quad \text{and} \quad K_2 = 4.26 \times 10^{-5}.$$

Therefore, both reactions,

$$H_2Tar + OH^- = HTar^{-1} + H_2O$$

and

$$HTar^{-1} + OH^- = Tar^{-2} + H_2O$$

are essentially quantitative. At $pH = 4.00$, the solutions of Equations 15-48, 15-49, and 15-50 indicate that in the final system,

$$\alpha_{H_2Tar} = 7.16 \times 10^{-2}$$
$$\alpha_{HTar^{-1}} = 6.51 \times 10^{-1}$$

and

$$\alpha_{Tar^{-2}} = 2.77 \times 10^{-1}$$

Since the *total* tartrate species in the system $= (500.0 \text{ ml})(0.100 \text{ mmole/ml}) = 50.0$ mmole, in the final solution there are 3.58 mmole H_2Tar, 32.6 mmole $HTar^{-1}$ and 13.8 mmole Tar^{-2}. Recall that we started with 50.0 mmole of H_2Tar. In order to form 32.6 mmole of $HTar^{-1}$, 32.6 mmole of NaOH are required. To form 13.8 mmole of Tar^{-2} requires 27.6 mmole of NaOH. Therefore the total NaOH which is required $= 60.2$ mmole, or 301 ml of 0.200 N NaOH.

POLYPROTIC ACID TITRATION CURVES

Titration curves for polyprotic acids resemble titration curves of monoprotic acids with the exception that they exhibit multiple inflection points corresponding to the various equivalence points. The magnitude of pH change near an equivalence point is related to the completeness of that reaction. The titration curve of 50.0 ml of 0.100 F H_3PO_4 with 0.100 N NaOH is shown in Figure 15-7. The titration curve in Figure 15-7 indicates that the reaction

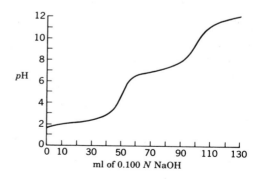

FIGURE 15-7.   Titration curve for titration of 50.0 ml of 0.100 F H_3PO_4 with 0.100 N NaOH.

$$H_3PO_4 + OH^- = H_2PO_4^- + H_2O$$

is essentially complete. This is predicted by the equilibrium constant for this reaction,

$$\frac{(H_2PO_4^-)}{(H_3PO_4)(OH^-)} = K_{eq} = K_1/K_w = 5.89 \times 10^{11}$$

The pH change at the second equivalence point also indicates a stoichiometric reaction for

$$H_2PO_4^- + OH^- = HPO_4^{-2} + H_2O$$

for which the mass action expression is

$$\frac{(HPO_4^{-2})}{(H_2PO_4^-)(OH^-)} = K'_{eq} = K_2/K_w = 6.16 \times 10^6$$

However, the reaction, $HPO_4^{-2} + OH^- = PO_4^{-3} + H_2O$, is not stoichiometric by any means. The equilibrium constant for this reaction is

$$K''_{eq} = K_3/K_w = 47.9$$

As a consequence, a third inflection is not observed in the phosphoric acid titration curve.

The titration curve in Figure 15-7 also points out the three buffer regions of the phosphoric acid system around $pH = 2.2$, $pH = 7.2$, and $pH = 12.3$.

POLYAMINE AND AMINO ACID SYSTEMS

Polyamine Systems. Polyamines, which function as weak bases, are commonly used as buffering agents and as complexing agents for metal ions. Their complexing ability is closely related to the basicity of the amine groups in the molecule. In complexing media, there is a direct competition between available protons and the metal ions to bond to basic sites of the polyamine. Thus a knowledge of the nature of the equilibrium acid-base chemistry of these types of molecules is essential for an understanding of their use and limitations as metal complexing agents.

Polyamines are treated somewhat the same as polyprotic acids. Consider the system ethylenediamine-water. The possible reactions include,

$$H_2NCH_2CH_2NH_2 + H_2O = H_3^+NCH_2CH_2NH_2 + OH^-$$

for which the mass action expression is,

$$\frac{(enH^+)(OH^-)}{(en)} = K_{b1}$$

where en = ethylenediamine, and the reaction

$$H_3^+NCH_2CH_2NH_2 + H_2O = H_3^+NCH_2CH_2NH_3^+ + OH^-$$

with the mass action expression,

$$\frac{(enH_2^{+2})(OH^-)}{(enH^+)} = K_{b2}$$

K_{b1} and K_{b2} represent base dissociation constants. The corresponding acid dissociation constants are more useful for calculation purposes, i.e.,

$$enH_2^{+2} + H_2O = enH^+ + H_3O^+$$

with

$$K_{a1} = \frac{(enH^+)(H_3O^+)}{(enH_2^{+2})} = 1.41 \times 10^{-7}$$

and

$$enH^+ + H_2O = en + H_3O^+$$

with

$$K_{a2} = \frac{(en)(H_3O^+)}{(enH^+)} = 1.17 \times 10^{-10}$$

The respective acid and base dissociation constants are related to the ion product of water as follows:

$$K_{a1}K_{b2} = K_w \qquad (15\text{-}62)$$

and

$$K_{a2}K_{b1} = K_w \qquad (15\text{-}63)$$

Acid-base calculations for these systems are carried out in the same manner as those which have been described for other polyprotic acid systems, e.g., phosphoric acid.

example/problem 15-22: Calculate the concentration of ethylenediamine dihydrogenchloride required to produce a buffer solution of $pH = 7.00$ which is 0.0100 F in ethylenediamine monohydrogen chloride.

solution. The $pH = 7.00$; therefore, $(H_3O^+) = 1.00 \times 10^{-7}$ M. From the equilibrium constants at this hydronium ion concentration

$$\frac{(enH^+)}{(enH^{+2})} = \frac{K_{a1}}{(H_3O^+)} = 1.41$$

and

$$\frac{(en)}{(enH^+)} = \frac{K_{a2}}{(H_3O^+)} = 1.17 \times 10^{-3}$$

thus $(en) \ll (enH^+)$. Therefore, the principal species in the solution are enH^+ and enH_2^{+2}. Since $(enH^+) = 0.0100$ F, $(enH_2^{+2}) = 0.0100/1.41 = 0.0071$ F, or the solution must be 0.0071 F in $en(HCl)_2$ to give a buffer of $pH = 7.00$.

Amino Acids. The simplest amino acid contains at least one acidic and one basic group. For example, the structure of glycine is represented by,

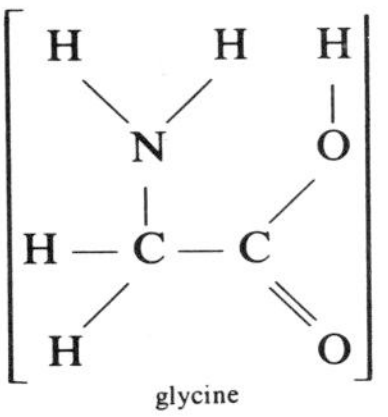

glycine

The α-amine group acts as a base and the carboxyl group behaves as an acid. As a matter of fact, when glycine is dissolved in water the conductivity indicates that glycine molecules have a very large dipole moment caused by significant charge separation in the molecules. This property suggests that the amino acid is an internally ionized molecule, commonly referred to as a "zwitterion" or "dipolar ion." Thus, in aqueous solution, glycine actually assumes the conformation,

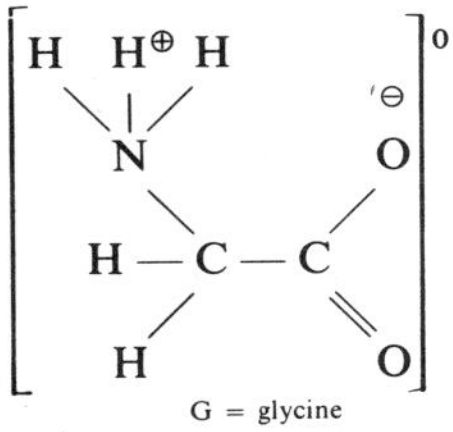

G = glycine

The negatively charged carboxylate group in the glycine "zwitterion" clearly has basic character. As a result, the molecule might accept a proton to form,

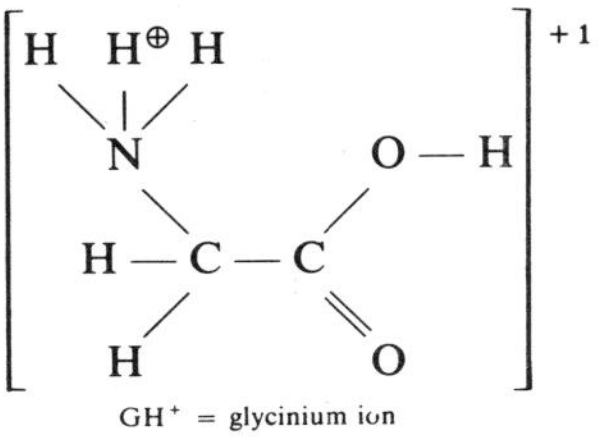

GH⁺ = glycinium ion

On the other hand, a strong base might strip the acidic proton from the amine segment of the "zwitterion" to yield,

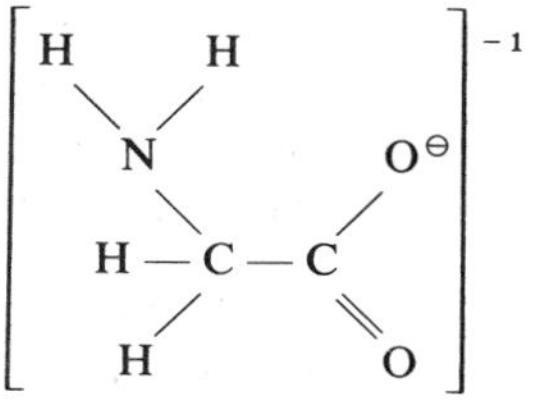

$$
\begin{bmatrix}
\text{H} & \text{H} \\
& \diagdown \diagup & \\
& \text{N} & \text{O}^{\ominus} \\
& \diagdown & \diagup \\
\text{H} - \text{C} & - \text{C} \\
\diagup & & \diagdown \\
\text{H} & & \text{O}
\end{bmatrix}^{-1}
$$

$G^- = \text{glycinate ion}$

The overall acid-base equilibria between species G, GH^+, and G^- are given by

$$GH^+ + H_2O = G + H_3O^+; \qquad K_{a1} = \frac{(H_3O^+)(G)}{(GH^+)}$$

and

$$G + H_2O = G^- + H_3O^+; \qquad K_{a2} = \frac{(H_3O^+)(G^-)}{(G)}$$

A list of the acid dissociation constants of various amino acids is presented in Table 15-5.

At different pH values, an amino acid may exist principally as a positively charged ion, a neutral molecule (with a large dipole moment) or a negatively charged ion. This is why electrophoresis separates amino acids which have different

TABLE 15-5 ACID DISSOCIATION CONSTANTS FOR REPRESENTATIVE AMINO ACIDS

Name	Neutral Structure	K_{a1} (pK_{a1})	K_{a2} (pK_{a2})	K_{a3} (pK_{a3})
Glycine	NH$_2$ | H$_2$CCOOH	4.46×10^{-3} (2.35)	1.86×10^{-10} (9.77)	
Serine	NH$_2$ | HOCH$_2$CHCOOH	6.30×10^{-3} (2.20)	5.61×10^{-10} (9.25)	
Cysteine	NH$_2$ | HSCH$_2$CHCOOH	1.10×10^{-2} (1.96)	4.36×10^{-9} (8.36)	5.25×10^{-11} (10.28)
Aspartic acid	NH$_2$ | HOOCCH$_2$CHCOOH	8.30×10^{-3} (2.08)	1.15×10^{-4} (3.94)	1.05×10^{-10} (9.98)

acid dissociation constants. At a given pH, different amino acids exist as either positive ions, neutral molecules or negative ions. The positive ion species migrate toward the negatively charged electrode, the neutral species are not deflected and the negative ion species migrate toward the positively charged electrode. This same variation in charge type with pH also is used as the basis for amino acid separations in ion exchange columns. Thus amino acid equilibria are extremely important both from theoretical and practical points of view. Acid-base calculations involving amino acids may be performed by using the same methods which have been developed for other polyprotic acid systems.

The pH at which an amino acid exists principally as the "zwitterion" neutral species and where the number of cations equals the number of anions is called the "isoelectric point." For glycine, this is the point at which essentially all of the amino acid is in the form of G, and where $(GH^+) = (G^-)$.

example / problem 15-23: Calculate the pH of 0.0150 F glycine.

solution. The possible equilibria are:

$$G + H_2O = GH^+ + OH^-; \qquad K_h = K_w/K_{a1} = 2.24 \times 10^{-12}$$
hydrolysis

$$G + H_2O = H_3O^+ + G^-; \qquad K_{a2} = 1.86 \times 10^{-10}$$
dissociation

$$G + G = GH^+ + G^-; \qquad K_{eq} = K_{a2}/K_{a1} = 4.17 \times 10^{-8}$$
disproportionation

Since G represents the intermediate species of the polyprotic acid system, we can use Equation 15-56:

$$(H_3O^+)^2 = \frac{K_{a1}K_{a2}(G) + K_{a1}K_w}{K_{a1} + (G)}$$

Solving,

$$(H_3O^+)^2 = 6.41 \times 10^{-13}$$

Therefore,

$$(H_3O^+) = 8.0 \times 10^{-7} \, M$$

and

$$pH = 6.10$$

example / problem 15-24: Determine the "isoelectric point" pH for the system glycine-water.

solution. By definition at the "isoelectric point" essentially all of the glycine is in the form of the neutral species and in addition

$$(GH^+) = (G^-)$$

Multiplying the mass action expressions K_{a1} and K_{a2}, we obtain

$$\frac{(H_3O^+)^2(G^-)}{(GH^+)} = K_{a1}K_{a2}$$

Since $(GH^+) = (G^-)$,

$$(H_3O^+)^2 = K_{a1}K_{a2} = 8.30 \times 10^{-13}$$

Thus

$$(H_3O^+) = 9.1 \times 10^{-7} M$$

and the "isoelectric point" $pH = 6.04$.

From Example Problems 15-23 and 24, the glycine "isoelectric point" pH is slightly lower than the pH of a 0.0150 F solution of glycine. Thus a *small* amount of strong acid would have to be added to a glycine solution to produce an "isoelectric solution."

AMINO ACID TITRATIONS

Amino acids may be titrated with either strong acids or strong bases. The titration curves for L-alanine, $CH_3 - \overset{\displaystyle NH_2}{\underset{\displaystyle H}{\overset{\displaystyle |}{\underset{\displaystyle |}{C}}}} - \overset{OH}{\underset{O}{C}}$ are shown in Figure 15-8.

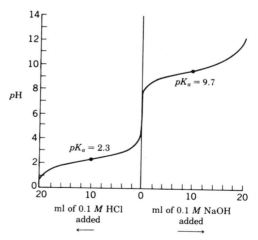

FIGURE 15-8. Titration curves for the reaction of 20.0 ml of 0.100 F L-alanine with 0.100 N NaOH and 0.100 N HCl. (From Conn and Stumpf, *Outlines of Biochemistry*, Wiley, 1963, p. 67.)

Aspartic acid, $HOOC-CH_2-CHCOOH$, with NH_2 attached, is representative of amino acids which have more than one carboxyl or amine group. The various ionic and molecular states of the compound are illustrated in this manner:

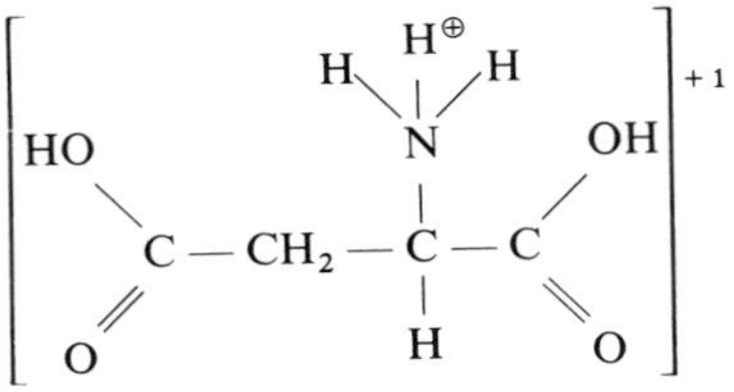

or H_3Ap^+

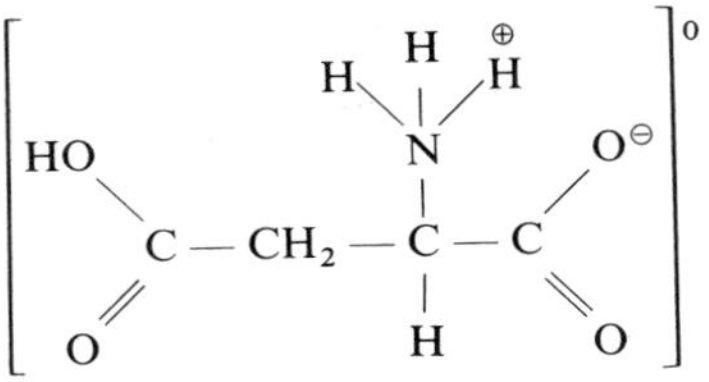

or H_2Ap

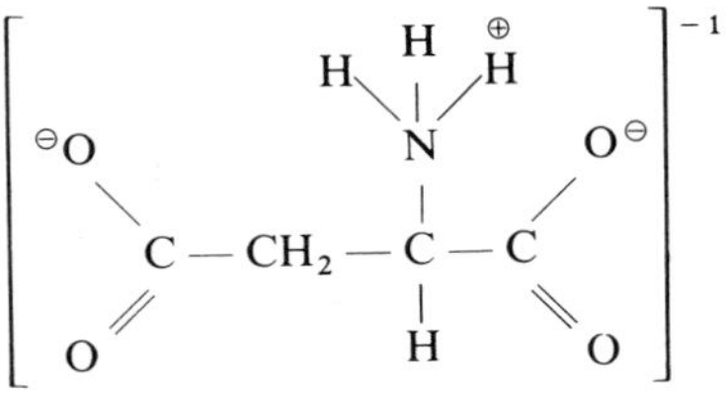

or HAp^-

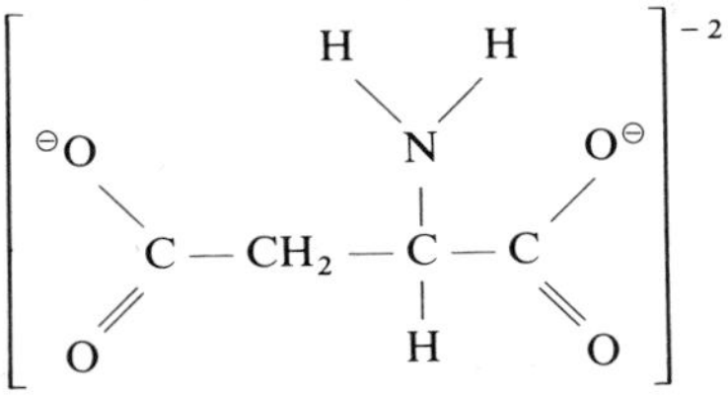

or Ap^{-2}

The equilibria for the aspartic acid-water system are represented by:

$$H_3Ap^+ + H_2O = H_3O^+ + H_2Ap; \quad K_{a1} = 8.3 \times 10^{-3}$$

$$H_2Ap + H_2O = H_3O^+ + HAp^-; \quad K_{a2} = 1.15 \times 10^{-4}$$

and

$$HAp^- + H_2O = H_3O^+ + Ap^{-2}; \quad K_{a3} = 1.05 \times 10^{-10}$$

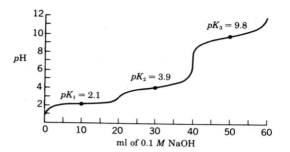

FIGURE 15-9. Titration curve for the reaction of 20.0 ml of 0.100 F aspartic hydrochloride with 0.100 N NaOH. (From Conn and Stumpf, *Outlines of Biochemistry*, Wiley, 1963, p. 69.)

A titration curve obtained in the reaction of 20.0 ml of 0.100 M aspartic hydro-chloride, $H_3Ap^+Cl^-$, with 0.100 N NaOH is given in Figure 15-9.

example / problem 15-25: Determine the "isoelectric point" pH for the system aspartic acid-water.

solution. At the "isoelectric point",

$$(H_3Ap^+) = (HAp^-)$$

and

$$(H_2Ap) \gg (H_3Ap^+) = (HAp^-)$$

Multiplying the mass action expressions for K_{a1} and K_{a2},

$$\frac{(H_3O^+)^2(HAp^-)}{(H_3Ap^+)} = K_{a1}K_{a2}$$

Thus

$$(H_3O^+)^2 = K_{a1}K_{a2}$$

and

$$(H_3O^+) = 9.8 \times 10^{-4}\ M$$

Therefore, the "isoelectric point" $pH = 3.01$.

NON-IDEAL EQUILIBRIA

At the beginning of this chapter, we pointed out that thermodynamic equilib-rium constants are based on the use of activities of the species involved rather than their molar concentrations. Recall that the activity of a species refers to the effective or "free concentration" of that species. In making the approximation that concentration is equal to activity, we have assumed that solute species are independent of each other and that there are no interactions between these species. However, even in dilute solutions there are fairly strong long range electrostatic interactions. The extent of the interactions between ions depends on the charge and size of the ions, as well as on the dielectric constant of the solvent. The overall effect of these interactions is to decrease the effective concentration or activity of the species. Thus the activity of any species is always less than the molar concentration except in *very* concentrated solutions where the repulsive electrostatic forces more than counterbalance the electrostatic attractive forces. Thus in most solutions the activity coefficient is less than unity, e.g., for component A,

$$a_A = f_A(A) \qquad f_A < 1.00$$

where the activity coefficient, f_A, is a measure of the non-ideality of the system.

The extended form of the Debye-Hückel limiting law (Equation 14-6) provides a means to estimate the value of ionic activity coefficients. Let us account for the activities of ions in a representative equilibrium calculation.

example / problem 15-26: One liter of a buffer solution is 0.0250 F in NaH_2PO_4 *and* 0.0250 F in Na_2HPO_4. Calculate the "true pH" of the solution. Compare this value with that estimated assuming all activity coefficients are unity. For phosphoric acid $K_2 = 6.16 \times 10^{-8}$.

solution.

(*a*) Approximate solution assuming all activity coefficients are unity,

$$\frac{(H_3O^+)(HPO_4^{-2})}{(H_2PO_4^-)} = 6.16 \times 10^{-8}$$

$$(H_2PO_4^-) = C_{H_2PO_4^-} - (H_3O^+) = 0.0250 - (H_3O^+)$$

$$(HPO_4^{-2}) = C_{HPO_4^{-2}} + (H_3O^+) = 0.0250 + (H_3O^+)$$

Considering the very small value of the equilibrium constant, we assume that $(H_3O^+) \ll 0.0250$ and solve,

$$(H_3O^+) = 6.16 \times 10^{-8} \frac{0.0250}{0.0250} = 6.16 \times 10^{-8} \ M$$

and

$$pH = 7.21$$

(*b*) Rigorous solution applying activity coefficients. The mass action expression takes the form

$$\frac{[f_{H_3O^+}(H_3O^+)][f_{HPO_4^{-2}}(HPO_4^{-2})]}{[f_{H_2PO_4^-}(H_2PO_4^-)]} = 6.16 \times 10^{-8}$$

Ionic strength $\mu = \frac{1}{2}[(Na^+) + (H_2PO_4^-) + 4(HPO_4^{-2})]$

$$\mu = 0.100$$

From Table 14-2, at $\mu = 0.100$,

$$f_{H_2PO_4^-} = 0.77 \quad \text{and} \quad f_{HPO_4^{-2}} = 0.355$$

Since

$$(H_2PO_4^-) = (HPO_4^{-2}) = 0.0250\ F,$$

$$\frac{a_{H_3O^+} \times 0.355 \times 0.0250}{0.77 \times 0.0250} = 6.16 \times 10^{-8}$$

Thus,

$$a_{H_3O^+} = 1.34 \times 10^{-7}\ M$$

and

$$pH = 6.87$$

Therefore, the "true pH" differs from the approximate pH by 0.34 unit. If the system $HPO_4^{-2} - PO_4^{-3}$ were examined, the difference would be even greater.

QUESTIONS AND PROBLEMS

Note: In all the following problems, assume that all solutions are at $25°C$ and that all activity coefficients are unity.

15-1. What is the pH of the following solutions?
 (a) 500 ml of a solution with an HCl concentration of $2.45 \times 10^{-3}\ F$. *Ans.* 2.61.
 (b) 300 ml of a solution with a NaOH concentration of $1.76 \times 10^{-2}\ F$.

Ans. 12.25.
 (c) A solution prepared by mixing together 250 ml of a solution with a hydronium ion concentration of 0.106 M and 350 ml of a solution with a hydronium ion concentration of $5.62 \times 10^{-2}\ M$. *Ans.* 1.11.
 (d) A solution prepared by mixing together 325 ml of a solution with a pH of 2.700 and 475 ml of a solution with a pH of 3.20. (Assume that the source of hydronium ion in each of the two original solutions was HCl.) *Ans.* 2.92.
 (e) A solution prepared by mixing together 225 ml of a solution with a NaOH concentration of 0.125 F, 325 ml of a solution with an HCl concentration of 0.110 F and 250 ml of distilled (degassed) water. *Ans.* 2.02.

15-2. What is the pH of the final solution when 15.00 ml of 0.250 F NaOH is added to 30.00 ml of 0.125 F HCl? *Ans.* 7.00.

15-3. What is the pH of the final solution when 14.90 ml of 0.250 F NaOH is added to 30.00 ml of 0.125 F HCl? *Ans.* 3.35.

15-4. 125 ml of 0.255 F propionic acid is diluted to 500 ml in a volumetric flask. What is the pH of this final solution? *Ans.* 3.04.

15-5. 100 ml of 0.325 F trimethylamine is diluted to 250 ml in a volumetric flask with distilled water. What is the pH of the final solution? *Ans.* 11.50.

15-6. 15.0 g of sodium propionate, C_2H_5COONa, is added to 500 ml of 0.250 F propionic acid. The mixture is diluted to one liter with distilled water. What is the pH of the final solution? *Ans.* 4.97.

15-7.   10.0 g of trimethylammonium chloride, $(CH_3)_3NHCl$, is added to 250 ml of 0.250 F trimethylamine. This mixture then is diluted to 500 ml with distilled water. What is the pH of the final solution?   *Ans.* 9.68.

15-8.   (a) What is the pH of 250 ml of 0.110 F ammonia?   *Ans.* 11.15.

   (b) What is the pH of a solution composed of 250 ml of the solution in part a, 7.54 g of NH_4Br and water of dilution to a final volume of 500 ml?   *Ans.* 8.80.

15-9.   What is the pH of the following solutions?
   (a) 200 ml of 0.124 F acetic acid.   *Ans.* 2.83.
   (b) 200 ml of 0.124 F acetic acid plus 50.0 ml of 0.110 N NaOH.   *Ans.* 4.21.
   (c) Solution in part b plus 100 ml of 0.110 N NaOH.   *Ans.* 5.06.
   (d) 200 ml of 0.124 F acetic acid plus 100 ml of 0.248 N NaOH.   *Ans.* 8.84.
   (e) 200 ml of 0.124 F acetic acid plus 105 ml of 0.248 N NaOH.   *Ans.* 11.60.
   (f) 9.15 g of sodium acetate (CH_3COONa) dissolved in distilled water and diluted to 1 liter.

15-10.   How much solid sodium acetate would have to be added to 2 liters of 0.125 F acetic acid to prepare a final buffer solution of pH 4.00? (Assume no volume increase on addition of salt.)   *Ans.* 3.59 g.

15-11.   How much 0.100 N NaOH must be added to a solution initially 0.200 F in acetic acid and 0.0200 F in sodium acetate to make the pH of the resulting solution be 5.00? Assume the volume of the initial acid-salt solution was 500 ml.   *Ans.* 600 ml.

15-12.   What is the pH of a solution formed by mixing 300 ml of a solution 0.240 F in NH_3 and 0.120 F in NH_4Cl with 200 ml of 0.150 N HCl?   *Ans.* 9.05.

15-13.   25.00 ml of a certain solution which contains *either* a mixture of HCl and H_3PO_4 *or* H_3PO_4 and NaH_2PO_4 was titrated with 0.100 N standard NaOH. The pH was monitored with a pH meter. 28.0 ml of base were required to reach the $H_2PO_4^-$ equivalence point and a *total* of 36.0 ml were required to reach the HPO_4^{-2} equivalence point. What were the components and their respective concentrations in the unknown?

$$Ans. (HCl) = 0.0800\ M; (H_3PO_4) = 0.0320\ M.$$

15-14.   A 50.0 ml solution which is 0.100 F in NaH_2PO_4 *and* 0.0500 F in Na_2HPO_4 is titrated with 0.250 N NaOH. What is the pH,
   (a) before any NaOH has been added?   *Ans.* 6.91.
   (b) after 20.0 ml of NaOH have been added?   *Ans.* 9.73.
   (c) after 30.0 ml of NaOH have been added?   *Ans.* 11.86.

15-15.   Succinic acid (indicate as H_2Sc) is a weak diprotic acid. Using reagents listed below, indicate how you would prepare a 1.000-liter buffer solution of pH = 4.80 which has a total succinate concentration (in all forms) of 0.0500 F, e.g.,

$$(H_2Sc) + (HSc^-) + (Sc^{-2}) = 0.0500\ F$$

Solutions available: 0.200 F H_2Sc; 0.100 N HCl; 0.100 N NaOH and distilled water.

   Ans. Add 488 ml of 0.100 N NaOH to 250 ml of 0.200 F H_2Sc and dilute to one liter with distilled water.

15-16.   It is desired to prepare a buffer solution of pH = 7.00 starting with 500 ml of a solution which is 0.400 F in Na_2HPO_4. Standardized 0.200 N solutions of both HCl and NaOH are available. Indicate the quantity (in ml) of which of the two reagent solutions you would add to the 500 ml Na_2HPO_4 solution to prepare the desired buffer.

   Ans. 619 ml of 0.200 N HCl.

15-17. Citric acid (abbreviated H_3Cit) and its salts represent a polyprotic acid system which often is used to buffer bacteriological media. How much 0.400 N NaOH solution must be added to 500 ml of 0.200 F citric acid to prepare a *final* buffer solution of $pH = 5.00$?

Ans. 504 ml.

15-18. A 50.0 ml solution which is 0.100 F in H_3PO_4 and 0.0500 F in NaH_2PO_4 is titrated with 0.250 N NaOH. What is the pH,

    (a) before any NaOH has been added?   *Ans.* 2.04.

    (b) after 20.0 ml of NaOH have been added?   *Ans.* 4.72.

    (c) after 30.0 ml of NaOH have been added?   *Ans.* 6.91.

15-19. Determine the general shape of the titration curve for the titration of 50.0 ml of 0.100 F serine hydrochloride with 0.200 N NaOH (K_a's given in Table 15-5).

15-20. Determine the isoelectric point pH for the amino acid cysteine.

REFERENCES

J. N. Butler, *Ionic Equilibrium*, Addison-Wesley, Reading, Mass., 1964. A very comprehensive treatment of the field of solution equilibrium calculations.

E. E. Conn and P. K. Stumpf, *Outlines of Biochemistry*, 2nd ed., Wiley, New York, 1966.

H. Freiser and Q. Fernando, *Ionic Equilibria in Analytical Chemistry*, Wiley, New York, 1963.

16 THE ROLE OF THE SOLVENT IN ACID-BASE CHEMISTRY

The first concepts of acids and bases were quite empirical. Classification was limited to sensory properties. Chemists noted early that limestone ($CaCO_3$) effervesces when treated with solvents like vinegar. Dilute solutions of these solvents exhibit a characteristic sour taste and they were named "acids" from the Latin term for vinegar, "acetum." Bases were also classified early according to unique observable characteristics such as the ability to dissolve oils and sulfur, to change plant dye colors and to counteract acid reactions. Rouelle in 1744 introduced the term "base" to represent this general class of compounds. They exhibit a characteristic "soapy" feel and form other compounds referred to as salts when reacted with acids. Any compound that reacts with an acid is by definition a base.

Lavoisier was the first to inquire why acids or bases behave as they do. He noted that when oxygenated sulfur and phosphorus compounds are placed in water, acids are formed. He proposed that the characteristic behavior of acids is due to the presence of oxygen. This theory was disproved in subsequent studies by Sir Humphrey Davy who went to great lengths to show that hydrochloric acid also contains oxygen. Similar experiments were tried in vain with hydriodic acid (HI) and hydrocyanic acid (HCN). Liebig finally asserted that an acid is a compound containing a hydrogen atom which can be replaced by a metal atom. This was a satisfactory classification for all of the acids known at that time.

CONCEPTS OF ACIDITY AND BASICITY

Arrhenius Theory. Between 1880 and 1890 the Arrhenius theory of electrolytic dissociation and ionization processes provided the first model on which to base our current understanding of acid-base character. Recall that the Arrhenius model describes an acid as any hydrogen-containing compound which gives hydrogen ions in aqueous solution, and a base is a compound which yields hydroxide ions in aqueous solution. The neutralization process is then represented by the reaction

395

$$H^+ + OH^- = H_2O$$

The Arrhenius definition thus provided the first mechanistic approach to acid-base behavior and was quite important in serving as a stimulus for the development of more sophisticated theories which were to come. The major problem of the Arrhenius model is that acid-base reactions are limited to aqueous solutions. It also limits bases to hydroxide compounds. This is unsatisfactory because it is well known that ammonia and many organic compounds show basic properties in their chemistry. Essentially all chemicals which exhibit acidic properties, however, do contain hydrogen. Thus the Arrhenius model reinforces the hydrogen ion concept of an acid.

Brønsted-Lowry Theory. In 1923, Brønsted and Lowry independently proposed that an acid is a species which tends to give up a proton (proton donor) and a base is a species that tends to accept a proton (proton acceptor). This definition encompasses Arrhenius acids and bases, but the more inclusive definition of a base significantly broadens the scope of acid-base chemistry.

In the Brønsted-Lowry model an acid-base reaction represents a competition between two different bases for a proton. Consider the compound HCl. This is an acid because it is able to donate a proton to something else. The resultant chloride ion is a base because it can accept a proton. This type of acid-base pair is called a conjugate pair; the chloride ion is the conjugate base of the acid HCl. For an acid to donate a proton, there must be a proton acceptor. In the ionization of an acid in a solvent, the latter performs as the base. If water is the solvent the reaction is

$$HCl + H_2O = H_3O^+ + Cl^-$$

The reverse reaction does not proceed to any significant extent because the water molecule is a much stronger base (proton acceptor) than the chloride ion. In general, the conjugate base of a strong acid is a weak base and, conversely, the conjugate base of a weak acid is a strong base. The Brønsted-Lowry theory will be treated more extensively later in this chapter.

Lewis Theory. G. N. Lewis in 1923 proposed four criteria which are necessary characteristics of acids or bases:

1. Acid-base reactions are fast reactions.
2. A stronger acid or base can replace a weaker acid or base from its compounds.
3. Indicators may be used to determine equivalence points in acid-base reactions.
4. Acids and bases are important catalysts.

Lewis explained all of these characteristics as acid-base reactions involving the formation of a coordinate covalent electron-pair bond. According to Lewis, the formation of a covalent bond suggests that a base is any species which can donate an electron-pair and an acid is any species which can accept an electron-pair. Neutralization is represented by

$$H^{\oplus} + :\overset{..}{\underset{..}{O}}:H^{\ominus} = H:\overset{..}{\underset{..}{O}}:H$$

in which the proton (an acid) accepts an electron-pair from the hydroxide ion (a base) to form a covalent bond. Another example is the reaction of a proton with an ammonia molecule:

$$H^{\oplus} + :\overset{H}{\underset{\underset{H}{..}}{N}}:H = H:\overset{H^{\oplus}}{\underset{\underset{H}{..}}{N}}:H$$

Here the ammonia molecule is a base and the proton is an acid. We can see that in the most general sense, any species with an electron orbital configuration capable of accepting an electron-pair to form a stable entity is an acid; conversely, any species with a "free" electron-pair (i.e., one which is in the valence shell but not involved in another covalent bond) is a base. In the reaction

$$Ag^{\oplus} + 2:\overset{H}{\underset{\underset{H}{..}}{N}}:H = \left[H:\overset{H}{\underset{\underset{H}{..}}{N}}:Ag:\overset{H}{\underset{\underset{H}{..}}{N}}:H \right]^{\oplus}$$

Ag^{+} is an acid and ammonia is a base. Lewis' classification of acids is founded on the presence of a unique electron distribution rather than the presence of a particular element. It is a more general approach than the Brønsted-Lowry concept. All materials classified as Lewis bases are also Brønsted bases. On the other hand, the number of Lewis acids far exceeds the number of Brønsted acids. The hydrogen ion is just one of many entities which will coordinate with an electron-pair from a base.

Comparison of the Brønsted and Lewis Theories. Both the Brønsted and the Lewis acid-base theories are useful. It is our contention, however, that the Brønsted approach is the more satisfactory for making quantitative acid-base calculations. The major advantage is that in any solvent the strength of a base is determined by its ability to attract and hold a proton in competition with the solvent and other basic molecules. According to the Lewis theory, however, the strength of a base in a given solvent depends on the nature of the acid used as a reference. When the electron-pair acceptor ion (or molecule) is varied, the strength of the coordinate bond changes and the basicity of the electron-pair donor changes. A comparison of the systems $Cr(II)-NH_3$ and $Cu(II)-NH_3$ in aqueous solution illustrates this problem. From the Lewis approach ammonia appears to be a stronger base in the Cu(II) system than in the Cr(II) system. In the Brønsted system there is only one reference component, namely, the proton, and various bases are compared in terms of competition for this proton.

THE BRØNSTED CONCEPT—THEORY AND PRACTICE

The relation between a base, B, and its conjugate acid, HB, is given in general terms by the equation

$$HB = H^+ + B$$

where HB may have neutral, negative, or positive charge and B has one less positive charge than HB. The above reaction might appropriately be called an "acid-base half-reaction" due to its similarity to a redox half-reaction,

$$Red = Ox + e^-$$

An acid gives up protons and a reducing agent gives up electrons. Neither half-reaction will proceed unless an acceptor is available since neither free electrons nor free protons exist in solution. The dissociation of an uncharged acid like hydrochloric acid is different from the dissociation of its salt, sodium chloride. In the salt, the atoms already exist as ions in the crystal lattice, in contrast to the neutral molecules of the acid. The dissociation of the uncharged acid molecules requires a *chemical reaction* between the base, H_2O, and the acid, HCl, with the resultant formation of ions:

$$HCl + H_2O = H_3O^+ + Cl^-$$

Acid Base Acid Base

Conjugate

Conjugate

Other examples of "complete" acid-base reactions involving hydrogen ion transfers from acids to bases to give the respective conjugate bases and conjugate acids are given in Table 16-1.

TABLE 16-1   TYPICAL ACID-BASE REACTIONS

H_3O^+	+	OH^-	=	H_2O	+	H_2O
 ⬡—COOH	+	H_2O	=	H_3O^+	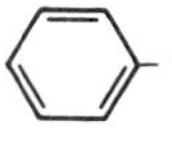 +	⬡—COO^-
$HClO_4$	+	H_2O	=	H_3O^+	+	ClO_4^-
H_3CCOOH	+	NH_3	=	NH_4^+	+	CH_3COO^-
H_2O	+	H_2O	=	H_3O^+	+	OH^-
HNO_3	+	H_2O	=	H_3O^+	+	NO_3^-
H_2SO_4	+	H_2O	=	H_3O^+	+	HSO_4^-

The strength of an acid, HB, in a given solvent, SH, is defined in terms of the extent to which the reaction $HB + SH = SH_2^+ + B^-$ proceeds. This reaction is a combination of two steps, ionization and dissociation:

$$HB + SH = \underset{\text{ion-pair}}{SH_2^+ B^-} = SH_2^+ + B^-$$

$$\underset{\text{ionization} \qquad \text{dissociation}}{}$$

The degree of ionization depends on the relative basic strengths of B and SH, and the degree of dissociation is a function of the dielectric constant of the solvent. The *overall dissociation* constant, K_a, for the acid HB is equal to the product of the ionization constant K_i and the dissociation constant K_d divided by $1 + K_i$,

$$K_a = \frac{a_{SH_2^+} \times a_{B^-}}{a_{HB} + a_{SH_2^+ B^-}} = \frac{K_i K_d}{1 + K_i} \tag{16-1}$$

where a_{HB}, $a_{SH_2^+}$, etc., represent activities. Thus the strength of an acid is defined quantitatively in terms of the magnitude of the K_a value. It is clear that the acid-base properties and dielectric constant of the solvent are important in determining acid-base behavior of solutes.

Dielectric Constant Effects. Any chemical reaction which involves a separation of charged ions is affected by the dielectric constant of the solvent. As we have pointed out, acid-base reactions involve an ionization step and a dissociation step. In aqueous solutions both of these steps occur rapidly and aqueous acid-base reactions are thus very fast reactions (e.g., much faster than aqueous precipitation, complexometric, and oxidation-reduction reactions). In any solvent, the extent of the ionization step depends on the relative strength of the conjugate acid-conjugate base pairs. The extent of the dissociation step depends on the charge type of the members of the ion-pair and the polarity of the solvent. The dielectric constant is a measure of this polarity—the higher the dielectric constant, the more polar the solvent. The extent of dissociation of ion-pair aggregates increases with the dielectric constant of the solvent. Clearly then, solvents with high dielectric constants are necessary for complete dissociation. The dielectric constant of a vacuum is arbitrarily defined as zero. The very polar water molecule has a dielectric constant of 80, whereas the value for the slightly polar acetic acid molecule is 7.14. Consequently, in water all products of acid-base reactions at moderate to low concentrations are essentially completely dissociated into solvated ions, whereas in glacial acetic acid these products exist principally as ion-pairs or ion-pair aggregates. Most of the more elementary techniques used to study acid-base reactions give a measure of the concentrations of one or more of the solvated ions. Thus, the overall dissociation constant, K_a, is the value which is normally determined. The dielectric constant of the solvent clearly has a pronounced effect on the value of the overall acid or base dissociation constant.

CLASSIFICATION OF SOLVENTS

Solvents are classified with respect to acid-base properties as either aprotic (or inert) or amphiprotic. Aprotic solvents are neither acidic nor basic, e.g., benzene and carbon tetrachloride. Amphiprotic solvents act as both proton acceptors and proton donors. There are gradations among the amphiprotic solvents from predominantly acidic to predominantly basic. Glacial acetic acid is very acidic, whereas liquid ammonia is very basic. Water and ethanol are neither strongly acidic nor strongly basic. All amphiprotic solvents undergo self-ionization or autoprotolysis reactions as illustrated by the following systems:

$$2H_2O = H_3O^+ + OH^-$$

$$2EtOH = EtOH_2^+ + OEt^-$$

$$2HOAc = H_2OAc^+ + OAc^-$$

$$2NH_3 = NH_4^+ + NH_2^-$$

or more generally,

$$2SH = SH_2^+ + S^- \quad \text{and} \quad K_s = (SH_2^+)(S^-)$$

where SH_2^+ is the solvated proton or "lyonium ion," S^- is the "lyate ion," and K_s is the autoprotolysis equilibrium constant. Protogenic amphiprotic solvents (e.g., sulfuric and formic acids) exhibit very weak basic properties and very strong acidic properties. Autoprotolysis constants for protogenic solvents are usually larger than that of water (e.g., $K_s = 10^{-6}$ for formic acid, whereas $K_s = 10^{-14}$ for water). Intermediate amphiprotic solvents possess weakly acidic protons and also act as very weak bases. Autoprotolysis constants for non-aqueous intermediate amphiprotic solvents tend to be smaller than that of water (e.g., $K_s = 10^{-19}$ for ethanol). Protophilic amphiprotic solvents (e.g., ethylenediamine) exhibit very weak acidic properties and relatively strong basic properties; their autoprotolysis constants are usually less than that of water. A list of solvents which are commonly used for acid-base titrations is presented in Table 16-2. The dielectric constants and autoprotolysis constants are indicated where they are known.

THE LEVELING EFFECT

We have stressed that the classification of an acid as strong or weak depends partly on the basic strength of the solvent. In aqueous systems, perchloric, hydro-

TABLE 16-2 SOLVENTS COMMONLY USED FOR ACID-BASE TITRATIONS

Solvent Classification	Subclassification	Name	Dielectric Constant (Debye units)	Autoprotolysis Constant pK_s
Aprotic		Chlorobenzene	5.8	
		Acetonitrile	37.5	
		Acetone	20.7	
		Chloroform	4.8	
		Methyl ethyl ketone	18.5	
		1,4-Dioxane	2.2	
Amphiprotic	Protogenic	Acetic acid	6.4	14.45
		Formic acid	58.0	6.2
	Intermediate	Water	80.0	14.0
		Methanol	31.0	16.7
		Ethanol	24.2	19.1
		Isopropanol	18.3	
		Ethylene glycol	37.7	
	Protophilic	Ethylenediamine	14.2	
		Pyridine	12.3	
		Ammonia	17.0	
		Aniline	6.9	
		Dimethyl formamide	34.8	

chloric, and nitric acids are all considered "strong acids," because in dilute solutions the reactions

$$HB + H_2O = H_3O^+ + B^-$$

proceed essentially 100% from left to right. Water does not differentiate between the inherent strength of these acids because water is a stronger base than their conjugate base anions. We might also say that HB is a stronger acid than H_3O^+ and that these acids are *leveled* to the strength of the solvated proton. The strongest acid which can exist in any solvent, SH, is SH_2^+. For example if formic acid is used as a solvent, all acids are leveled to the strength of $HCOOH_2^+$, and the order of acid strength is perchloric, hydrochloric, and nitric. Formic acid is not as strong a base as the conjugate anions of these acids, and the dissociation reactions,

$$HB + HCOOH = HCOOH_2^+ + B^-$$

proceed to different extents, with perchloric acid showing the greatest tendency to "dissociate." Compounds which are "weak" acids in water may become strong acids in a more basic solvent. For example, benzoic acid is a weak acid in aqueous solution, but it is a "strong" acid in liquid ammonia or ethylenediamine; i.e., the reaction,

$$HOBz + NH_3 = NH_4^+ + OBz^-$$

is essentially complete. Thus ammonia is a stronger base than the benzoate ion, and benzoic acid is a stronger acid than NH_4^+. On the other hand, benzoic acid is not appreciably dissociated in glacial acetic acid; i.e., the reaction

$$HOBz + HOAc = H_2OAc^+ + OBz^-$$

is not observed.

The interaction of a base, B, with a solvent requires that the solvent has acidic properties. Dissociation of a base does not occur in aprotic solvents such as carbon tetrachloride and benzene unless an acid is added. Clearly, the extent of dissociation of a base increases with increasing acid strength of the solvent. Amines are good examples of basic solutes which are weak bases in water but do not behave as bases in liquid ammonia or ethylenediamine. These solvents are much less acidic than water. However, in very acidic solvents (e.g., acetic and sulfuric acids) amines behave as very strong bases. A base leveling effect also is encountered with acidic amphiprotic solvents. For example, in aqueous solution an aliphatic amine such as methylamine, CH_3NH_2, is more than 10^4 times as strong a base as an aromatic amine such as aniline, $C_6H_5-NH_2$. However, in strongly acidic solvents such as glacial acetic acid, aliphatic and aromatic compounds are both strong bases and cannot be differentiated with respect to relative strengths. This is an example of the "leveling effect" of a solvent on a base. In glacial acetic acid the reaction

$$CH_3NH_2 + HOAc = CH_3NH_3^+ + OAc^-$$

proceeds quantitatively because OAc^- is the strongest base which can exist in acetic acid. Thus the basicity of methylamine is "leveled" to that of OAc^-. We find that the strongest base which can exist in any solvent is the "lyate ion." Any base which is stronger than the lyate ion reacts with the solvent to form this ion. For example, the oxide ion (e.g., from Na_2O or CaO) reacts quantitatively with water to form OH^- (the "lyate ion" of water):

$$O^{-2} + H_2O = 2OH^-$$

The oxide ion is a stronger base than OH^- and consequently it is "leveled" to OH^- in water.

Briefly summarized, the leveling effect tells us that:

1. A strongly acidic solvent differentiates the strength of less acidic solutes, and levels the strength of basic solutes to that of the lyate ion.

2. A strongly basic solvent differentiates the strength of less basic solutes, and levels the strength of acidic solutes to that of the lyonium ion.

3. To make a weak base appear to be strong, use a strongly acidic solvent.

4. To make a weak acid appear to be strong, use a strongly basic solvent.

ACID-BASE TITRATIONS IN NON-AQUEOUS SOLVENTS

Fundamental studies concerning the nature of titration reactions in non-aqueous solvents represent a new frontier in chemistry where most of the important progress has been made since about 1957. The majority of non-aqueous titrations involves neutralizations of organic bases or acids and the direct determinations of acidic and basic functional groups. In addition to their importance in organic analysis, non-aqueous acid-base titrations are used extensively in pharmaceutical analysis, e.g., to determine constitutents present in antihistamines, antibiotics, and sulfonamides. Direct titrations are possible in non-aqueous acid-base reactions since they proceed to completion within a few microseconds.

In the areas of organic oxidation-reduction, precipitation, and complexometric titrations, one of the greatest problems is that the reactions are considerably slower than acid-base reactions, Frequently, in order to accelerate the reactions, an excess of the titrant is added, and this excess is determined subsequently by an appropriate back-titration procedure.

There are numerous advantages offered by acid-base titrations in non-aqueous media, the most important of which is that a much larger number of acids and bases can be titrated in non-aqueous solvents than in aqueous solution. For example, a weak acid with a pK_a of 9 or greater cannot be determined accurately in water because of the competition of the solvent for the strong base titrant. But the weak acid can be titrated in ethylenediamine, which is considerably more basic than water and will not react with a strong base titrant. The availability of a large variety of non-aqueous solvents allows the choice of a solvent which will assist but not interfere with a specific acid-base titration. A properly formulated non-aqueous acid-base titration procedure provides results which are very accurate and often more precise than those obtained from a corresponding titration in aqueous media. In the material to follow, we will consider briefly some of the practical considerations which apply to non-aqueous acid-base titrations. The student is referred to the excellent monograph by Kucharský and Šafařik for a more comprehensive review of the multitude of applications of non-aqueous titrations. Kolthoff and Bruckenstein present a rigorous theoretical treatment of acid-base chemistry in non-aqueous media in the *Treatise on Analytical Chemistry*.

Titrants. Since perchloric acid is the strongest mineral acid, acidic titrants normally consist of solutions of perchloric acid in either anhydrous acetic acid or dioxane. Acetic acid solutions which are 0.1 to 1.0 F in perchloric acid commonly are used. Perchloric acid is essentially 100% ionized in acetic acid; it exists as the

ion pair, $CH_3C^+ \overset{\displaystyle OH}{\underset{\displaystyle OH}{\diagdown}} ClO_4^-$ (or $H_2OAc^+ClO_4^-$), as well as the solvated ion,

H_2OAc^+.

Basic titrants include quaternary tetraalkyl ammonium hydroxides, which are stronger bases than the alkali metal hydroxides. Although the product salts of alkali metal ions are quite insoluble in non-aqueous media, quaternary ammonium salts are very soluble. Tetrabutylammonium hydroxide in isopropanol is the most commonly used base titrant. To insure that the titrant solvent does not interfere with the principal reaction, the concentration of the titrant solution is usually high relative to the concentration of the substance titrated. Only a small volume of titrant is added in comparison to the volume of the titration mixture.

Choice of Solvent for Acid-Base Titration. The following considerations are pertinent to the choice of a solvent for a specific non-aqueous acid-base titration:

1. The solvent should permit a *large change* in the solvated proton concentration near the equivalence point. Other things being equal, the smaller the autoprotolysis constant, the better the end point.

2. The substance to be titrated must be soluble, either in the solvent or in an excess of the titrant which then may be back-titrated.

3. The product of the titration must be soluble, or if it is a precipitate, it must be compact and crystalline and not gelatinous. Gelatinous precipitates tend to interfere with accurate end-point determinations.

4. The solvent should not introduce interfering side reactions with either the substance to be titrated or the titrant.

5. Preferably, the solvent should be inexpensive and easily purified.

When several acids or bases in a mixture are "leveled" to the same strength, they may not be differentiated by titration. For example, the concentration of each constituent in a mixture of perchloric acid and sulfuric acid cannot be determined in a titration with a strong base in aqueous solution. Both of these acids are leveled to hydronium ion which is then titrated with the base. As a result, only the *total amount* of strong acid may be determined. In glacial acetic acid, perchloric acid is approximately 235 times as strong as sulfuric acid. Even this large difference is not enough to give two distinct equivalence points in a titration of this mixture in glacial acetic acid. Furthermore, the bisulfate ion is too weak to be titrated in this solvent. However, in a titration of a perchloric acid and sulfuric acid mixture in a methyl isobutyl ketone solvent, three distinct breaks in "pH" occur when t-butyl ammonium hydroxide in isopropanol is used as the titrant. The breaks correspond to the successive neutralizations of perchloric acid, the first proton of sulfuric acid and finally the bisulfate ion. Curve A of Figure 16-1 shows the titration curve obtained with a glass electrode-calomel electrode cell. The e.m.f. of this electrode system is approximately proportional to the "pH" of the system. Additional acid-differentiating titrations also are illustrated in Figure 16-1.

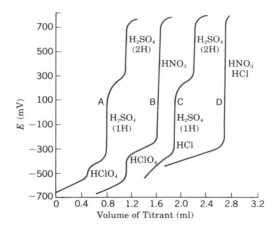

FIGURE 16-1. Titration curves of acid mixtures in the solvent methyl isobutyl ketone using 0.2 F t-butylammonium hydroxide as the titrant and a glass electrode-saturated calomel electrode cell. [After Bruss and Wyld, *Anal. Chem.*, **29**, 232 (1957).]

Inert solvents may be added to either protogenic or protophilic solvents to modify differentiating titrations. The presence of the inert solvent decreases the amphiprotic character of both acidic and basic solvents. For example, butylamine and pyridine are both titrated as strong bases in glacial acetic acid, but in a solvent which consists of 10% acetic acid and 90% chloroform, two distinct equivalence points are noted corresponding to the neutralizations of butylamine and then pyridine.

Normally, the titration of a weak acid in an inert solvent involves the addition of a small volume of concentrated base dissolved in an amphiprotic solvent such as an alcohol. Thus, after the first addition of titrant, the system contains a small amount of amphiprotic solvent (the alcohol) in an inert solvent. The "effective" autoprotolysis constant for the system is that of the amphiprotic solvent mixed with the inert solvent. When the amount of amphiprotic solvent is small, the "effective" autoprotolysis constant is small and the "pH" break is large near the equivalence point. This is the reason why highly concentrated solutions of bases are used as titrants. Isopropyl alcohol is commonly used as the solvent for tetra-alkylammonium hydroxides because it is the least acidic of the amphiprotic solvents.

In summary, for titrations of weak acids and weak bases, inert solvents provide the largest break in "pH" near the equivalence point. Inert solvents are also preferable in successive titrations of acids and bases in mixtures. When solubility problems are encountered with inert solvents, protogenic solvents are used for weak base titrations and protophilic solvents are used in weak acid titrations.

END POINT DETERMINATION IN NON-AQUEOUS TITRATIONS

Unfortunately, in non-aqueous media we do not have accurate values for the dissociation constants of chemical indicators, nor do we have quantitative relationships which relate the e.m.f. of electrochemical cells to constituent concentrations. So how can we find accurate end points in non-aqueous titrations? Let us briefly examine some of the indicator systems for non-aqueous titrations.

Potentiometric End Point. In a typical non-aqueous potentiometric acid-base titration, we might use this cell:

$$\text{Ag} \mid \text{AgCl, HCl (0.10 } N) \mid \begin{array}{c} \text{Glass} \\ \text{Membrane} \\ \hline \text{Non-Aqueous} \\ \text{Solution} \end{array} \mid\mid \begin{array}{c} \text{Saturated Calomel} \\ \text{Electrode} \end{array}$$

As in aqueous solution, in most non-aqueous solvents the glass electrode appears to respond to the difference between the activity of the solvated proton in the solution inside the glass membrane and the activity of solvated proton in the solutions on the outside. However, a quantitative interpretation of this potential difference is not obvious. In the first place, ion activities in one solvent cannot be simply related to ion activities in another solvent. In addition, when we measure the e.m.f. of the cell just shown, we include a sizable, unknown, liquid junction potential between the aqueous calomel electrode and the non-aqueous solution. This liquid junction potential may vary considerably during the course of a non-aqueous titration, depending on the nature of the solvent and the titrants. Liquid junction potentials must remain reasonably constant during the course of the titration for high precision. In many cases the e.m.f. of the above cell does vary approximately linearly with the pSH_2 of the non-aqueous solution. It should be pointed out, however, that the e.m.f. variation in no way corresponds to the theoretical variation derived for aqueous solutions from the Nernst equation. In other words, a *change* in 1.00 unit of pSH_2 *does not* correspond to a change in e.m.f. of 59.16 mV at 25° C in non-aqueous solvents. As a result, the pH scale of a pH meter is meaningless in non-aqueous titrations and the millivolt scale(s) should be used. So, for titrations in ethanol or glacial acetic acid, the glass-calomel electrode system appears to respond to changes in $-\log (EtOH_2^+)$ and $-\log (H_2OAc^+)$, respectively (or the "pH" of these solutions). When an acid is titrated in an inert solvent (e.g., a ketone) with t-butyl ammonium hydroxide in isopropanol, the glass electrode responds to changes in the isopropanol solvated proton concentration. In highly basic solvents, such as butylamine and ethylenediamine, the glass electrode does not function as an indicator electrode and an antimony electrode is used instead. Some examples of potentiometric non-aqueous titration curves are illustrated in Figures 16-2 through 16-4.

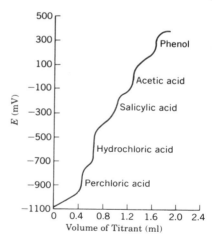

FIGURE 16-2. Titration curve for strong, weak, and very weak acid mixture in methyl-isobutyl ketone using 0.2 F t-butylammonium hydroxide in isopropanol as the titrant. Indicating electrode system: glass-platinum (in titrant). [After Bruss and Wyld, *Anal. Chem.*, **29**, 232 (1957).]

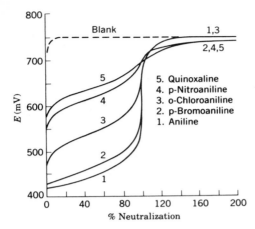

FIGURE 16-3. Titration curves for various aromatic amines in anhydrous acetic acid using 0.10 F perchloric acid in glacial acetic acid as the titrant. Indicating electrode system: glass-calomel. (From Fritz and Hammond, *Quantitative Organic Analysis*, Wiley, 1957, p. 32.)

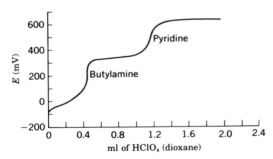

FIGURE 16-4. Titration curve for butylamine-pyridine mixture in acetonitrile using 0.10 F perchloric acid in dioxane as the titrant. Indicating electrode system: glass-calomel placed very close together. [From Fritz, *Anal. Chem.*, **25**, 407 (1953).]

Chemical Indicators. Indicators for non-aqueous acid-base titrations behave similarly to those that are employed in aqueous titrations in either giving up or accepting protons and changing color in the process. An indicator, therefore, may dissociate in solvent SH,

$$\underset{\text{color A}}{\text{HIn}} + \text{SH} = \text{SH}_2^+ + \underset{\text{color B}}{\text{In}^-}$$

Clearly the predominant form of the indicator depends on the SH_2^+ concentration. So far this story is no different from that for an indicator in aqueous solution. However, in non-aqueous media many solvents are available and the behavior of a particular indicator depends on the acidity, basicity, or inertness of the solvent as well as its dielectric constant.

Some indicators have simple color changes; others successively pass through a wide range of color shades. For example, as crystal violet is increasingly protonated in glacial acetic acid, it changes from violet to blue-green to green to yellow. Methyl violet passes through similar changes. To determine the color change which best indicates the end point, a potentiometric titration should be run with the indicator present. The color change which occurs nearest the potentiometric equivalence point should then be used as the end point in future titrations of the same kind. A list of indicators for titrations of weak acids and weak bases is given in Table 16-3.

TABLE 16-3 Indicators Commonly Used in Non-Aqueous Titrations

Indicator	Constituent Titrated	Solvent
Crystal violet or Methyl violet	Weak bases	Acetic acid; acetonitrile
Methyl red	Weak bases	Dioxane; glycol-isopropanol
Dibenzalacetone	Weak bases	Nitromethane
Azo-violet or Thymol blue or o-Nitroaniline	Weak acids	Dimethylformamide

THE HAMMETT ACIDITY FUNCTION

Hammett has studied the equilibrium phenomena of a series of acid-base indicators in solutions representing a wide range of acidity. *In these studies he introduces an acidity function, H_0, which is a measure of the tendency of a solution to transfer a proton to a neutral base.* Hammett defines H_0 by the equation,

$$H_0 = -\log a_{\text{SH}_2^+}\left[\frac{f_{\text{B}}}{f_{\text{BH}^+}}\right] \qquad (16\text{-}2)$$

where B is the neutral base to which the solution transfers a proton, $a_{SH_2^+}$ is the activity of the solvated hydrogen ion, and f_B and f_{BH^+} are the activity coefficients of the neutral base and its conjugate acid.

We wish to derive an expression for H_0 which is amenable to experimental determination. In order to do this we will begin with some of Hammett's preliminary indicator experiments.

Suppose we have a very concentrated strong acid solution such as a mixture of sulfuric acid and water and attempt to determine the extent of dissociation of a weak indicator base, B. Classical conductivity or potentiometric methods are not satisfactory, because these methods involve measuring a property of the solution as a whole. In a sulfuric acid-water mixture, the conductivity is very high as a result of the ions produced by the reaction

$$H_2SO_4 + H_2O = H_3O^+ + HSO_4^-$$

Now, if a small amount of a neutral base, B, is added, any *changes* in these concentrations due to dissociation of B,

$$B + H_3O^+ = BH^+ + H_2O$$

will not change the conductivity appreciably. However, if we select a neutral base whose conjugate acid absorbs electromagnetic radiation at a substantially different wavelength than the base, we can determine the concentrations of BH^+ and B by spectrophotometry and thus determine the extent of dissociation of B in the solution under study. For a series of strongly acidic solutions containing the very weak neutral base, we can determine the variation in proton-donating power of the solutions by monitoring the extent of dissociation of B.

Hammett presents a more quantitative approach to this problem. In his treatment, the base strength of B is measured by the acidity constant of its conjugate acid, given in terms of activities rather than concentrations, i.e.,

$$pK_a^B = -\log \frac{a_{SH_2^+} a_B}{a_{BH^+}} \tag{16-3}$$

He begins with a dilute aqueous solution of sulfuric acid, in which the activity coefficients approach unity; however, they do not approach unity in other solvents. Therefore, in dilute aqueous solutions,

$$pK_a^B = pH - \log \frac{(B)}{(BH^+)} \tag{16-4}$$

Since the pH can be determined quite accurately, pK_a^B can be easily evaluated if $(B)/(BH^+)$ can be determined by spectrophotometry.

Continuing with Hammett's treatment, let us consider a second neutral base C which is slightly weaker than B. A solution, for example, $\sim 10\% \ H_2SO_4$, is selected in which B and C are both partially dissociated to measurable extents. Due to the high $a_{SH_2^+}$ in the solution, a small quantity of B added to one portion of the solution and a small quantity of C to another portion does not change $a_{SH_2^+}$ significantly. For all intents and purposes it is the same for both solutions.

The dissociation constant of the conjugate acid of C is

$$pK_a^C = -\log \frac{a_{SH_2^+} a_C}{a_{CH^+}} \qquad (16\text{-}5)$$

Equations 16-4 and 16-5 are combined to give,

$$pK_a^C - pK_a^B = -\log \frac{a_C}{a_{CH^+}} + \log \frac{a_B}{a_{BH^+}} \qquad (16\text{-}6)$$

or

$$pK_a^C - pK_a^B = -\log \frac{(C)}{(CH^+)} + \log \frac{(B)}{(BH^+)} - \log \frac{f_C f_{BH^+}}{f_{CH^+} f_B} \qquad (16\text{-}7)$$

If the ratio of activity coefficients is essentially unity, the last term in Equation 16-7 can be neglected. Experiments support this approximation for sulfuric acid solutions, for mixtures of perchloric, nitric and hydrochloric acids with water, as well as for solutions in formic acid and concentrated solutions of sulfuric acid in acetic acid. The activity coefficient term is essentially constant and is equal to zero in dilute aqueous solutions where all activity coefficients have values of 1. Therefore, in solutions of high dielectric constant (and as an approximation for *any* solution), the activity coefficient term can be neglected,

$$pK_a^C - pK_a^B = -\log \frac{(C)}{(CH^+)} + \log \frac{(B)}{(BH^+)} \qquad (16\text{-}8)$$

Thus we determine pK_a^C from the known value of pK_a^B and of (B) and (BH^+) in one portion of the solvent, and (C) and (CH^+) in another portion of the same solvent.

In the next step, we choose a third neutral base indicator D, with $pK_a^D < pK_a^C$ so that the degree dissociation of both C and D can be measured in a somewhat more acidic solution than that used in the last experiment for B and C:

$$pK_a^D - pK_a^C = -\log \frac{(D)}{(DH^+)} + \log \frac{(C)}{(CH^+)} \qquad (16\text{-}9)$$

Provided that pK_a^C is known from above, pK_a^D can also be determined.

The base strength of successively weaker indicators can be measured in sulfuric acid solutions ranging up to the anhydrous acid with this stepwise approach. Table 16-4 gives values of pK_a derived using this approach in sulfuric acid solutions,

TABLE 16-4 INDICATOR CONSTANTS, pK_a, OF VERY WEAK NEUTRAL BASES

Indicator	Solvent				
	HCl + H_2O	HNO$_3$ + H_2O	H_2SO_4 + H_2O	HClO$_4$ + H_2O	HCO$_2$H
Aminoazobenzene	(+2.80)	---	---	---	---
Benzeneazodiphenylamine	+1.52	---	---	---	---
p-Nitroaniline	+1.11	(+1.11)	(+1.11)	(+1.11)	---
o-Nitroaniline	−0.17	−0.20	−0.13	−0.19	(−0.17)
p-Chloro-*o*-nitroaniline	−0.91	−0.97	−0.85	−0.91	−0.94
p-Nitrodiphenylamine	---	---	−2.38	---	−2.51
2,4-Dichloro-6-nitroaniline	---	---	−3.22	−3.18	−3.31
p-Nitroazobenzene	---	---	−3.35	−3.35	−3.29
2,6-Dinitro-4-methylaniline	---	---	−4.32	---	---
2,4-Dinitroaniline	---	---	−4.38	−4.43	---
N,N-Dimethyl-2,4,6,-trinitroaniline	---	---	−4.69	---	---
Benzalacetophenone	---	---	−5.61	---	---
β-Benzoylnaphthalene	---	---	−5.92	---	---
p-Benzoyldiphenyl	---	---	−6.19	---	---
6-Bromo-2,4-dinitroaniline	---	---	−6.59	---	---
Anthraquinone	---	---	−8.15	---	---
2,4,6-Trinitroaniline	---	---	−9.29	---	---

as well as in other mixtures of strong acids in water and in anhydrous formic acid. For each solvent, the value in parentheses serves as a reference point. Thus the pK_a of aminoazobenzene measured spectrophotometrically in dilute HCl solutions is the primary reference, and the values of other indicators listed for HCl solutions are derived by stepwise comparison. The value for *p*-nitroaniline so obtained serves as a secondary standard for other strong acids, and the average value for *o*-nitroaniline found in these solutions is a reference point for solutions in formic acid. In Table 16-4 we find that, within experimental error, the relative strength of two bases is independent of the medium in which they are compared. A part of the small variations is caused by differences in light absorptivities in different media.

The indicator experiments just described demonstrate that all quantities of the type $f_B f_{CH^+}/f_{BH^+} f_C = 1$. This is possible only if the ratio f_B/f_{BH^+} has the same value for all bases. Therefore, the acidity function is independent of the base used for its evaluation and is a characteristic property of the solution. In strong proton-donor solutions, $a_{SH_2^+}$ cannot be measured directly. However, recall that,

$$a_{SH_2^+} = \frac{K_a^B a_{BH^+}}{a_B} = \frac{K_a^B (BH^+) f_{BH^+}}{(B) f_B} \qquad (16\text{-}10)$$

Substituting the value of $a_{SH_2^+}$ from Equation 16-10 into Equation 16-2, we obtain,

$$H_0 = -\log K_a^B \frac{(BH^+) f_{BH^+}}{(B) f_B} \times \frac{f_B}{f_{BH^+}}$$

$$H_0 = -\log K_a^B - \log \frac{(BH^+)}{(B)}$$

$$H_0 = pK_a^B + \log \frac{(B)}{(BH^+)} \qquad (16\text{-}11)$$

So, to determine the tendency of a solution to transfer a proton to a neutral base, all we have to do is add a small amount of indicator of known pK_a and measure the ratio $(B)/(BH^+)$ spectrophotometrically. We can also turn this around and determine pK_a values.

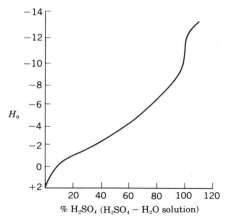

FIGURE 16-5. Hammett acidity function variation with % composition in system $H_2SO_4 - H_2O$. [From Hammett and Deyrup, *J. Am. Chem. Soc.*, **54**, 2721 (1932).]

From the form of the acidity function, we can see that the acidity function is not identical with pH. However, it equals pH in dilute aqueous solutions where $f_B/f_{BH^+} \rightarrow 1$. It should be stressed that the value H_0 does not apply to the tendency of a solution to transfer a proton to an electrically charged base. Other functions have been suggested for these cases (H_- for anionic bases and H_+ for cationic bases). These functions are not properties of the solvent alone but depend also on the nature of the reference base.

From the definition of H_0 we can see that the more negative the value, the higher is the proton donor ability of the solution. We can picture a range of acidity from water, $H_0 = 7$, to anhydrous sulfuric acid, $H_0 = -13$. The conclusion is that anhydrous sulfuric acid is 10^{20} more powerful than water as a proton donor. Acidity function plots are shown in Figures 16-5 and 16-6. The use of H_0 is very convenient in the study of the mechanisms of acid-catalyzed reactions.

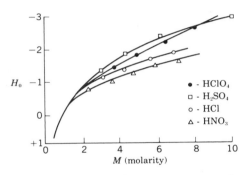

FIGURE 16-6.   Hammett acidity function in moderately concentrated aqueous solution. [From Hammett and Paul, *J. Am. Chem. Soc.*, **56**, 287 (1934).]

QUESTIONS AND PROBLEMS

16-1.   Give the autoprotolysis reaction and the corresponding mass action equilibrium expression for the following solvents:

    (*a*) ethylenediamine, $H_2N(CH_2)_2NH_2$
    (*b*) sulfuric acid
    (*c*) formic acid, HCOOH
    (*d*) isopropanol, H_3CCHOH
                       |
                      CH_3

    (*e*) pyridine,

16-2. Justify the following statements:

(a) Phenol ($K_a = 1.2 \times 10^{-10}$ in water) may be quantitatively titrated in ethylenediamine using tetrabutylammonium hydroxide; however, phenol cannot be quantitatively titrated in water with sodium hydroxide.

(b) Perchloric acid and nitric acid may be titrated differentially in methyl isobutyl ketone; however this titration is not possible in water.

(c) Pyridine ($K_b = 1.5 \times 10^{-9}$ in water) can be titrated quantitatively in glacial acetic acid with perchloric acid; however, it cannot be titrated quantitatively in water with hydrochloric acid.

16-3. Predict *with justification* a solvent and titrant combination which is suitable for quantitative analysis of the following compounds: (aqueous acid and base dissociation constants are given in parentheses)

(a) propionic acid ($K_a = 1.34 \times 10^{-5}$)

(b) aniline, $\langle\rangle$—NH_2 ($K_b = 4.2 \times 10^{-10}$)

(c) hypobromous acid, HOBr ($K_a = 2.5 \times 10^{-9}$)

(d) iodic acid, HIO_3 ($K_a = 1.6 \times 10^{-1}$)

(e) a mixture of propionic acid ($K_a = 1.14 \times 10^{-5}$) and acetic acid ($K_a = 1.75 \times 10^{-5}$)

(f) a mixture of ammonia ($K_b = 1.78 \times 10^{-5}$) and pyridine, $\langle\rangle N$ ($K_b = 1.5 \times 10^{-9}$)

REFERENCES

J. S. Fritz and G. S. Hammond, *Quantitative Organic Analysis*, Wiley, New York, 1957; Chapter 3.

L. P. Hammett, *Physical Organic Chemistry*, McGraw-Hill, New York, 1940. Acidity function discussed in Chapter 9.

I. M. Kolthoff, *Treatise on Analytical Chemistry*, Part 1, Volume 1, I. M. Kolthoff and P. S. Elving, Editors, Interscience, New York, 1959; Chapter 11. Excellent discussions of concepts of acids and bases.

J. Kucharsky and L. Šafařik, *Titrations in Non-Aqueous Solvents*, Elsevier, Amsterdam, 1965.

17 EFFECTS OF MOLECULAR STRUCTURE ON ACIDITY

There are numerous experimental methods by which the relative strengths of various acids and bases in different solvent systems are determined. A fundamental question raised by the results of these studies is: "Why are some acids and bases stronger than others?" For example, in aqueous solution why is hydrobromic acid a stronger acid than hydrofluoric acid; why is phenol a stronger acid than propanol, and *para*-nitrobenzoic acid stronger than benzoic acid? To a large degree the answers to these questions are found in analyses and comparisons of molecular structures. We find that the introduction of various functional groups, which are neither acidic nor basic, in the structure of an organic acid or base greatly affects the acid and base properties of the molecule as a whole. A most dramatic example of this phenomenon is trichloroacetic acid which is a much stronger acid than the parent compound, acetic acid, in aqueous solution. We will discuss the three general categories of inductive effects, resonance effects and steric effects in an attempt to correlate variations in acid-base strength with molecular structure.

INDUCTIVE EFFECTS

We have indicated previously that the dissociation constant is a measure of the strength of the acid. Among the many Brønsted acids studied, the carboxylic acids have been most exhaustively examined in terms of relating substituent effects to the extent of dissociation in the solvent water. Table 17-1 lists pK_a ($-\log K_a$) values for some of these acids.

For acid dissociations, changes in structure which promote the loss of the acidic proton from the acid molecule or hinder proton return to the conjugate base increase the degree of the dissociation (decrease pK_a) of the acid. A comparison of pK_a values for various substituted carboxylic acids with the pK_a value of acetic acid is instructive in correlating structural effects and acid strength. In the first group of acids in Table 17-1, the acidity increases with the introduction of a positively charged group (e.g., $H_3N^\oplus$). This may be interpreted on purely electrostatic grounds since the positive charge tends to shift the electron density in the σ bonded system *away* from the acidic proton, making it easier to remove, e.g.,

417

TABLE 17-1 pK_a VALUES FOR SOME REPRESENTATIVE CARBOXYLIC ACIDS IN SOLVENT H_2O AT 25°C

Acid	Formula	pK_a
Acetic acid	CH_3COOH	4.76
Glycine hydrochloride	$H_3N^{\oplus}\!\!-CH_2COOH\ Cl^{\ominus}$	2.35
δ-Aminovaleric acid hydrochloride	$H_3N^{\oplus}\!\!-(CH_2)_4COOH\ Cl^{\ominus}$	4.27
Hydrogen malonate anion	$^{\ominus}O_2CCH_2COOH$	5.69
Hydrogen adipate anion	$^{\ominus}O_2C(CH_2)_4COOH$	5.41
Fluoroacetic acid	FCH_2COOH	2.66
Chloroacetic acid	$ClCH_2COOH$	2.86
Dichloroacetic acid	$Cl_2CHCOOH$	1.30
Trichloroacetic acid	Cl_3CCOOH	0.65
β-Chloropropionic acid	$Cl(CH_2)_2COOH$	4.0
Hydroxyacetic acid	$HOCH_2COOH$	3.83
Cyanoacetic acid	$N\equiv CCH_2COOH$	2.43
Malonic acid	$HOOCCH_2COOH$	2.83
Propionic acid	CH_3CH_2COOH	4.87
Trimethylacetic acid	$(CH_3)_3CCOOH$	5.05
Formic acid	$HCOOH$	3.77

Taken from Gould, *Mechanism and Structure in Organic Chemistry,* Holt, Rinehart and Winston, New York, 1959; p. 201.

$$H_3N^{\oplus} \leftarrow \overset{\overset{\displaystyle H}{|}}{\underset{\underset{\displaystyle H}{|}}{C}} \leftarrow C \overset{\displaystyle O}{\underset{\displaystyle O \leftarrow H}{}}$$

This kind of effect is most prounoned when the positively charged substituent is close to the carboxyl group. For example, $H_3N^{\oplus}\!\!-CH_2COOH$ is about 300 times as strong an acid as CH_3COOH, whereas there is a much smaller increase in acid strength for $H_3N^{\oplus}\!\!-(CH_2)_4COOH$ where the positive charge is five atoms away from the carboxyl group.

Likewise, we can anticipate that the introduction of a negative charge will shift electron density *toward* the proton, making it more difficult to remove and thus increase the pK_a. Let us compare the hydrogen malonate anion, $O_2^{\ominus}CCH_2COOH$, with acetic acid and hydrogen malonate with malonic acid, $HOOCH_2COOH$. Hydrogen malonate may be thought of as acetic acid with a negative carboxylate group, $COO^{\ominus}$, substituted for an α hydrogen. The malonate anion has four equivalent basic sites compared to two for acetic acid. A statistical approach shows that hydrogen malonate should be twice as strong a base as the acetate anion or, analogously, hydrogen malonate should be half as strong an acid as acetic acid. The electrostatic effect is in the right direction to explain this discrepancy, making hydrogen malonate more basic and less acidic.

Dipole interactions as well as ionic charges cause inductive effects within a molecule. Compared to carbon and hydrogen atoms, fluorine, chlorine, nitrogen, and oxygen atoms possess proportionately greater unscreened nuclear charge and are therefore better electron-pair attractors, or, in other words, these atoms are more electronegative than either carbon or hydrogen atoms. When a more electronegative atom is substituted for the hydrogen atom in a $C — H$ couple, there is a shift in electron density toward the more electronegative atom and polarization results. As might be expected, those atoms nearest the substitution position experience the greatest polarization. The effect of substituting a more electronegative group on a carboxylic acid parallels the effect of a positively charged group, i.e., there is a greater tendency to lose the acidic proton and the acid strength is increased. In Table 17-1, note that halogen substitution for an α hydrogen of acetic acid causes a considerable increase in acid strength. Di- and tri-halogen substituted acids are even stronger. Glycolic acid, $HOCH_2COOH$, in which the electronegative oxygen atom of the OH group has replaced an α hydrogen of acetic acid, is ten times as strong as acetic acid. Chlorine substitution in the β position in propionic acid also increases the strength of the acid, but the effect is less than in substitution where the electron attractor is closer to the acidic proton.

Functional groups which contain a highly electronegative atom doubly or triply bonded to a more electropositive atom also increase the acidity of the molecule. Typical examples are: $— C \equiv N$, $— NO_2$, $— COOH$ and $— C = O$.

The electrons in the π-bonding orbitals of the more electropositive atom of each of these groups are more polarizable than the strongly localized σ-bonded electrons, such as those in an alcohol group. Consequently, in the alcohol group,

$— \overset{\overset{\displaystyle H}{|}}{\underset{\underset{\displaystyle H}{|}}{C}} — \overset{..}{\underset{..}{O}}H$, even though the oxygen atom is more electronegative than the adjacent carbon, the electrons in the σ bond are localized and no effective positive charge is given to the carbon; thus, the inductive effect of the OH group on the rest of the molecule is not significant. On the other hand, substituents like the

aldehyde group, $-C\overset{\displaystyle O}{\underset{\displaystyle H}{\diagup\diagdown}}$, can exhibit considerable negative inductance on the

rest of the molecule. We can explain this as follows. In the aldehyde group, the oxygen atom is more electronegative than the carbon atom. The double bond between these two atoms consists of one σ and one π bond. We have indicated that the carbon electron in a strongly localized σ bond between these atoms is not significantly polarized; however, the carbon electron in the π bond is polarized toward the oxygen atom, leaving an effective partial positive charge on the

carbon, i.e., $-\overset{\delta^+}{C}\overset{\displaystyle O^{\delta^-}}{\underset{\displaystyle H}{\diagup\diagdown}}$ where δ^+ and δ^- signify partial positive and negative

charges, respectively. We can indicate this effect by analyzing the polar resonance forms of these groups,

in which the atom with the positive charge is the one nearer to the remainder of the molecule. These groups act as electron attractors, drawing electrons away from acidic protons on the remainder of the molecule and thus increasing the acidity of the molecule. Resonance forms of some of these other functional groups are analogous,

$$-\overset{\overset{\displaystyle \ddot{O}}{\diagup\!\!\!\diagup}}{C}\diagdown_{\displaystyle \overset{..}{O}H} \longleftrightarrow -\overset{\overset{\displaystyle \ddot{O}^{\ominus}}{\diagup}}{\overset{\oplus}{C}}\diagdown_{\displaystyle \overset{..}{O}H}$$

Note from Table 17-1 that when three methyl groups are substituted for the three α hydrogens in acetic acid, the acidity decreases by a factor of 2. However, a more significant change is noted if we replace a hydrogen nearer the acidic proton $\left(\text{such as } H - C\overset{\displaystyle \diagup\!\!\!\diagup O}{\diagdown OH} \right)$ with a methyl group (to form CH_3COOH).

The methyl group lowers the extent of dissociation by a factor of 10. Therefore, in comparison we conclude that the hydrogen atom is a *better* electron-withdrawing agent than a methyl group and, by analogy, it is better than all other alkyl groups. The most common explanation for this effect is hyperconjugation. This is represented as follows:

$$\underset{\displaystyle H}{\overset{\displaystyle H}{H-\overset{|}{\underset{|}{C}}-C}}\overset{\diagup\!\!\!\diagup O}{\diagdown O-H} \longleftrightarrow \overset{H^{\oplus}}{\underset{\displaystyle H}{H-\overset{|}{\underset{|}{\overset{\ominus}{C}}}-C}}\overset{\diagup\!\!\!\diagup O}{\diagdown O-H} \longleftrightarrow \overset{\displaystyle H^{\oplus}}{\underset{\displaystyle H}{H-\overset{|}{C}=C}}\overset{\diagup O^{\ominus}}{\diagdown O-H}$$

that is, electron density moves toward the acid proton and decreases the acidity compared to $H - C\overset{\displaystyle \diagup\!\!\!\diagup O}{\diagdown OH}$ In contrast to alkyl substitution of α hydrogens in

acetic acid and the resulting decrease in acidity, when unsaturated (π-bonded) hydrocarbon groups are substituted, the acidity *increases* by a factor of 2. This is noted with vinyl, $- CH = CH_2$, and phenyl group, $-\langle\bigcirc\rangle$, substitutions.

This behavior indicates that an unsaturated carbon atom is a stronger electron attractor than a saturated carbon atom. An explanation has been offered in terms of differences in hybridizations of these two types of atoms. The σ bond from the saturated C to the rest of the molecule is of the sp^3 hybrid class, and the corresponding σ bond from an unsaturated C is an sp^2 hybrid. The 2s orbital has proportionately greater electron density closer to the nucleus than the $2p$ orbital. Therefore, since an sp^2 hybrid bond has a greater percentage of "s-character" than its sp^3 analog, the unsaturated carbon has greater electron charge density closer to the nucleus than the saturated carbon and is a better electron withdrawer. By analogy, a carbon atom which is triply bonded to a hydrogen and singly bonded to the rest of the molecule is an even better electron withdrawer since the hybridization of its bonds (sp) with the rest of the molecule has even greater "s-character."

TABLE 17-2 INDUCTIVE EFFECTS OF FUNCTIONAL GROUPS SUBSTITUTED FOR HYDROGEN

$+I$	$-I$		
— CH$_3$	— C(H)=O	— NH$_3^{\oplus}$	— F
— CH$_2$R	— C(R)=O	— NR$_3^{\oplus}$	— Cl
— CHR$_2$	— C(=O)OH	— NO$_2$	— Br
— CR$_3$	— C(=O)OR	— OH	
— C(O$^{\ominus}$)=O	— CH = CH$_2$	— OR	
— NH$_2$	⟨benzene ring⟩	— SH	
	— C ≡ N	— SR	
	— C ≡ CH		

So far we have been discussing the effects of substitution of various functional groups for hydrogen in aliphatic systems. Accepted conventions specify that functional groups which are stronger electron attractors than hydrogen exhibit negative inductance ($-I$) effects, and those which are weaker electron attractors than hydrogen have positive inductance ($+I$) effects. Table 17-2 lists inductive effects of some of the more common functional groups.

RESONANCE EFFECTS

When we examine variations in acidity and basicity in aromatic compounds, we find that predictions based only on inductive effects are often in error. As an example, if only inductive effects were operative, p-hydroxy benzoic acid would be a stronger acid than benzoic acid, but just the opposite is found to be true. Inductive effects indicate that m-nitrophenol should be a stronger acid than p-nitrophenol, which is in error. These same inductive effects predict that benzylamine should be a slightly stronger base than aniline however, benzylamine is a stronger base than aniline by a factor of 30,000! The direct analogy with inductive effects as they are evidenced in σ bonded aliphatic systems is clearly inadequate in explaining substituent effects in aromatic and other conjugated (alternating single-double bonds) systems.

We have given several examples of how electrostatic effects are transmitted along the σ-bonded chain of aliphatic molecules. We have noted how this transmission falls off sharply along the chain with increasing distance from the point of charge disturbance. However, in an aromatic or conjugated system electrostatic effects are picked up and distributed over the entire π-electron system. Therefore, atoms which are relatively far from the point of electrostatic disturbances are "feeling" this distrubance just as much as the atoms which are in close proximity. This kind of "π-cloud" transmission is called a "resonance" or "conjugation effect." It is illustrated by the resonance structures for various types of substituted aromatic compounds. Two good examples are nitrobenzene(I) and the phenoxide anion(II):

(I)

(II)

Nitrobenzene clearly withdraws electron density from the aromatic ring and particularly from the *ortho* and *para* positions. The phenoxide ion, on the other hand, delocalizes its negative charge throughout the ring with greatest concentration on the *ortho* and *para* sites. A most important characteristic of resonance effects is their tendency to be transmitted more strongly to alternate atoms in the conjugated system.

The ability of a molecule or ion to undergo charge delocalization through a conjugated system tends to stabilize the molecule or ion. This is referred to as "resonance stabilization." As an example, consider the relative acidities of phenol ($pK_a = 10$) and methanol ($pK_a = 18$). From the inductive effect, methanol should be less acidic than phenol since the phenyl group is known to be a better electron withdrawer than an alkyl group. However, the inductive effect alone does not explain the great magnitude of the difference. The "resonance effect" helps to explain this large difference in acidity. For example, the phenolate ion is stabilized by charge delocalization relative to the methoxide ion in which the negative charge is concentrated on one atom. This tends to make the phenolate ion a weaker base than the methoxide ion and, therefore, phenol is a stronger acid than methanol. Thus, in this comparison we find that both the inductive effect and resonance stabilization of the conjugate base increase the acidity. We can compare aromatic bases to aliphatic bases in the same manner. Aniline, $C_6H_5NH_2$, is a much weaker base ($pK_b = 9.4$) than aliphatic amines ($pK_b = 3.3$). The phenyl group in aniline withdraws electrons from the amine functional group more than the alkyl group in aliphatic amines. Withdrawal of electron density from the basic nitrogen atom then tends to decrease its basicity. Once again, the magnitude of the difference cannot be described by a difference in inductive effects alone. The high electron density of the aniline nitrogen atom tends to delocalize throughout the benzene ring and lowers the basicity relative to an aliphatic amine, where the high electron density is completely localized on the amine nitrogen atom. Delocalization of electron density in aniline is represented by the resonance structures:

Quantitative studies indicate that resonance effects account for about 2.5 of the 6.1 pK units difference in basicities of aromatic and aliphatic amines.

Many electron-withdrawing groups which show negative inductance effects on saturated carbon chains have the opposite effect on conjugated systems if they can participate in the π-electron resonance. Groups such as $-NH_2$, $-Cl$, $-OR$, $-O-COR$, $-F$, and $-Br$ have a normal tendency to withdraw electrons, but they also possess a non-bonded electron-pair which is available to the resonance cloud. In the earlier examples the resonance effect is greater than the inductance effect. Other groups which show negative inductance, such as

$$-NO_2, \quad -C \equiv N, \quad -COOH, \quad -COOR, \quad -CHO, \text{ and } -C \overset{\displaystyle O}{\underset{\displaystyle R}{\diagup\!\!\diagdown}}, \text{ also with-}$$

draw π-electron density from conjugated systems. By analogy to inductive effects, substituent groups which supply π-electron density to conjugated systems by resonance effects are classified as $+R$ groups and those which withdraw π-electron density are $-R$ groups. Resonance and inductive substituent effects are summarized in Table 17-3. Note that substituents which exhibit $+R$ effects characteristically (except for $-CH_3$ and $-CR_3$) have atoms which possess one or more unshared electron-pairs. However, for $-R$ substituent groups, the atom which σ bonds to the rest of the molecule is multiply bonded to a more electronegative atom (except for $-CF_3$).

Resonance effects are differentiated from inductive effects by studying *para* substitution in aromatic systems. In *para* substitution, inductive effects are quite small due to the great distance that separates the substituent from the reaction center. In *meta* substitution inductive effects are more significant than resonance effects. In *ortho* substitution, we observe both strong inductive and resonance effects and, in addition, there are superimposed steric or crowding effects. Studies of the relative acidities of benzoic acid and its substituted derivatives offer a more quantitative evaluation of these effects. Benzoic acid exhibits a $pK_a = 4.20$, whereas p-hydroxy benzoic acid is a weaker acid with $pK_a = 4.58$. This is not surprising since the acid carboxyl group is more affected by the $+R$ effect of the *para*-substituted hydroxy group than by its $-I$ inductive effect. On the other hand, the pK_a of m-hydroxy benzoic acid is 4.08, a stronger acid than the parent benzoic acid. The $-I$ inductive effect of the hydroxy group apparently predominates in *meta* substitution. For p-fluorobenzoic acid ($pK_a = 4.14$), the $+R$ effect is much smaller than its $-I$ effect. Resonance effects are much larger for substituents whose linking atom to the conjugated system is a first row element (i.e., $-F$, $-OH$, $-NH_2$, etc.). This is explained in terms of the resonance effect involving direct p-orbital interaction with the π-bonded orbitals in the conjugated system. Interaction is stronger (i.e., overlap more effective) when the energy and size of

TABLE 17-3 RESONANCE AND INDUCTIVE EFFECTS OF
FUNCTIONAL GROUPS SUBSTITUTED FOR HYDROGEN

$+R, +I$ Groups	$+R, -I$ Groups	$-R, -I$ Groups
$-O^{\ominus}$	$-F$	$-NO_2$
$-S^{\ominus}$	$-Cl$	$-C \equiv N$
$-CH_3$	$-Br$	$-\overset{\displaystyle O}{\underset{\diagdown H}{\overset{\diagup}{C}}}$
$-CR_3$	$-I$	$-\overset{\displaystyle O}{\underset{\diagdown R}{\overset{\diagup}{C}}}$
	$-OH$	$-\overset{\displaystyle O}{\underset{\diagdown OH}{\overset{\diagup}{C}}}$
	$-OR$	
	$-O-\underset{\underset{O}{\parallel}}{C}-R$	$-\overset{\displaystyle O}{\underset{\diagdown OR}{\overset{\diagup}{C}}}$
	$-SH$	$-\overset{\displaystyle O}{\underset{\diagdown NH_2}{\overset{\diagup}{C}}}$
	$-SR$	$-CF_3$
	$-NH_2$	
	$-NR_2$	
	$-NH-\underset{\underset{O}{\parallel}}{C}-R$	

the interacting orbitals are similar. In these respects, the outer $2p$ orbitals of the first row elements are quite similar to the aromatic π-electron system. However, the p orbitals of the heavier elements are somewhat different in energy and size than the bonded orbitals, and less interaction is possible. This explains the decreased magnitude of resonance effects noted in heavier element substituents. We conclude that variations in acidity in conjugated systems can be explained with considerable accuracy by analyses of inductive and resonance effects.

HYDROGEN BONDING AND ACID STRENGTH

Hydrogen bonding is an electrostatic interaction between a small concentration of positive charge (nucleus of hydrogen atom) and a high density of free valence electrons (not involved in another chemical bond) such as that which exists on atoms of oxygen, nitrogen and fluorine. Water molecules offer good examples of hydrogen bonding.

Hydrogen bond

This short range electrostatic interaction should affect acidities of substituted acids. Let us examine the series of substituted benzoic acids listed in Table 17-4. We observe that p-hydroxy benzoic acid is less acidic than benzoic acid by a factor of two. This is predictable because the $+R$ effect of the hydroxy groups predominates in *para* substitution. However, substitution of a hydroxy group in the *ortho* positions raises the acidity (with respect to benzoic acid) by a factor of 16. The hydroxy group in *ortho* substitution exhibits $+R$ and $-I$ effects which tend to cancel each other out. Also note that when two hydroxy groups are substituted, the acidity is increased by a factor of 1000. On the other hand, when a methoxy, — OCH_3, group which exhibits $+R$ and $-I$ effects similar to — OH is substituted in the *ortho* position, there is only a very slight increase in acidity. From this comparison we see that $+R$ and $-I$ effects cannot account for the great increase in acidity noted in *ortho*-hydroxy substitutions. The significant differences between the — OH and — OCH_3 are (a) size and (b) the fact that — OCH_3 has no acidic protons which can participate in hydrogen bonding. In a comparison of *ortho*-methoxy benzoic acid with benzoic acid, the steric effect offered by the size of the — OCH_3 group does not appear to affect the acidity greatly.

TABLE 17-4 DISSOCIATION CONSTANTS OF SUBSTITUTED BENZOIC ACIDS IN WATER AT 25° C

Name	Formula	$K_a \times 10^5$
Benzoic acid		6.3
o-Methoxybenzoic acid		8.1
p-Methoxy benzoic acid		3.4
o-Hydroxy benzoic acid		105
p-Hydroxy benzoic acid		2.9
2,6-Dihydroxy benzoic acid		5000

We can illustrate the effect of H-bonding with *o*-hydroxy benzoic acid:

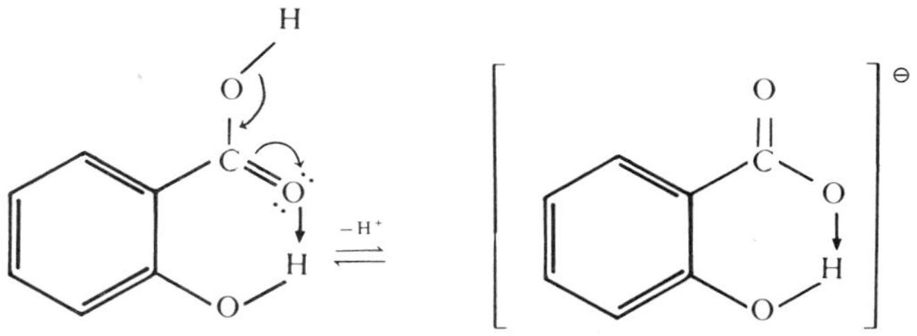

The OH hydrogen tends to pull electron density from the oxygen of the carbonyl and shifts electron density away from the carboxyl acidic proton, making it more accessible for interaction with a solvent molecule. So the acidity is higher than that indicated for benzoic acid. The conjugate base anion is also stabilized with respect to the benzoate anion since there is greater charge delocalization around the ring systems. Both hydroxy groups in 2,6-hydroxy benzoic acid participate in hydrogen bonding,

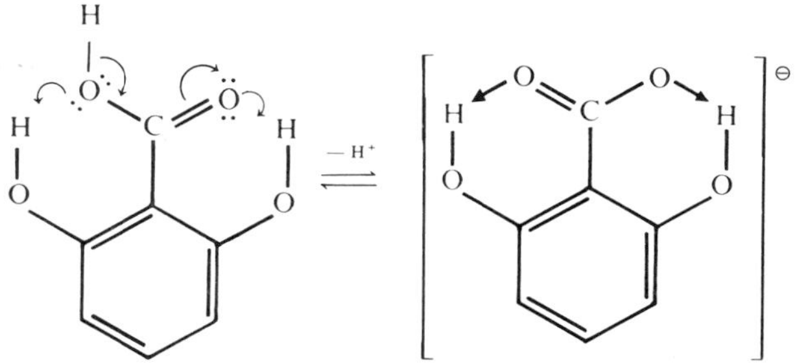

The conjugate base anion is highly stabilized since the negative charge is delocalized around three rings. We can see from the structure that intramolecular hydrogen bonding exists in the anions in both of the compounds we have examined. The first ionization constants of these acids would be expected to be very large. Since the second acidic proton is incorporated in a stabilized cyclic hydrogen bonded negative ion, the ratio K_1/K_2 is expected to be abnormally high and experiments verify this. It should be pointed out that hydrogen bonding is quite rare in aliphatic dicarboxylic acids, except in very sterically crowded acids like diethyl malonic and tetramethyl succinic acids. In less hindered acids, the carboxyl groups are farther apart allowing no hydrogen bonding. However, some unsaturated dicarboxylic acids like maleic acid do exhibit hydrogen bonding:

STERIC EFFECTS

The substitution of large bulky groups into a molecule also can affect the acidity. For example, the size of the group and substitution position may be such that it interferes with a possible resonance configuration of either the acid or its conjugate base and thus lowers the resonance energy. This effect is called steric inhibition of resonance and is demonstrated in the three isomers of *tertiary*-butyl benzoic acids. The *meta* and *para* acid strengths are about the same, but the *ortho* isomer is a stronger acid by a factor of 10. In order to achieve charge inter-action, and consequent charge delocalization in the resonance structures of the benzoate anion, the carboxylate group must be coplanar with the benzene ring. However, the very large *tertiary*-butyl group, when placed in the *ortho* position, pushes the carboxyl group out of the plane of the benzene ring and decreases the resonance energy and increases the acid strength.

In unconjugated systems, there is very little steric hindrance to the approach of a solvent molecule or a solvated proton, unless very large groups such as two *tertiary*-butyl groups are attached to a carbon atom which, in turn, is bonded to the basic atom. Thus steric factors appear to affect acid strength to a significant extent only in conjugated systems.

QUESTIONS AND PROBLEMS

17-1. Predict which compound in the following couples is the stronger acid (that is, has the smaller pK_a). In each case, *justify your choice*.

(a) $N \equiv CCH_2COOH$ or H_3CCOOH

(b) H_3CCOOH or $(H_3C)_3CCOOH$

(c) H_3COH or   ⬡— OH

(d) —COOH   or   —COOH

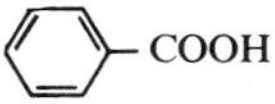

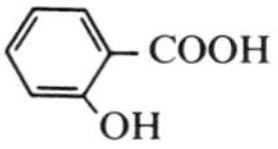

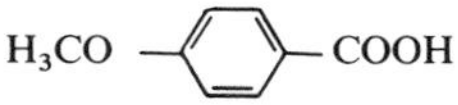

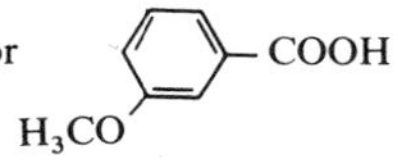

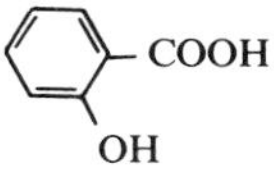

(e) H_3CO —— COOH   or   —COOH

(f) —COOH   or   HO —— COOH

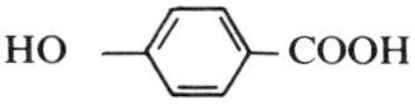

17-2. Predict which compound in the following couples is the stronger base. *Justify your choice.*

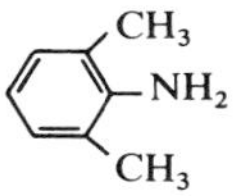

(a) —NH_2 or H_3CNH_2

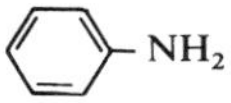

(b)   or H_3C —— NH_2

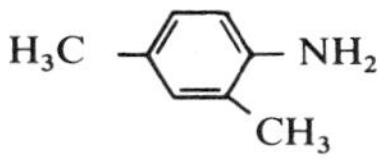

(c)    or

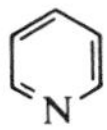

REFERENCES

E. S. Gould, *Mechanism and Structure in Organic Chemistry,* Holt, Rinehart and Winston, New York, 1959; Chapters 4 and 7. Very good discussions of the effects of molecular structure on acidity and basicity.

I. M. Kolthoff, *Treatise on Analytical Chemistry,* Part 1, Volume 1, I. M. Kolthoff and P. S. Elving, Editors, Interscience, New York, 1959; Chapter 11. Excellent discussions of concepts of acids and bases.

18 KINETICS

There are many facets to the study of chemical reactions. The stoichiometry of a reaction specifies the weight relationships between the reactants and the products. The equilibrium constant of a reaction defines the extent to which a reaction will go to completion. The mechanism of a reaction describes the detailed manner in which products are obtained from reactants. Finally, the rate of a reaction is an expression for the speed at which the reaction takes place. In this chapter, we introduce some of the concepts of mechanisms and rates, generally referred to as "reaction kinetics."

For quantitative analysis, the chemist prefers reactions that take place very fast and go essentially to completion, and, whenever possible, he will choose reagents and conditions accordingly. From the stoichiometry, he can then compute the composition of the sample, as in gravimetric and volumetric analysis. Such measurements tell us essentially nothing about *how* the reaction occurred. Relatively few reactions actually take place as written. One which probably does so is the reaction between H_2 and I_2 in the gas phase:

$$H_2 + I_2 = 2HI$$

In this reaction, a molecule of hydrogen collides with a molecule of iodine. There is a definite probability that a rearrangement of chemical bonds will take place, yielding two molecules of hydrogen iodide.

The corresponding reaction between H_2 and Br_2 is not so simple; the first step is the dissociation of a Br_2 molecule:

$$Br_2 = 2Br$$

followed by a chain of reactions:

$$Br + H_2 = HBr + H$$

$$H + Br_2 = HBr + Br, \text{ etc.}$$

The detailed mechanism of the apparently simple reaction:

$$2H_2 + O_2 = 2H_2O$$

is so complex that it is not yet known for certain. The simple balanced equation we are used to writing obviously is not intended to tell us the detailed path of a given reaction. It is primarily from a study of reaction rates that we learn about reaction mechanisms.

Some reactions take place nearly instantaneously—most ionic reactions in aqueous solution are examples of very fast reactions; for instance,

$$H_3O^+ + OH^- = 2H_2O$$

Others go extremely slowly—the radioactive disintegration of Th^{232} requires 10^{10} years for the reaction to go just half way. Special techniques are needed to study these extremes of rates, but a wide variety of analytical methods are useful in studying reactions whose rates are intermediate—say, with half-lives from a few seconds to a few hours.

RATE CONSTANT

The rate of a reaction is measured by the rate of change with time of the concentration (or pressure) of the products. It is assumed that the stoichiometry is known so that changes in concentration of products are simply related to changes in concentration of reactants. For example, if it takes place as written, the rate of the reaction

$$aA + bB = xX + yY$$

can be expressed in terms of derivatives as:

$$\text{Rate} = \frac{d(X)}{x\,dt} = \frac{d(Y)}{y\,dt} = -\frac{d(A)}{a\,dt} = -\frac{d(B)}{b\,dt} \qquad (18\text{-}1)$$

The reason for the a, b, etc., in the denominators of Equation 18-1 should be clear from the stoichiometry; the rate of a reaction is unique, and must be the same regardless of which concentration is used. The negative signs on the last two terms reflect a decrease in concentration of the reactants as time increases. Rates, with some exceptions, change with time, so a derivative must be used to express the rate at a given time.

The concentrations in Equation 18-1 can be replaced with any measured variable that is directly proportional to concentration; e.g., absorbance, conductance, optical rotation, peak intensity (mass spectroscopy), peak height or area (chromatography), milliliters of titrant, pressure of a gas, etc. If the stoichiometry is known, the change in concentration of one species is sufficient to determine the rate provided that all reactants are present initially in equivalent amounts. If one or more reactants are in excess, the species to be followed must be carefully selected or large correction terms may be required. In general, we choose to follow the concentration of that species which can be most easily measured. In a typical reaction, the concentration of a reactant might change as depicted in Figure 18-1, in which the rate is the negative of the slope of the curve at any point. Reaction rates are always given positive values. The numerical value depends on the units of concentration and time, or other variable measured.

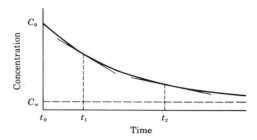

FIGURE 18-1. Variation of concentration with time for a typical reaction. Slope of curve at t_1 and t_2 gives instantaneous rate at these times.

At a given temperature, the rate is usually a function of the concentration of the reactants. Indeed, if the reaction actually occurs as written, the rate is proportional to the frequency of collisions of the *reacting* molecules, and can be expressed as:

$$\text{Rate} = k(A)^a(B)^b \qquad (18\text{-}2)$$

where k is known as the *rate constant* for the reaction. For example, for the hydrogen-iodine reaction,

$$\text{Rate} = k(H_2)(I_2)$$

In practice, a and b may not be the same as the stoichiometric coefficients, and are seldom greater than unity. Since the mechanism may not involve a direct collision of A and B (as in the $H_2 + Br_2$ reaction), the rate expression may involve a complex function of the concentrations as well as rate constants for intermediate reactions. For H_2 plus Br_2:

$$\text{Rate} = \frac{d(\text{HBr})}{dt} = \frac{k(H_2)(Br_2)^{1/2}}{1 + k'(\text{HBr})/(Br_2)} \qquad (18\text{-}3)$$

Rate expressions determined empirically are often the best evidence for an assumed mechanism. If the rate constants determined over a range of initial concentrations are actually constant, we can be fairly confident that the proposed mechanism is correct. Rate expressions and rate constants are applied either to the whole reaction or to intermediate reactions as appropriate.

ORDER OF A REACTION

The sum of the exponents in the rate expression (Equation 18-2) is called the *order of the reaction*. The hydrogen-iodine reaction is "second-order." If the rate expression is not a simple product of concentrations, the "order" has no meaning and is not used (e.g., Equation 18-3). The order of a reaction is an empirical concept derived from the observed rate expression. It is not necessarily a whole number—fractional orders are well-known.

The order of a reaction is not necessarily a fixed number. For instance, the $H_2 + I_2$ reaction is normally second-order. But we might use a very large excess of H_2 so that the pressure (concentration) of H_2 changes negligibly during the reaction. In this case, its value can be included in the rate constant:

$$\text{Rate} = k^*(I_2) \tag{18-4}$$

because the frequency of collisions varies only with the concentration of I_2. Under these conditions the reaction is called *pseudo-first-order* in iodine. A reaction may be first-order in some components, second-order in others, etc.

In elucidating mechanisms of complex reactions, it is often very convenient and helpful to allow only one concentration to change while maintaining all others constant (by using a large excess, buffering, etc.). Each of the several reactants is varied in turn so that the rate dependence on each species can be determined separately. Otherwise most kinetic problems could not be solved. As an example, the inversion of sucrose is acid catalyzed:

$$C_{12}H_{22}O_{11} + H_2O \xrightarrow{H^+} 2C_6H_{12}O_6$$

and from its rate expression, it would appear to be third-order:

$$\text{Rate} = -d(C_{12}H_{22}O_{11})/dt = k(C_{12}H_{22}O_{11})(H_2O)(H^+) \tag{18-5}$$

However, H^+ is a catalyst only and its concentration is essentially constant, as is the concentration of water if it is the solvent. Under these conditions the reaction is pseudo-first-order in sucrose. It might also be pseudo-first-order in water if some other solvent were used.

MOLECULARITY OF A REACTION

In arriving at a rate expression, one must propose a mechanism in which a certain number of species must collide in order to react. The number of such species is called the *molecularity* of the reaction. A unimolecular reaction is always first-order, a bimolecular reaction is second-order, etc. but the reverse is not necessarily true.

INTEGRATED RATE EXPRESSIONS

Zero-Order Reactions. The definition of reaction order includes those reactions for which the rate is independent of all concentrations:

$$-\frac{d(A)}{dt} = k \tag{18-6}$$

which upon integration between the limits $t = 0$ and t, and $(A)_0$ (the initial concentration of A) and (A) yields:

$$(A)_0 - (A) = kt \tag{18-7}$$

There are very few cases of zero total order. Most of the known examples involve heterogeneous reactions on catalytic surfaces. Once the surface is completely covered the rate is independent of changes in concentration.

First-Order Reactions. Because the reactant is being consumed, the instantaneous rate changes continuously with time. To study the rate, we follow the concentration of a product, (X), or the reactant, $(A) = (A)_0 - (X)$.

$$-\frac{d(A)}{dt} = \frac{d(X)}{dt} = k(A) = k[(A)_0 - (X)] \tag{18-8}$$

Separating the variables in Equation 18-8 yields

$$-\frac{d(A)}{(A)} = k dt$$

which on integration yields

$$-\int_{(A)_0}^{(A)} \frac{d(A)}{(A)} = k \int_0^t dt$$

or

$$\ln \frac{(A)_0}{(A)} = kt \tag{18-9}$$

Equation 18-9 is written in a more useful form:

$$(A) = (A)_0 e^{-kt} = (A)_0 \, 10^{-kt/2.303} \tag{18-10}$$

which gives the concentration of A at any time, or in logarithmic form:

$$\log (A) = \log (A)_0 - \frac{kt}{2.303} \tag{18-11}$$

In order to test whether or not a reaction is first-order (in A), a number of values of (A) are determined at various times during the reaction. A plot of $\log (A)$ vs. t should be linear (Equation 18-11) with a slope of $-k/2.303$ and a y-intercept of $\log (A)_0$, as shown in Figure 18-2. Many texts use the symbols a and b for the *initial* concentrations of reactants A and B, and x for the instantaneous concentra-

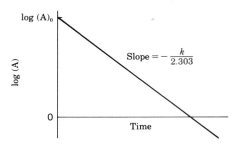

FIGURE 18-2.   Linear plot of a first-order reaction.

tion of a product (or the *decrease* in concentration of the reactant). Thus Equation 18-11 becomes

$$\log \frac{a}{a - x} = \frac{kt}{2.303}$$ (18-12)

The symbol x is frequently used as a *reaction variable*, and the rate is expressed as dx/dt. In addition to providing a check on first-order behavior, such a plot is used to determine the rate constant and the initial concentration if this is unknown.

Half-Life of First-Order Reactions.   The time required for one-half of a substance to react in a given reaction is called the half-life of that reaction. At this time, $(A)/(A)_0 = 1/2$ and from Equation 18-9 or 18-11:

$$k = \frac{2.303}{t_{1/2}} \log 2$$

or

$$t_{1/2} = \frac{2.303 \log 2}{k} = \frac{0.693}{k}$$ (18-13)

First-order reactions can be characterised either by their rate constants or their half-lives. One of the common examples of first-order reactions is radioactive decay.

Second-Order Reactions.   The rate expression for a reaction may depend on the product of two concentrations, such as:

$$-\frac{d(A)}{dt} = -\frac{d(B)}{dt} = k(a - x)(b - x)$$ (18-14)

where a and b are the initial concentrations of A and B, and x is the instantaneous concentration of one of the products. This reaction is second-order overall, but first-order with respect to A and first-order with respect to B. In the simplest case of second-order reactions, the initial concentrations of reactants are equal, $a = b$, and

$$-\frac{d(A)}{dt} = k(a - x)^2 = \frac{dx}{dt} \tag{18-15}$$

Integration of Equation 18-15, between the limits $x = x$ and 0, and $t = t$ and 0, gives

$$k = \frac{1}{t} \times \frac{x}{a(a - x)} \tag{18-16}$$

More generally, $a \neq b$ in Equation 18-14, in which case integration yields

$$k = \frac{2.303}{t(a - b)} \log \frac{b(a - x)}{a(b - x)} \tag{18-17}$$

In the special case where a large excess of one of the reagents is used, for example, $b \gg a$, then

$$a - b \approx -b \quad \text{and} \quad b - x \approx b$$

and Equation 18-17 reduces to

$$k = \frac{2.303}{tb} \log \frac{a}{a - x} \tag{18-18}$$

Since b is constant, the form of Equation 18-18 is identical to Equation 18-12. Under these conditions, the reaction is pseudo-first-order.

Half-Life of Second-Order Reactions. A second-order reaction in which both initial concentrations are equal follows Equation 18-16. The half-life is determined by noting that at $t = t_{1/2}$, $x = a/2$; from which it follows:

$$t_{1/2} = \frac{1}{ka} \tag{18-19}$$

It is important to note that the half-life of a second-order reaction is inversely proportional to initial concentration, whereas the half-life of a first-order reaction is independent of concentration.

Third-Order Reactions. There are very few examples of third-order reactions, and unless all reactants are present in stoichiometric amounts, the rate expressions become very complex.

440   CONSECUTIVE REACTIONS

When an overall reaction goes through a series of intermediates, the product of the first reaction becomes the reactant for the second, etc. The rate expressions may become very complex, but can be simplified if the intermediate reactions are first-order, or can be made pseudo-first-order. Such a series will be represented schematically by these reactions:

$$A \xrightarrow{k_1} B \qquad B \xrightarrow{k_2} C$$

where k_1 and k_2 are the respective rate constants. In addition to the reactions just given, the reverse reactions must also occur, but for the moment we will assume that the reverse rates are small compared to the forward rates. Under these conditions, the rate expressions are:

$$-\frac{d(A)}{dt} = k_1(A) \tag{18-20}$$

$$\frac{d(B)}{dt} = k_1(A) - k_2(B) \tag{18-21}$$

$$\frac{d(C)}{dt} = k_2(B) \tag{18-22}$$

Integration of Equation 18-20 gives

$$(A) = (A)_0 e^{-k_1 t} \tag{18-23}$$

where $(A)_0$ is the initial concentration of A. Substitution of (A) from 18-23 into 18-21 gives

$$\frac{d(B)}{dt} = k_1(A)_0 e^{-k_1 t} - k_2(B) \tag{18-24}$$

and if $(B)_0 = 0$, integration of 18-24 gives

$$(B) = \frac{(A)_0 k_1}{k_2 - k_1}(e^{-k_1 t} - e^{-k_2 t}) \tag{18-25}$$

From stoichiometric considerations (conservation of mass) or from summation of Equations 18-20, 18-21, and 18-22:

$$\frac{d(A)}{dt} + \frac{d(B)}{dt} + \frac{d(C)}{dt} = 0 \tag{18-26}$$

Now if $(B)_0 = (C)_0 = 0$, then

$$(A) + (B) + (C) = (A)_0 \tag{18-27}$$

or

$$(C) = (A)_0 - (A) - (B) \qquad (18\text{-}28)$$

and

$$(C) = (A)_0 \left\{ 1 + \frac{1}{k_1 + k_2} (k_2 e^{-k_1 t} - k_1 e^{-k_2 t}) \right\} \qquad (18\text{-}29)$$

We now have in Equations 18-23, 18-25, and 18-29, expressions for (A), (B), and (C) as functions of $(A)_0$, time and the two rate constants. Figure 18-3 shows how the concentrations vary with time for a typical case where $k_1 = 0.1$ min.$^{-1}$ and $k_2 = 0.05$ min.$^{-1}$.

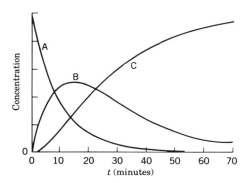

FIGURE 18-3. Concentration-time curves for series first-order reactions.

It is easily seen that component A decreases in an exponential fashion, as it should for a first-order reaction. Component B increases at first, but there is a point at which the decomposition of B to form C occurs at exactly the same rate as the formation of B from A. This is the maximum on the B curve. It is the point which $d(B)/dt = 0$, or from Equation 18-24,

$$k_1 (A)_0 e^{-k_1 t} = k_2 (B) \qquad (18\text{-}30)$$

It can be shown that the maximum concentration of B is

$$(B)_{max} = (A)_0 \kappa^{\kappa/(1 - \kappa)} \qquad (18\text{-}31)$$

where κ is k_2/k_1. The form of Equation 18-31 is such that as k_2/k_1 increases, $(B)_{max}$ decreases. This means that the faster B is converted to C, relative to its formation from A, the lower is the concentration of B that can exist.

Although there are a number of restrictions placed in this derivation of series rates (especially the neglecting of reverse rates), many chemical systems in fact follow the kinetics as given; for example, the radioactive decay series, and the hydrolysis (solvolysis) of esters in which the solvent concentration is large and constant.

EFFECT OF TEMPERATURE ON REACTION RATE

The rate of many chemical reactions increases by a factor of two or three for every 10° rise in temperature. The rate generally increases in a fashion depicted in Figure 18-4a. It is more convenient to plot log k as a function of $1/T$, because the relationship is often linear as in Figure 18-4b.

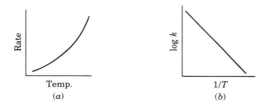

FIGURE 18-4.   Reaction rate as a function of temperature.

The Activated State Concept.   The temperature dependence of reaction rates was first explained by Arrhenius who postulated that an energy barrier exists between the reactants and products. Only those molecules with sufficient energy are able to react. The extra energy required to get over the barrier is called the *activation energy.* This state of affairs is illustrated in Figure 18-5, in which the potential energy of the "system" is plotted vs. the "reaction coordinate." The *reaction coordinate* is any variable which measures the extent of the reaction (time or concentration of product, for example, although it is a qualitative concept).

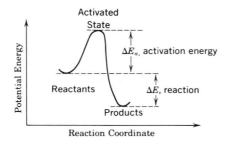

FIGURE 18-5.   Potential energy along the reaction coordinate.

Molecules are able to acquire the necessary energy of activation by collisions. An increase in temperature adds energy to the system, the reactants are able to acquire the activation energy more quickly, and the rate is increased.

Reactants and products are at stable potential energy minima. Because the products are more stable than the reactants, the reaction proceeds as fast as molecules can reach the "activated state" and cross the potential energy maximum (the barrier).

For a unimolecular reaction, the activated state is some condition of the molecule such that a bond is stretched or distorted just to the breaking point. In a bimolecular reaction, the activated state consists of two reactant molecules which have collided with sufficient energy and with favorable geometry for reaction.

Many reactions obey the Arrhenius rate expression:

$$k = Ae^{-E_a/RT} \tag{18-32}$$

or, in logarithmic form,

$$\log k = \log A - \frac{E_a}{2.3RT} \tag{18-33}$$

In these equations, A is a constant sometimes called the "frequency factor" and is related to the probability of the activated state changing to products or back to reactants; E_a is the activation energy. Both terms can be obtained from the plot in Figure 18-4b. Activation energies vary greatly, and this is reflected in the great variation in rates already noted.

CATALYSIS

A catalyst is a substance which changes the rate of a chemical reaction without appearing in the net reaction and without changing the equilibrium position of the main reaction. The catalyst does this by providing a parallel reaction path or mechanism with a lower activation energy. The catalyst forms a lower energy activated complex with the reactant. When the activated complex breaks up to form product, the catalyst is regenerated. This is shown schematically in Figure 18-6.

Nearly all chemical reactions are subject to catalysis, either positive or negative. The fantastic array of complex chemicals synthesized by living systems are examples of what can be done from simple reactants but with very specialized catalysts known as "enzymes."

Acid-Base Catalysis. Many substances are more reactive in protonated form:

$$S + H^+ \xrightarrow{\ k_1\ } SH^+$$

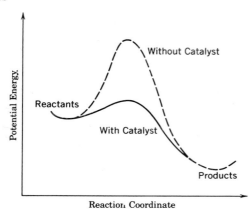

FIGURE 18-6. Effect of catalyst on the reaction path.

Protonation reactions are very fast, so that the subsequent formation and decomposition of the intermediate, RSH^+, to give product P, will be rate-determining:

$$SH^+ + R \xrightarrow{\quad k_2 \quad} P + H^+$$

The overall rate for the reaction is

$$\text{Rate} = k_2(SH^+)(R) = \frac{k_2}{K_a}(S)(H^+)(R) \tag{18-34}$$

where K_a is the dissociation constant of the acid, SH^+. The overall rate depends on the hydronium ion concentration and not the particular acid from which it was derived. The hydrolysis and alcoholysis of esters and the inversion of sucrose follow this kind of kinetics.

More generally, the catalysis is not limited to hydronium ion, but also includes Brønsted acids and bases.

$$S + HA \xrightarrow{\quad \text{fast} \quad} S \cdot HA$$

$$S \cdot HA + R \xrightarrow{\quad \text{slow} \quad} P + HA$$

for which:

$$\text{Rate} = (S) \, \Sigma k_i(HA)_i \tag{18-35}$$

where the summation includes all acids which may be involved in the reaction.

Enzyme Catalysis. In a simple but typical case, we may represent catalysis by an enzyme as follows:

$$E + S \underset{k_2}{\overset{k_1}{\rightleftharpoons}} E \cdot S \xleftarrow{k_3} P + E$$

where E is the enzyme, S the substrate, $E \cdot S$ the activated complex, and P the product. The rate of formation of the complex is given by:

$$\frac{d(E \cdot S)}{dt} = k_1(E)(S) \tag{18-36}$$

and the rate of the reverse reaction is given by:

$$-\frac{d(E \cdot S)}{dt} = k_2(E \cdot S) \tag{18-37}$$

At equilibrium, the two rates are equal and

$$\frac{k_2}{k_1} = \frac{(E)(S)}{(E \cdot S)} = K_m \tag{18-38}$$

Although K_m was derived by equating rate expressions, it is apparently the dissociation constant of the enzyme complex, $E \cdot S$. The total amount of enzyme must remain constant:

$$(E)_T = (E) + (E \cdot S) \tag{18-39}$$

Therefore,

$$K_m = \frac{[(E)_T - (E \cdot S)](S)}{(E \cdot S)} \tag{18-40}$$

Solving for $(E \cdot S)$, we obtain:

$$(E \cdot S) = \frac{(E)_T(S)}{K_m + (S)} \tag{18-41}$$

At low concentration of substrate, the initial reaction velocity, V_0, is directly proportional to the initial concentration of substrate (first-order dependence):

$$V_0 = k_3(E \cdot S) \tag{18-42}$$

But as the initial substrate concentration is increased, the initial reaction velocity levels off and approaches a constant maximum velocity, as seen in Figure 18-7. The substrate-independent region is an example of zero-order kinetics. In this region, the reaction rate is controlled by the decomposition of the complex, $E \cdot S$, governed by k_3:

$$V_0^{max} = k_3(E \cdot S)^{max} = k_3(E)_T \tag{18-43}$$

Combining Equations 18-41, 18-42, and 18-43, we obtain

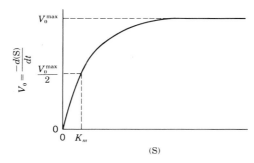

FIGURE 18-7. Initial reaction velocity of enzyme catalyzed reaction as a function of substrate concentration.

$$V_0 = \frac{V_0^{\max}(S)}{K_m + (S)} \qquad (18\text{-}44)$$

Equation 18-44 is known as the *Michaelis-Menten equation* and gives us an alternate definition for K_m, which is known as the *Michaelis constant*:

$$K_m = (S)\left\{\frac{V_0^{\max}}{V_0} - 1\right\} \qquad (18\text{-}45)$$

From Equation 18-45, it is clear that if $V_0 = 1/2V_0^{\max}$, then $K_m = (S)$; that is, K_m is the substrate concentration which gives an initial reaction velocity equal to one-half the maximum velocity.

A more direct procedure for determining K_m is to invert Equation 18-44:

$$\frac{1}{V_0} = \frac{K_m + (S)}{V_0^{\max}(S)} = \frac{1}{V_0^{\max}} + \frac{K_m}{V_0^{\max}(S)} \qquad (18\text{-}46)$$

This is known as the Lineweaver-Burk equation. It is a convenient way of determining K_m from rate data, because a plot of $1/V_0$ vs. $1/(S)$ is a straight line, with an intercept of $1/V_0^{\max}$ and a slope of $K_m/V_0^{\max}$, as shown in Figure 18-8.

The Michaelis constant is a measure of enzyme activity; however, it should be pointed out that the definition given in Equation 18-38 is valid only if the equilibrium for the formation of E·S from E and S is well-established; that is, k_1 and k_2 are much greater than k_3. In fact, it can be shown that

$$K_m = \frac{k_2 + k_3}{k_1} \qquad (18\text{-}47)$$

which reduces to Equation 18-38 if $k_2 > k_3$.

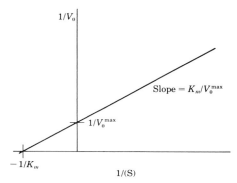

FIGURE 18-8. Lineweaver-Burk plot of the Michaelis-Menten equation.

OTHER APPLICATIONS OF KINETIC STUDIES

In addition to providing a better understanding of how chemical reactions occur, kinetic data have many uses.

The study of relative rates of related reactions and the associated activation energies gives some insight into the detailed structure and conformations of the species. The ultimate goal is to relate specific rate constants to molecular properties.

In chemical analysis, we make use of rate data to select the optimum conditions —or to select conditions in which an interfering reaction will be suppressed. The use of catalysts to speed up a reaction is, of course, well known. In some cases, the presence of a catalyst makes it possible to determine traces that would be otherwise overlooked.

Clearly, kinetics, like thermodynamics, pervades all chemistry. The concepts introduced in this chapter are used by every kind of chemist.

QUESTIONS AND PROBLEMS

18-1. The rate constant for the solvolysis of t-butyl chloride in 80% ethanol $-$ 20% water is 9.2×10^{-6} sec^{-1} at 25° C. If a solution initially contained 0.05 M t-butyl chloride, how long would it take for the solvolysis to be 99.0% complete?   *Ans.* 139 hr.

18-2. The kinetics of the spontaneous decomposition of Fy to Fz were followed by spectrophotometry. (Fy absorbs at 340 mμ, whereas Fz does not.) The following data were obtained:

448

time, min.	1	4	7
conc of Fy, *M*	6.3	3.1	1.6

(a) What is the rate constant of the reaction? *Ans.* 2.3 min^{-1}.

(b) What was the initial concentration of Fy? *Ans.* 8.0 *M*.

(c) Calculate the half-life of the reaction. *Ans.* 2.0 min.

18-3. The kinetics of the spontaneous decomposition of Gy to Gz were followed by polarography:

time, sec	0	20	60	120	200
conc of Gz m*M*	0	37	75	94	99

(a) Determine the order of the reaction. *Ans.* First-order.

(b) Calculate the rate constant. *Ans.* 2.4 × 10^{-2} sec^{-1}.

(c) Calculate the half-life of the reaction. *Ans.* 29 sec.

(d) What percent of Gy was converted to Gz at 50 sec? *Ans.* 69%.

18-4. A reaction, 2A → B is found to be second-order. If a 1.00 *M* solution of A is prepared and then examined 10.0 hr later, only half as much A is found in the solution.

(a) What is the rate constant for this reaction? *Ans.* $k_2 = 0.1$ 1-mole^{-1} hr^{-1}.

(b) When will the reaction be 95% complete? *Ans.* 190 hr.

(c) What is the "half-life" of a 0.500 *M* solution of A? *Ans.* 20 hr.

REFERENCES

A. A. Frost and R. G. Pearson, *Kinetics and Mechanism*, 2nd ed., Wiley, New York, 1961.

S. W. Benson, *The Foundations of Chemical Kinetics*, McGraw-Hill, New York, 1960.

significant differences. The primary ionization by beta particles accounts for only about one-quarter of the total ionization; the remainder results from secondary ionization. For a given energy, the velocity of a beta particle is much larger than for an alpha particle. In air, ionization stops when the energy has been reduced to 12.5 eV, which is the ionization potential of an oxygen molecule. On the other hand, the beta particle may lose a large fraction of its energy in a single collision. Beta particles are widely scattered by collisions with atomic nuclei, but energy loss is caused almost entirely by interactions with electrons. The range in air of beta particles is about 100 cm, during which a 0.5-MeV particle will produce 60 ion-pairs/cm. An idealized curve for the absorption of beta particles is given in Figure 19-2. Actual curves do not exhibit such a sharp cut-off because

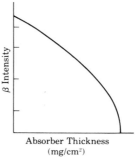

Absorber Thickness
(mg/cm²)

FIGURE 19-2. Idealized absorption curve for beta particles.

of secondary ionization effects. The penetrating power of beta particles is commonly expressed in terms of the mg/cm² of aluminum required for 100% absorption. With absorbers of low atomic number, the penetrating power is independent of the particular substance used.

Gamma Rays. When a nucleus in an excited state returns to its ground state, the most common way involves the emission of electromagnetic radiation. The energies are large (10 keV to 7 MeV) and the radiation is called gamma rays.

The specific ionization caused by gamma rays is much less than for alpha or beta particles; therefore, gamma rays have much greater ranges. Again, the production of ions costs about 35 eV per ion-pair, although for gamma rays the ionization is due almost entirely to secondary processes:

1. *Photoelectric effect.* This is the most important process at low energies. The gamma ray ejects a bound electron from an atom or molecule. The entire energy of the gamma ray is used up—partly in releasing the electron and partly in the kinetic energy it takes with it.

2. *Compton effect.* This is the predominant process in the 0.6- to 4-MeV range. Instead of giving up its entire energy to the departing electron, only a part of its energy is transferred. Thus the gamma ray now has much less energy and is also traveling in a different direction.

3. *Pair-production process.* This process takes place only if the energy exceeds 1.02 MeV and increases with increasing energy. Above this energy threshold, an electron-positron pair can be created by conversion of energy into "mass." The positron produced has an extremely short lifetime—its fate is immediate annihilation with an electron with the simultaneous emission of two 0.51-MeV photons. Thus pair-production always results in low-energy secondary radiation.

There is no well-defined range for gamma rays. All three processes lead to exponential absorption of the form given by Beer's law. In this case, we write:

$$I_d = I_o e^{-\mu d} \tag{19-4}$$

where I_o is the original intensity, I_d is the intensity transmitted through a thickness d, and μ is an absorption coefficient. The half-thickness, $d_{1/2}$, is defined as the thickness required to reduce I_d to $I_o/2$, or $d_{1/2} = 0.693/\mu$. Half-thickness values may be translated into photon energies, the details of which are beyond the scope of this discussion.

Neutrons. The interaction of neutrons (which carry no charge) with electrons is practically negligible. Primary ionization by neutrons is not observed. It is only because of secondary effects resulting from collisions with atomic nuclei that we are able to detect neutrons.

"Fast" neutrons are of little interest to us, but after they have been slowed down, the resulting "thermal" neutrons are very efficient at producing nuclear reactions. This not only gives a means of detecting neutrons, but also provides a source of artificially created isotopes.

DETECTION AND MEASUREMENT OF RADIOACTIVITY

The several kinds of particles and rays produced during the disintegration of a radioactive nuclide leave a large number of ions along their paths. It is these ions which are normally detected and measured. Several techniques are used, any one of which may be the best for a particular application.

Photographic Emulsion. An ionizing particle or ray will cause an activation and subsequent darkening of a photographic plate. Thus the path becomes visible and the degree of darkening is a measure of the total activity. This method is used to locate the exact distribution of radioactive material in a thin slice of the sample (e.g., a tracer in a slice of tissue). The most common application is for film badges used to monitor total exposure of laboratory personnel exposed to radiation. The blackening of photographic plates which had been placed close to samples of uranyl sulfate led to the historic discovery of radioactivity by Bequerel in 1896.

The Ionization Chamber. Many detectors make use of the electrical conductivity of a gas which has been partially ionized by radiation passing through it. In the ionization chamber, an electric field is applied between two electrodes separated by a gas. The kind of gas used depends on the particular application and the geometry of the electrodes is selected to give the optimum performance. These details will be discussed shortly for the Geiger counter—a common example of an ionization chamber.

Charged particles or rays passing into the chamber will produce ion-pairs which, in the absence of an electric field, will recombine and will not be detected. As the voltage between the electrodes is increased, the electrons will be collected at the anode and positive ions at the cathode. At low voltages, the magnitude of this "pulse" of ion current is approximately proportional to the applied voltage as shown in Figure 19-3 in the region up to V_1. At voltages greater than V_1 there is a region of nearly constant pulse height, indicating that all of the ions produced by the radiation are being collected before they have a chance to recombine.

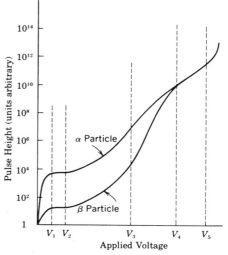

FIGURE 19-3. Variation of pulse height with applied voltage in an ionization chamber or counter. (From Friedlander, Kennedy and Miller, *Nuclear and Radiochemistry*, Wiley, 1964, p. 142.)

This is called the "saturation region." There is a range of voltage over which the exact voltage setting is not critical and systems designed to operate in this region are called *ionization chambers*. Some of these instruments are designed to give a separate signal or "pulse" for each disintegration. The height of the pulse depends in part on the number of ion-pairs produced. Other instruments incorporate a large time constant so that the current is averaged out to a more or less steady state. In this way the average rate of disintegration is determined, rather than the individual events. The currents produced in ionization chambers are of the order of 10^{-15} amp. Vibrating-reed electrometers are commonly used as amplifiers.

Proportional Counters. As the voltage in the ionization chamber is increased beyond V_2 in Figure 19-3, the current again increases because the electrons moving through the higher electric field acquire sufficient energy to cause secondary ionization. In this way, the original ionization is multiplied and a larger pulse is obtained.

In the region between V_2 and V_3 (Figure 19-3), the *pulse height* increases with applied voltage, but more important, it *is proportional to the initial ionization*. Note, however, that the *counting rate* does not depend on voltage in the proportional region. Thus we can have a voltage plateau for alpha particles which produce a large number of primary ions. Under the same conditions we might not see beta particles, which are 100 times less ionizing. At a higher voltage, where the multiplication factor is greater, both the alpha and the beta particles will be counted. This kind of performance is illustrated in Figure 19-4. Compared to the Geiger counter, the discharge is limited to the immediate region of the entering particle and the paths traversed by the secondary ions. Thus the dead time (recovery time between pulses) is very short, about 1 μsec, and the counter is useful for rates up to 200,000 counts/sec. Multiplication factors vary up to 10^4, but this still requires considerable external amplification.

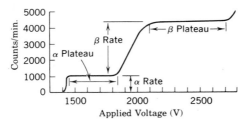

FIGURE 19-4. Effect of applied voltage on the counting rate of a proportional counter receiving both alpha and beta particles.

The Geiger Counter. The proportional region of a counter, as just described, is limited at the upper voltage end by the onset of photoionization. At high voltages, the electrons formed in the initial and secondary ionization are accelerated so much that photons are emitted when the electrons strike the central anode. The photons so released spread the discharge along the wire, resulting in an "avalanche" of electrons reaching the anode. Typical geometry of a Geiger counter is illustrated in Figure 19-5. The interior of the tube may be filled with a mixture of argon (which provides the ionizable substance) and some heavier gas such as alcohol, methane, or chlorine (which quenches the avalanche).

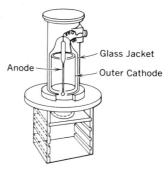

FIGURE 19-5. Schematic diagram of a Geiger counter and sample holder.

Each ionizing particle entering the tube thus triggers an enormous discharge, or pulse, which no longer depends on the number of primary ion-pairs produced. The electrons reach the central anode very quickly because of the extremely high field around the wire. Typically, this takes about 5×10^{-7} sec. But then the wire is surrounded by a sheath of positively charged fragments, which effectively reduces the voltage gradient below the level needed for ion multiplication. Thus the counter is inoperative and must recover before another pulse can take place. It takes about 100 to 500 μsec for the positive ions to reach the outer cathode, and this is the inherent "dead time" of the counter after each pulse. When the positive ions strike the cathode they might well release secondary electrons and set off a new (unwanted) pulse if it were not for the "quenching" effect of the ether, alcohol, or methane contained in the filling gas. These polyatomic molecules manage to absorb much of the energy of the positive ions by collisions.

The plateau region of a Geiger counter is shorter and less well-defined than for a proportional counter—the region between V_4 and V_5 in Figure 19-3. The optimum voltage should be determined for each instrument. As indicated by the steep rise in the curve beyond V_s, if the upper voltage limit is exceeded, the quenching effect breaks down and the tube goes into a continuous discharge condition.

Geiger counters produce a very large pulse (1 to 10 V) which requires little if any amplification for detection. Counters that use an organic vapor for quenching deteriorate after 10^8 counts. Tubes using halogen vapors as quenching agents last indefinitely. Because of the long dead time, counting rates are limited to about 15,000 counts/min. There is, of course, no possibility of determining the energy of the original ionizing particle, because the pulse is an "all or nothing" phenomenon.

Scintillation Counters. Many of the early studies of natural radioactivity were done by observing the fluorescence produced when an alpha particle struck a screen impregnated with zinc sulfide. This crude method produced considerable eye strain, but it has been highly refined by using better scintillators and photomultiplier detectors.

For counting beta particles, crystals of anthracene or stilbene release pulses of photons which are detected by an adjacent photomultiplier tube. Liquid solutions of stilbene or *p*-terphenyl in xylene or toluene are also good scintillators for beta particles, and if these solutions are loaded with boron or cadmium compounds, they will even detect neutrons.

For the measurement of gamma rays, large crystals of sodium iodide are preferred. The crystal is activated with about 1% of thallium iodide. Unfortunately, the crystals are highly hygroscopic and must be protected from the atmospheric moisture. A typical scintillation counter is illustrated in Figure 19-6.

Scintillation counters have very high counting efficiencies and very short dead times (0.25 μsec for NaI crystals and less than 0.01 μsec for stilbene crystals).

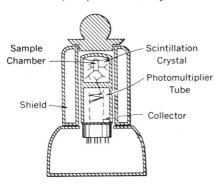

Sample Chamber — Scintillation Crystal

Photomultiplier Tube

Shield — Collector

FIGURE 19-6. Schematic diagram of a scintillation counter and auxiliary apparatus.

Another very important feature is that the height of the pulse is proportional to the energy of the original particle.

AUXILIARY INSTRUMENTATION

Scalers. Radioactive disintegrations often occur at very high rates, faster than any mechanical counter could operate. A scaling circuit is used in such a way that only every other count is passed along. A number of these circuits in series thus produces only $1/2^n$ counts for each original pulse, where n is the number of scaling units, or the scaling factor. The number of events withheld is indicated on a series of glow lamps, with a mechanical counter measuring only the scaled-down signals. More drastic (and also more convenient) scaling is accomplished by circuits which pass along only every tenth count, the so-called "decade scalers." Electric timers may be incorporated in the scaling unit which automatically start and stop for the counting interval, or may stop the counting at a predetermined time or total number of counts.

Pulse-Height Discriminators. If the amplitude (or height) of the pulse is proportional to the energy of the original ionizing particle, the measurement of the pulse height may be useful in identifying the nature of the radiation.

A single-channel analyzer incorporates a device which will pass signals only if they exceed a certain minimum size; those signals below the threshold are dissipated and not counted. A similar circuit can also exclude those signals which exceed a specific maximum value. Thus a "window" is created, and only those signals within a fixed amplitude are counted. Now, if this "window" can be moved along the energy spectrum, it is possible to obtain a radiation spectrum; that is, a plot of the distribution of number of counts as a function of energy of the radiation received by the counter.

Multiple-channel analyzers are still more versatile. By means of suitable circuitry they can sort out the pulses on the basis of size and send each pulse into a particular counting device which counts only those pulses of a given range of energy. Thus the whole spectrum is obtained at once. Analyzers containing 100 to 400 such channels are now available.

COUNTING ERRORS AND CORRECTIONS

The meaningful counting of radioactivity is not as simple as it may seem. There are a number of complications inherent in the phenomenon itself as well as specific problems within the instruments.

Background Radiation. Even in a laboratory not contaminated by previous radiochemical work, there will be small amounts of radioactivity from naturally occurring isotopes in the surroundings and from cosmic radiation. Even with the best shielding, the cosmic effect is not completely eliminated. The background counting rate must be determined and subtracted from the measured counting rate, and if the two rates are comparable, the "true" rate of the sample will be subject to large errors. Background rates of 30 cpm are not uncommon for beta counters.

Extremely "low-level" counters may be surrounded by auxiliary counters which can eliminate the background signals by a "coincidence" circuit, wherein the signal from the auxiliary counter cancels a coincident signal in the main counter.

Coincidence Corrections. During the time when the counter is "dead," i.e., recovering from a previous discharge, any new entering particle will be lost. Especially with Geiger counters, this loss of count may be significant and can be corrected for.

If τ is the dead time after each count and R_o is the observed counting rate in counts per sec, then the total dead time per sec is τR_o. If R^* is the "true" counting rate which would be observed if all particles were counted, then the loss because of "coincidence" is

$$R^* - R_o = \tau R_o R^*$$

or

$$R^* = \frac{R_o}{1 - \tau R_o} \qquad (19\text{-}5)$$

If the dead time of the counter is not known, it cannot be determined from Equation 19-5, which contains two unknowns, R^* and τ. To determine τ, we may employ two sources with observed rates R_1, R_2, and R_{12} when counted separately and "stacked." The sum of R_1^* and R_2^* must equal $R_{12}^* + R_B^*$ because the background is included twice when R_1 and R_2 are measured separately:

$$R_1^* + R_2^* = R_{12}^* + R_B^* \qquad (19\text{-}6)$$

Since R_B is much less than the other rates, we can ignore its coincidence correction. Substituting from Equation 19-5 into Equation 19-6, we obtain

$$\frac{R_1}{1 - R_1\tau} + \frac{R_2}{1 - R_2\tau} = \frac{R_{12}}{1 - R_{12}\tau} + R_B$$

Next, clear the fractions and discard terms in τ^2 and $R_B\tau$, which leads to a practical equation:

$$\tau = \frac{R_1 + R_2 - R_{12} - R_B}{2R_1 R_2} \qquad (19\text{-}7)$$

Counting Geometry. Radiation generally escapes from the sample in all directions as shown in Figure 19-7 and only those particles actually directed

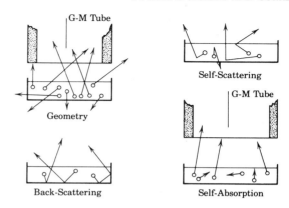

FIGURE 19-7. The fate of radiation from a sample, showing losses due to geometry, self-scattering, back-scattering, and self-absorption.

toward the counter can be counted. Obviously, the arrangement of counter and source including the distance between the two should be reproducible so that the same fraction of particles will always be counted. With proportional and scintillation counters, the sample is often placed within the counter, which improves the counting efficiency enormously.

It should be clear that we rarely count all of the disintegrations and therefore, when we speak of "activity" of a sample, we should distinguish between the activity we measure and the true activity. Systems calibrated with a sample of known activity are often used. In any event, measurements must be made in a consistent manner.

Self-Scattering and Self-Absorption. Beta particles in particular are subject to deflection and/or absorption by the sample itself. Both of these effects are reduced by using a thinner sample. If the sample is a thin layer, these effects can be neglected, or if the sample is very thick, the effects become independent of thickness. But at intermediate thickness, the self-absorption effect follows a Beer's law dependence on thickness and the correction is more difficult to apply.

Back-Scattering. Some of the beta particles which would escape through the back of the sample (opposite to the counter) may be reflected by the material of the sample holder. This phenomenon is called "back-scattering," and adds to the measured counting rate. The amount of back-scattering depends on the nature of the material in the sample holder and its thickness. The error is most easily reduced by using the same type of sample holder for all comparable measurements.

Counting Statistics. Although the half-life of a given sample of radioactive material can be measured with considerable accuracy because of the large numbers of nuclides involved, the individual disintegrations occur in a random fashion. It is impossible to predict when a given nuclide will disintegrate.

As a typical example, we might obtain the following number of counts in successive 1-minute intervals:

Minute	cpm	Minute	cpm
1	93	6	104
2	95	7	100
3	110	8	102
4	101	9	95
5	96	10	104
Avg. for 1st 5 min.	99	Avg. for 2nd 5 min.	101
	Avg. for 10 min. = 100 cpm		

The counts per minute vary from 93 to 110, and one would have to be very lucky indeed to pick the right minute in which the average rate would be obtained. The average for the first five minutes varies from that of the second five, and the ten minute average is still different but more likely to be correct. By "correct," we mean the average rate we would observe if we could count for an infinitely long time. But this would be quite the wrong thing to do (even if we had the time), because the rate must change with time according to the decay law (which leads to yet another type of correction!).

Assuming that individual events are random, we can apply statistical laws to predict the reliability of our measurements. In a large series of measurements of the same quantity, 68% of the measurements have a deviation from the mean no greater than one "standard deviation," given the symbol σ. Thus the standard deviation is a measure of the scatter of a set of observations around their mean value, and it indicates the probable reliability of a single measurement. In activity measurements, the standard deviation is equal to the square root of the total number of counts taken:

$$\sigma = \sqrt{N} \tag{19-8}$$

The standard deviation must increase with the number of counts, but the relative standard deviation decreases with the number of counts

$$\text{rel. std. dev.} = \frac{\sigma}{N} = \frac{\sqrt{N}}{N} = \frac{1}{\sqrt{N}}$$

or

$$\% \text{ rel. std. dev.} = \frac{100}{\sqrt{N}} \qquad (19\text{-}9)$$

The standard deviation, which can be computed from a single counting run, tells us how confident we can be of our answer. There is a 68% chance (a confidence level of 68%) that our answer is within 1 σ of the true mean, a 50% chance that our answer is within 0.68 σ of the true mean, a 95% chance that our answer is within 2 σ of the true mean. The standard deviation of the counting rate is:

$$\sigma_R = \frac{\sqrt{N}}{t} = \sqrt{\frac{R}{t}} \qquad (19\text{-}10)$$

For example, if a sample gave 6400 counts in 2 min., the standard deviation is

$$\sigma = \sqrt{6400} = 80 \text{ counts}$$

or the relative standard deviation is

$$100/\sqrt{6400} = 1.25\%$$

and the standard deviation in the counting rate is

$$\sigma_R = \frac{\sqrt{6400}}{2} \quad \text{or} \quad \sqrt{\frac{6400/2}{2}} = 40 \text{ cpm}$$

Thus we have 68% level of confidence that the true rate is within ± 40 of 3200 cpm. If we should prefer to be 95% confident that our answer is within $\pm 1.25\%$ of the true rate, $2\sigma_R$ must equal 0.0125:

$$2\sigma_R = \frac{2}{\sqrt{N}} = 0.0125$$

from which $\sqrt{N} = 160$ and $N = 25{,}600$ counts. Thus we must take at least 25,600 counts which will take 8 minutes.

The background count is also random in nature and subject to the same error treatment. When two rates are added or subtracted the net standard deviation is given by

$$\sigma_R = \sqrt{\sigma_A^2 + \sigma_B^2} \qquad (19\text{-}11)$$

where A represents the sample activity and B the background. When the background rate is much smaller than sample rate, errors in the background rate will be negligible compared to the error in sample rate. Therefore, it would not pay to spend much time counting the background. On the other hand, if the two rates are of the same order of magnitude, the time spent counting the background is just as important as time spent on the sample itself. The optimum way to divide your time between background and sample is

$$\frac{t_B}{t_A} = \sqrt{\frac{R_B}{R_A}} \tag{19-12}$$

Change of Rate with Time. The counting rate, like the number of remaining radioactive nuclides, must decay exponentially with time. Thus, if the counting time is too long, the rate will change appreciably while you are counting. If the counting time is less than one-tenth of the half-life, this effect is negligible. A correction can be made if necessary, but is not often required.

MIXTURES OF RADIOISOTOPES

Unless the mixture is extremely potent, for example, the interior of a nuclear reactor, we can assume that each nuclide behaves independently of all others, no matter what kind. The total activity then is the sum of the individual activities. We should note, however, that counters are not equally sensitive to all kinds of radiation so that sensitivity factors must be applied to each type of activity. Some counters, as we have seen, are inherently discriminating, so that some kinds of activity may be completely eliminated from the observation.

If more than one kind of activity is being counted, it is unlikely that each will have the same half-life. The shortest lived isotope will disappear first and there will be a noticeable change in slope of the decay curve if the two half-lives vary by more than a factor of two. The decay curve for a mixture of two isotopes with half-lives of 48 min and 8 hr is shown in Figure 19-8. The composite curve can be analyzed by extrapolating the final straight portion back to zero time and subtracting the activity of long-lived isotope from the total observed activity. Three components can be handled in similar fashion, but experimental uncertainties make more than three very difficult. Whenever possible, it is much easier to use discrimination to handle complex mixtures. As a last resort, one must employ chemical separations.

SOME APPLICATIONS OF RADIOISOTOPES

Tracers. Except for the very lightest elements (lighter than carbon), radio-isotopes are chemically identical with stable isotopes. Thus they may be used to

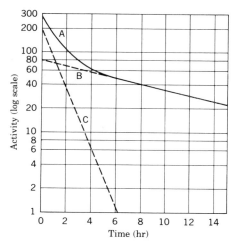

FIGURE 19-8. A composite decay curve of a mixture of two isotopes. A, total activity. B, extrapolated activity of isotope with half-life of 8 hours. C, hypothetical curve for activity of isotope with half-life of 48 minutes. (From Friedlander, Kennedy and Miller, *Nuclear and Radiochemistry*, Wiley, 1964, p. 75.)

"tag" a compound in a way that will be undetectable until the nuclide disintegrates. The history of the tagged compound and/or its successors can be followed through a chemical reaction, an industrial process, a biological process or even a geological process. The "tag" must be an atom that is not exchangeable with the surroundings; for example, tritium would be useless as a tag on an acid if it were inserted in the carboxyl group.

Many organic and biochemical compounds are available with C^{14} or tritium "tags" in known positions. Compounds that are not available can be synthesized by using tagged reagents as starting materials. The use of tracers is limited primarily by the imagination of the user. In biological systems, of course, we must consider possible damage to the surroundings. When necessary, and especially for carbon, oxygen, nitrogen, and hydrogen, stable heavy isotopes may be inserted as tags and detected later by mass spectrometry.

Activation Analysis. Radioactive isotopes of nearly all elements can be created artificially by bombardment with slow neutrons. In principal, any sample can be "activated" by placing it in a high flux of neutrons such as in an atomic pile (nuclear reactor). The amount of activity produced is a function of the neutron flux, the cross section for neutron capture of the bombarded element, and the time of activation. Thus each element has a given sensitivity for activation by this method and all elements are not necessarily activated. A complex sample will require good discrimination in the counting or else some chemical separation to isolate the various activities. The overall sensitivity depends not only on the activation process, but also on the ease of detection of the isotope produced. Preferably, it should have a half-life in the medium range. Sensitivities vary widely, but with a neutron flux of 10^{12} cm^{-2} sec^{-1}, most elements can be detected in the range of 10^{-16} to 10^{-11} g. For a number of elements, this is by far the most sensitive method available.

Analysis by Isotope Dilution. For many complex samples, there may be no suitable quantitative method to isolate a particular component. If the interferences are difficult to remove or nullify, a method called isotope dilution analysis may provide the answer. A radioactive form of the pure substance to be determined is required. This is "diluted" in the original sample, and if even a small portion of the component can be recovered in a pure form, then a measurement of the reduced activity will give the percent yield of the separation process.

Suppose a sample contains iron, but interferences invalidate other methods. We add W_0 g of Fe^{59}Cl$_3$ (not necessarily a pure isotope) that has a specific activity A_0. The sample is mixed so that the Fe^{59} is equally distributed throughout the sample. A portion of the total iron is then separated (precipitation, extraction, etc.) and isolated in a pure weighable form. If the original sample contained W_1 g of iron, then the fraction of the initial activity found in this portion is the dilution ratio, $W_0/(W_0 + W_1)$, or

$$A_0 \frac{W_0}{W_0 + W_1} = A_1$$

where A_1 is the specific activity of the isolated portion. It follows that

$$W_1 = W_0 \left(\frac{A_0}{A_1} - 1 \right) \tag{19-13}$$

This method has been valuable for the analysis of otherwise intractable organic and biochemical mixtures as well as geochemical and archeological samples.

RADIATION SAFETY

Although experiments normally done in elementary laboratory work present no more radiation hazard than luminous watch dials or normal cosmic radiation, we must call attention to some potential hazards. Contamination is especially insidious because there may be no apparent symptoms—the damage may show up in your offspring.

Inhalation of radioactive material is particularly to be avoided because the lungs are extremely sensitive and the contamination is difficult to remove. Ingestion may not be as bad because stomach pumps are rather effective if used in time. Absorption through the skin is also nasty, especially through cuts and blemishes and around the eyes. The hands can tolerate 20 times as much radiation as the abdominal region. One must be concerned with both the familiar radioactive or physical half-life and also the biological half-life; that is, how fast the contamination is eliminated from the body by normal biological functions.

Sensible precautions include:

1. Use a survey instrument to determine actual level of activity present and thus the need for further precautions.
2. Use hoods and dry boxes whenever possible.
3. Use trays or absorbent paper to contain possible spills.
4. Use gloves, tongs, etc., to avoid contact.
5. Keep as much distance as practicable between source and personnel.
6. Use adequate shielding if necessary.
7. Store all radioactive materials in shielded vaults when not in use.
8. Warn other personnel or visitors whenever danger is present.
9. Don't panic. If you are in difficulty, get help.
10. For any work with more than a few microcuries of activity, consult a more complete Safety Manual before beginning to work.

QUESTIONS AND PROBLEMS

19-1. Calculate the weight of (a) 2 millicuries of P^{32}, (b) 10 microcuries of I^{131}.

Ans. (a) 3.5×10^{-9} g.

19-2. What fraction of the activity remains in the two samples of Problem 19-1 after 10 days? *Ans.* P^{32}, 61.3%.

19-3. If the dead time of a Geiger counter is 200 μsec, what is its counting efficiency for counting rates of 2000, 200 and 20 counts per sec? *Ans.* 60%, 96%, 99.6%.

19-4. The beta activity of a sample was followed for a period of three hours, during which the following data were taken. Plot the decay curve and analyze the curve for: number of components, half-lives, identity of nuclides, and initial activity of each component.

Time, min.	Activity, cpm	Time, min.	Activity, cpm
10	540	80	55
10	540	80	55
20	315	90	50
30	200	100	45
40	138	120	38
50	99	140	30
60	80	160	27
70	65	180	24

19-5. Two ml of a solution containing Co^{++} and Cu^{++} are passed through an ion exchange column. The Co^{++} fraction is collected in a flask and 0.1000 g of radioactive tagged $Co^{60}Cl_2$ (specific activity = 5000 counts/min.-g) is added to the flask. An excess of sulfide ion is then added to precipitate the Co^{++} as CoS. A 0.0500-g portion of the CoS is isolated and counted, giving an activity of 275 counts/min. (corrected for background and coincidence). What is the concentration of Co^{++} in the original solution?   *Ans.* 6.8 mg/ml.

19-6. A certain sample gives 450 counts/min. What is the relative percent standard deviation, if the sample is counted for 15 min.?   *Ans.* 5.5 cpm.

19-7. The observed (uncorrected) counting rate for a sample is 38.0 counts/min. while under the same conditions the background rate is 15.0 counts/min. If both background and sample are counted for 20 min., what is the relative standard deviation of the corrected activity?

19-8. The dead time of counter is determined by measuring sample A, 10,060 counts/min.; sample B, 10,950 counts/min.; sample A and B together, 20,310 counts/min. Calculate the value of the dead time.   *Ans.* 190 μsec.

19-9. Some wood samples are discovered in a geological land-cut in which there is evidence of glaciation having occurred at some time in the past. The carbon-14 present in the samples decomposes at a rate of 7.00 atoms per minute per gram of wood. Carbon-14 in fresh wood decomposes at a rate of 15.30 atoms per minute per gram of wood. Carbon-14 is a weak β emitter with a half-life of 5760 years. How many years have elapsed since glaciation occurred in the area under study?   *Ans.* $t = 6.52 \times 10^3$ yr.

REFERENCES

G. R. Choppin, *Experimental Nuclear Chemistry*, Prentice-Hall, Englewood Cliffs, N. J., 1961.

G. Friedlander, J. W. Kennedy, and J. M. Miller, *Nuclear and Radiochemistry*, 2nd ed., Wiley, New York, 1964.

R. T. Overman and H. M. Clark, *Radioisotope Techniques*, McGraw-Hill, New York, 1959.

INDEX

469

FOUR-PLACE LOGARITHMS TO BASE 10

No.	0	1	2	3	4	5	6	7	8	9	1 2 3	4 5 6	7 8 9
10	0000	0043	0086	0128	0170	0212	0253	0294	0334	0374	4 8 12	17 21 25	29 33 37
11	0414	0453	0492	0531	0569	0607	0645	0682	0719	0755	4 8 11	15 19 23	26 30 34
12	0792	0828	0864	0899	0934	0969	1004	1038	1072	1106	3 7 10	14 17 21	24 28 31
13	1139	1173	1206	1239	1271	1303	1335	1367	1399	1430	3 6 10	13 16 19	23 26 29
14	1461	1492	1523	1553	1584	1614	1644	1673	1703	1732	3 6 9	12 15 18	21 24 27
15	1761	1790	1818	1847	1875	1903	1931	1959	1987	2014	3 6 8	11 14 17	20 22 25
16	2041	2068	2095	2122	2148	2175	2201	2227	2253	2279	3 5 8	11 13 16	18 21 24
17	2304	2330	2355	2380	2405	2430	2455	2480	2504	2529	2 5 7	10 12 15	17 20 22
18	2553	2577	2601	2625	2648	2672	2695	2718	2742	2765	2 5 7	9 12 14	16 19 21
19	2788	2810	2833	2856	2878	2900	2923	2945	2967	2989	2 4 7	9 11 13	16 18 20
20	3010	3032	3054	3075	3096	3118	3139	3160	3181	3201	2 4 6	8 10 13	15 17 19
21	3222	3243	3263	3284	3304	3324	3345	3365	3385	3404	2 4 6	8 11 12	14 16 18
22	3424	3444	3464	3483	3502	3522	3541	3560	3579	3598	2 4 6	8 10 12	14 15 17
23	3617	3636	3655	3674	3692	3711	3729	3747	3766	3784	2 4 6	7 9 11	13 15 17
24	3802	3820	3838	3856	3874	3892	3909	3927	3945	3962	2 4 5	7 9 11	12 14 16
25	3979	3997	4014	4031	4048	4065	4082	4099	4116	4133	2 3 5	7 9 10	12 14 15
26	4150	4166	4183	4200	4216	4232	4249	4265	4281	4298	2 3 5	7 8 10	11 13 15
27	4314	4330	4346	4362	4378	4393	4409	4425	4440	4456	2 3 5	6 8 9	11 13 14
28	4472	4487	4502	4518	4533	4548	4564	4579	4594	4609	2 3 5	6 8 9	11 12 14
29	4624	4639	4654	4669	4683	4698	4713	4728	4742	4757	1 3 4	6 7 9	10 12 13
30	4771	4786	4800	4814	4829	4843	4857	4871	4886	4900	1 3 4	6 7 9	10 11 13
31	4914	4928	4942	4955	4969	4983	4997	5011	5024	5038	1 3 4	6 7 8	10 11 12
32	5051	5065	5079	5092	5105	5119	5132	5145	5159	5172	1 3 4	5 7 8	9 11 12
33	5185	5198	5211	5224	5237	5250	5263	5276	5289	5302	1 3 4	5 6 8	9 10 12
34	5315	5328	5340	5353	5366	5378	5391	5403	5416	5428	1 3 4	5 6 8	9 10 11
35	5441	5453	5465	5478	5490	5502	5514	5527	5539	5551	1 2 4	5 6 7	9 10 11
36	5563	5575	5587	5599	5611	5623	5635	5647	5658	5670	1 2 4	5 6 7	8 10 11
37	5682	5694	5705	5717	5729	5740	5752	5763	5775	5786	1 2 3	5 6 7	8 9 10
38	5798	5809	5821	5832	5843	5855	5866	5877	5888	5899	1 2 3	5 6 7	8 9 10
39	5911	5922	5933	5944	5955	5966	5977	5988	5999	6010	1 2 3	4 5 7	8 9 10
40	6021	6031	6042	6053	6064	6075	6085	6096	6107	6117	1 2 3	4 5 6	8 9 10
41	6128	6138	6149	6160	6170	6180	6191	6201	6212	6222	1 2 3	4 5 6	7 8 9
42	6232	6243	6253	6263	6274	6284	6294	6304	6314	6325	1 2 3	4 5 6	7 8 9
43	6335	6345	6355	6365	6375	6386	6395	6405	6415	6425	1 2 3	4 5 6	7 8 9
44	6435	6444	6454	6464	6474	6484	6493	6503	6513	6522	1 2 3	4 5 6	7 8 9
45	6532	6542	6551	6561	6571	6580	6590	6599	6609	6618	1 2 3	4 5 6	7 8 9
46	6628	6637	6646	6656	6665	6675	6684	6693	6702	6712	1 2 3	4 5 6	7 7 8
47	6721	6730	6739	6749	6758	6767	6776	6785	6794	6803	1 2 3	4 5 5	6 7 8
48	6812	6821	6830	6839	6848	6857	6866	6875	6884	6893	1 2 3	4 4 5	6 7 8
49	6902	6911	6920	6928	6937	6946	6955	6964	6972	6981	1 2 3	4 4 5	6 7 8
50	6990	6998	7007	7016	7024	7033	7042	7050	7059	7067	1 2 3	3 4 5	6 7 8
51	7076	7084	7093	7101	7110	7118	7126	7135	7143	7152	1 2 3	3 4 5	6 7 8
52	7160	7168	7177	7185	7193	7202	7210	7218	7226	7235	1 2 2	3 4 5	6 7 7
53	7243	7251	7259	7267	7275	7284	7292	7300	7308	7316	1 2 2	3 4 5	6 6 7
54	7324	7332	7340	7348	7356	7364	7372	7380	7388	7396	1 2 2	3 4 5	6 6 7
	0	1	2	3	4	5	6	7	8	9	1 2 3	4 5 6	7 8 9

FOUR-PLACE LOGARITHMS TO BASE 10

No.	0	1	2	3	4	5	6	7	8	9	1	2	3	4	5	6	7	8	9
55	7404	7412	7419	7427	7435	7443	7451	7459	7466	7474	1	2	2	3	4	5	5	6	7
56	7482	7490	7497	7505	7513	7520	7528	7536	7543	7551	1	2	2	3	4	5	5	6	7
57	7559	7566	7574	7582	7589	7597	7604	7612	7619	7627	1	2	2	3	4	5	5	6	7
58	7634	7642	7649	7657	7664	7672	7679	7686	7694	7701	1	1	2	3	4	4	5	6	7
59	7709	7716	7723	7731	7738	7745	7752	7760	7767	7774	1	1	2	3	4	4	5	6	7
60	7782	7789	7796	7803	7810	7818	7825	7832	7839	7846	1	1	2	3	4	4	5	6	6
61	7853	7860	7868	7875	7882	7889	7896	7903	7910	7917	1	1	2	3	4	4	5	6	6
62	7924	7931	7938	7945	7952	7959	7966	7973	7980	7987	1	1	2	3	3	4	5	6	6
63	7993	8000	8007	8014	8021	8028	8035	8041	8048	8055	1	1	2	3	3	4	5	5	6
64	8062	8069	8075	8082	8089	8096	8102	8109	8116	8122	1	1	2	3	3	4	5	5	6
65	8129	8136	8142	8149	8156	8162	8169	8176	8182	8189	1	1	2	3	3	4	5	5	6
66	8195	8202	8209	8215	8222	8228	8235	8241	8248	8254	1	1	2	3	3	4	5	5	6
67	8261	8267	8274	8280	8287	8293	8299	8306	8312	8319	1	1	2	3	4	4	5	5	6
68	8325	8331	8338	8344	8351	8357	8363	8370	8376	8382	1	1	2	3	3	4	4	5	6
69	8388	8395	8401	8407	8414	8420	8426	8432	8439	8445	1	1	2	2	3	4	4	5	6
70	8451	8457	8463	8470	8476	8482	8488	8494	8500	8506	1	1	2	2	3	4	4	5	6
71	8513	8519	8525	8531	8537	8543	8549	8555	8561	8567	1	1	2	2	3	4	4	5	5
72	8573	8579	8585	8591	8597	8603	8609	8615	8621	8627	1	1	2	2	3	4	4	5	5
73	8633	8639	8645	8651	8657	8663	8669	8675	8681	8686	1	1	2	2	3	4	4	5	5
74	8692	8698	8704	8710	8716	8722	8727	8733	8739	8745	1	1	2	2	3	4	4	5	5
75	8751	8756	8762	8768	8774	8779	8785	8791	8797	8802	1	1	2	2	3	3	4	5	5
76	8808	8814	8820	8825	8831	8837	8842	8848	8854	8859	1	1	2	2	3	3	4	5	5
77	8865	8871	8876	8882	8887	8893	8899	8904	8910	8915	1	1	2	2	3	3	4	4	5
78	8921	8927	8932	8938	8943	8949	8954	8960	8965	8971	1	1	2	2	3	3	4	4	5
79	8976	8982	8987	8993	8998	9004	9009	9015	9020	9025	1	1	2	2	2	3	4	4	5
80	9031	9036	9042	9047	9053	9058	9063	9069	9074	9079	1	1	2	2	3	3	4	4	5
81	9085	9090	9096	9101	9106	9112	9117	9122	9128	9133	1	1	2	2	3	3	4	4	5
82	9138	9143	9149	9154	9159	9165	9170	9175	9180	9186	1	1	2	2	3	3	4	4	5
83	9191	9196	9201	9206	9212	9217	9222	9227	9232	9238	1	1	2	2	3	3	4	4	5
84	9243	9248	9253	9258	9263	9269	9274	9279	9284	9289	1	1	2	2	3	3	4	4	5
85	9294	9299	9304	9309	9315	9320	9325	9330	9335	9340	1	1	2	2	3	3	4	4	5
86	9345	9350	9355	9360	9365	9370	9375	9380	9385	9390	1	1	2	2	3	3	4	4	5
87	9395	9400	9405	9410	9415	9420	9425	9430	9435	9440	0	1	1	2	2	3	3	4	4
88	9445	9450	9455	9460	9465	9469	9474	9479	9484	9489	0	1	1	2	2	3	3	4	4
89	9494	9499	9504	9509	9513	9518	9523	9528	9533	9538	0	1	1	2	2	3	3	4	4
90	9542	9547	9552	9557	9562	9566	9571	9576	9581	9586	0	1	1	2	2	3	3	4	4
91	9590	9595	9600	9605	9609	9614	9619	9624	9628	9633	0	1	1	2	2	3	3	4	4
92	9638	9643	9647	9652	9657	9661	9666	9671	9675	9680	0	1	1	2	2	3	3	4	4
93	9685	9689	9694	9699	9703	9708	9713	9717	9722	9727	0	1	1	2	2	3	3	4	4
94	9731	9736	9741	9745	9750	9754	9759	9763	9768	9773	0	1	1	2	2	3	3	4	4
95	9777	9782	9786	9791	9795	9800	9805	9809	9814	9818	0	1	1	2	2	3	3	4	4
96	9823	9827	9832	9836	9841	9845	9850	9854	9859	9863	0	1	1	2	2	3	3	4	4
97	9868	9872	9877	9881	9886	9890	9894	9899	9903	9908	0	1	1	2	2	3	3	4	4
98	9912	9917	9921	9926	9930	9934	9939	9943	9948	9952	0	1	1	2	2	3	3	4	4
99	9956	9961	9965	9969	9974	9978	9983	9987	9991	9996	0	1	1	2	2	3	3	3	4
	0	1	2	3	4	5	6	7	8	9	1	2	3	4	5	6	7	8	9